CO-ORDINATED SCIENCE

GCSE BOOK 1

Tim Bloomfield, Ken Dobson, Jane Drury,
Clive Griffin, Richard Irving, Colin McCarty,
Mary Ratcliffe, Richard Shewry and Andy Toone

EDITED BY KEN DOBSON

CollinsEducational

An imprint of HarperCollins*Publishers*

CollinsEducational, an imprint of HarperCollins*Publishers*

77-85 Fulham Palace Road, Hammersmith, London W6 8JB.

© Suffolk County Council 1992
First published 1992
Reprinted 1992

ISBN 0 00 327491 8

Designed by Derek Lee

Picture research by Marilyn Rawlings

Artwork by John Booth, Ray Burrows, Tom Cross, Gay Galsworthy, Sally Neave, Pantek Arts, Archie Plumb and Jeremy Gower.

Cartoons by Martin Shovel

Index by Laurence Errington

Typeset by Dorchester Typesetting Group Ltd, Dorchester, Dorset DT1 1UA

Printed and Bound in Hong Kong

Acknowledgements

The author and publishers are grateful to the following for permission to reproduce copyright material on the pages indicated:

(T, top; B, bottom; C, centre; L, left; R, right)

Ace Photo Agency/C.T.H. Smith 69 L, Benelux Press 27 C
A.E.A. Technology, Harwell 179 L
Bryan and Cherry Alexander 108
Allsport UK/Vandystadt 115 T, Gary Mortimore 115 BL, Bob Martin 115 BR, Tony Duffy 116 TL, Mike Powell 116 BR, 118 TR, Gary Mortimore 118 CL, Kit Houghton 120 TR, Tony Duffy 120 BL, 120 BR, Bob Martin 122, Oli Tennant 126 T, Bruno Bade 142 TL, David Leah 149 B
Arcaid/Mark Fiennes 161 BL
Architectural Association Slide Library/A. Higgott 112 T, Mark Reid 163 BC, A. Higgott 163 BR
Ardea London 3 top row L, Wardene Weisser 3 third row L, François Gohier 3 third row R, Jack A. Bailey 7 BR, Jean Paul Ferrero 49, François Gohier 104, R, John Clegg 135 T, Donald Burgess 136 BR, P. Morris 136 TR
Aviation Picture Library/Austin J. Brown 30 T
Biofotos 55 TR, 55 BR, 131, 136 BL, 136 BC
Barnaby's Picture Library/Chapman 47 BR
John Birdsall Photography 3 second row C, 10 T, 42, 43 BL, 43 BC
Biophoto Associates 48 TR, 134 TR, 139 B, 158 BL, 162, 193 R
Anthony Blake Photo Library 43 TR
British Geological Survey 104 L
British Petroleum, 170 CL, 170 TL
British Trust for Conservation Volunteers/S. Pythian 170 BL
Bubbles Photo Library 47 C, Loisjoy Thurston 52
S. D. Burt 97 BC
Camera Press/B.G. Silberstein 106 L, Terence Spencer 118 BR, Fred Coombs 161 TR

J. Allan Cash Photolibrary 96, 112 C, 158 BR, 165 T
John Cleare/Mountain Camera 182
Collections/Brian Shuel 161 CR, 161 BC
Lupe Cunha 3 bottom row L, 6 T, 47 TC, 47 TL, 142 TR, 142 CR
Stephen Dalton/Oxford Scientific Films 31 B
Environmental Picture Library/Nigel Dickinson 81 BL
ETSU/Department of Energy 177 L
Mary Evans Picture Library 11 B, 18 TR
Vivien Fifield 193 BL
Geoscience Features Picture Library 64, 111, 130 TR, 135 B, 137 CR, 191
Greenpeace Communications/Walker 81 BC, Ferraris 84 CR
Robert Harding Picture Library 163 CR
Holt Studios/Mary Cherry 3 second row L, Nigel Cattlin 83, 84 TR and 130 BL, Andrew Morant 161 C
Hulton Picture Company 137 BR
Hutchison Library/ Kerstin Rogers 130 BR, Liba Taylor 170 TR
ICCE Photo Library/Mark Boulton 81 BR, Andy Purcell 85 CR, Mark Boulton 177 TR
ICI Bio Products, Billingham 28 T
The Independent/Nicholas Turpin 173, Nicholas Schoon 175
Andrew Lambert 22 TL, 22 TR, 26 B, 37 T, 40, 41 TR, 41 BR, 43 CR, 57 L, 58, 68, 69 BR, 126 B, 127, 144 CR, 146 TL, 146 BR, 147 L, 150
Frank Lane Picture Agency/M. Nimmo 48 BL, H. Clark 81 T, Terry Whittaker 91, R. Thompson 95 TL, D. Hoadley 95 TR, Hugo Binzo 95 BL
Life Science Images/Ron Boardman 4 TR, 131, 139 T, 142 CL, 153 T, 153 C
London Fire Brigade 153 B
Magnum Photos/Bruno Barbey 172, Renni Burri 179 R, 183
Meteorological Office/Dundee 97 C and 98 B, J. A. Walton 97 BR
Military Picture Library/Tim Fisher 3 second row R, 65
Natural History Museum 148, 158 TR
National Medical Slidebank 30 B
National Power 177 BR
Peter Newark's Pictures 18 B, 147 C
Phoenix Mountaineering 157
Novosti Press 62
Olympia and York 165 C
R. K. Pilsbury 97 BL
Planet Earth Pictures/R. L. Matthews 2, Ken Lucas 3 top row R, Pete Atkinson 118 CR, Kurt Amsler 165 B
Popperfoto 22 B, 35
Press Association 29, 101
Rex Features/Sipa/Foulon 158 CL
Ann Ronan Picture Library 181
Royal Botanic Gardens, Kew 57 R
Science Photo Library/Dr Colin Chumbley 5 T, David Scharf 10 C, Secchi-Le laque/Roussel – UCLAF/CNRI 10 B, CNRI 11 C, Biology Media 11 T, Dr Tony Brain 23 B, Heini Schneebeli 30 C, S. I. V. 31 T, Dr Ray Clark 37 C, Katrina Thomas 47 TR, Francis Leroy/Biocosmos 51 TR, Petit Format/Nestlé 51 TC and 51 BC, Jim Stevenson 51 BR, Andrew MacLenaghan 69 TR, Adam Hart-Davis 73 R, Jeremy Burgess 73 L, John Walsh 85 TR, Soames Summerhays 95 C, Alfred Pasieka 107 TR and 107 CR, US Geological Survey 110, Dr Morley Read 130 L, NASA 130 TC, David Parker 134 BR, Dr Jeremy Burgess 135 C, Hank Morgan 138, Dr Steve Patterson 142 BC, Chemical Design 147 R, Dr C Hammond/Leeds University 149 C, Axel Bartell 152, Lab Molecular Biology/MRC 158 BC, Peter Menzel 161 BR, Simon Fraser 178 TR, Sheila Terry 178 BR, Novosti 178 BL, M. I. Walker 193 TL
S.D. Pictures 163 TR
Frank Spooner Pictures/Gamma 3 bottom row R, David Barritt/Gamma 50, Gary Williams/Gamma 98 T
Sport and General 120 BC
Sydney Plating Company 76
Syndication International 55 C
Andrew Synd/Microscopix 23 T, 23 C
Telefocus 47 BL
UPI/Bettmann 20 T, 20 B
Visionbank 106 R
J. A. Walton 97 BR
W.A. Technology, Cambridge 142 BR
C. James Webb 59, 142 BL
Wiggins Teape 130 BR

CONTENTS

PART 1 Topics for study

PART 2 Reference section

CHAPTER ONE

STAYING ALIVE

The art of survival

When we go to bed at night, most of us are fairly sure that we are going to wake up again the next morning. We tend to take our survival – our staying alive – for granted.

But imagine suddenly waking up, and finding yourself in a new and very unfriendly environment. It could be a tropical rain forest in South America, the grassy plains of Africa, or even the back streets of a huge city. Try to imagine being alone and naked, with only your bare hands to help you survive. How long do you think you would last in such a place without food, water, tools, shelter and medicines?

Millions of people all over the world face a constant struggle to stay alive from one day to the next. Their main enemies in this daily war are just the same things that you would have to face in your new 'home': lack of food and clean water, little shelter from harsh weather, and disease.

If the battle against any one of these is lost, you die.

People survive!

Humans have only been present on this planet for about 2 million years. But life began on Earth more than 300 million years ago. Despite all the problems they face in staying alive, humans have become a dominant species on earth. This means they are better at surviving than many other living creatures that surround them. How long this may last is difficult to tell.

Plants and animals use all sorts of different methods to help them stay alive in dangerous and hostile places. At first sight, compared with the animals you can see in the photographs, humans do not appear to be particularly impressive!

We have no fangs, claws or talons, unlike the predator animals which must catch and kill their prey. Our soft skin gives us little defence against attackers compared with the leathery hide of a rhinoceros or the quills on a porcupine's back. Humans cannot fly, run very fast or swim well, and we have no natural camouflage to help us hide away from danger. So why have human beings been such a successful species so far?

Brain power

A highly developed brain brings the possibility of intelligence. Intelligence means that we can work out how things happen. Once this knowledge is gained we can act, or behave, in ways that should increase our chances of survival. We can learn, remember and invent. One of the most important human developments was organised farming. This ensures a regular supply of food. Water can be purified for drinking. We can build shelters against bad weather and continue to develop medicines against diseases. A high-velocity rifle will kill any dangerous animal before it has even seen or smelt that we are there.

But remember that on your own you are probably still quite helpless. As helpless as a human baby that has not yet learnt the skills of survival. Humans are social animals – they have always worked together in groups. If all the members of the group co-operate and contribute to the group's survival in different ways, then every member of the group is more likely to survive to a ripe old age.

Why we do what we do

Behaviour is the key to human survival. But the right behaviour depends on having good senses. Imagine that you have been blind-folded very thoroughly, so that you cannot see even the faintest glimmer of light. Then you have ear muffs placed over your ears so that you cannot hear even the faintest of sounds. Next, a breathing mask is placed over your mouth and nose and joined to an air supply. This lets you breathe underwater. The mask has no taste or smell. Finally, you are lowered into a huge tank of water until you are completely submerged.

The water is so still and calm that you have no sensation of touch anywhere upon your skin. The water is at exactly the same temperature as your body. There is no pressure, no roughness or smoothness, and no pain. Everything is utterly black and completely silent.

The effects can be quite alarming. You would rapidly become disoriented, insecure and very anxious. Such experiments cannot be kept going for long because they can damage the volunteers' mental states permanently. Above everything else, this just shows how important our senses really are. They are our link to the world we live in. All our senses are based on living cells called *receptors*. They receive, or 'take in', the changes that take place around us.

The better all our receptors or senses are working, the more information about the world we can take in. The brain accepts all of this information, even though most of it is unimportant, and we ignore it. If you are reading this sentence carefully, your brain is ignoring sounds and smells from all around you.

When necessary, however, we use the information to decide how to act: in other words how to *behave*.

▲ Penfield's homunculus ('small man'). The bigger the body parts, the bigger the brain area that they are linked to.

Emergency action!

You are walking home alone one night along a dark street, and a car suddenly appears, travelling at speed. It seems to swerve towards you. You suddenly feel frightened. You jump backwards away from the oncoming car, which screeches to a halt ten metres away. The door opens and the light comes on . . .

How did you know the car was there?

Your senses of sight and hearing made you aware of the car. Your brain worked out that it could be a possible threat. You saw the car approaching. You heard the car approaching. You saw and heard the car swerving towards you. Your senses were *stimulated*.

Your eyes and ears received many stimuli. *Stimulus* means any of the changes happening around you that are detected by your senses. In this example, some of the stimuli were: the sight of the car itself; seeing the car move towards you and change direction; the sound of the car, and so on.

A stimulus picked up by a receptor cell is the very first stage in deciding what to do, or how to behave.

How did you know what to do?

The information received by your receptors or senses was passed on to your brain. Your brain co-ordinated this data and made a decision about the best way of dealing with what all of this information was telling it.

Any system of control or behaviour must be able to react to change. There must be a co-ordinating and controlling centre capable of deciding which changes are important and what should be done about them. In human beings, this system is the *central nervous system*, or CNS. This consists of the brain and the spinal cord. It is connected to all other parts of the body by nerves.

What did your brain decide to do?

You felt fear, and then quickly used the muscles in your legs and other parts of your body to jump backwards away from harm. This is called a *response*. You reacted to the situation so as to stay alive.

How did your response come about?

Your brain transmitted messages along nerves to the correct muscles in your body. The muscles acted to move you away from the danger. In this example, the muscles are called the *effectors* because they carried out or 'effected' your response. In animals, effector systems that bring about appropriate responses to stimuli are usually the body's muscles because movement is often involved in a response.

We now have a complete model of simple behaviour.

- *Stimulus* – a change detected by receptors;
- *Receptor system* – detects stimuli;
- *Control system* – co-ordinates information and decides upon the response;
- *Effector system* – carries out the appropriate response.

Biologists sometimes call this basic system the 'stimulus–response' model of behaviour.

▼ This cross section of a human brain shows the main parts of the brain.

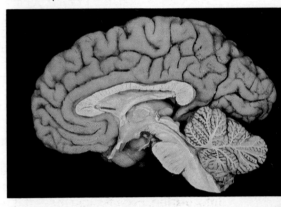

► The stimulus–response model of behaviour.

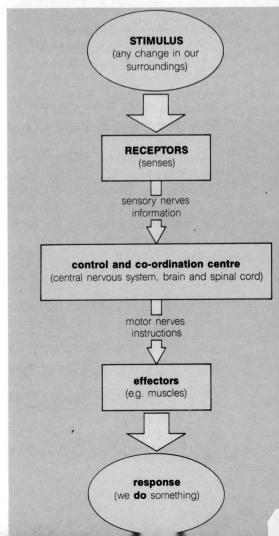

Perception – the working of the brain

Our perception – how we 'see' the world – depends upon the activity of the brain and the information it receives. This mechanism, like so many other brain functions, is far from being fully understood.

All of the information going into the brain from the senses, and all the information passing out of the brain to our effectors, is essentially in the same form. Messages are conducted along the *sensory* and *motor* nerves as 'bursts' of tiny electrical impulses. Whether it is information from the eyes, ears or skin, the brain receives the data as patterns of electric signals. This is very much like the way a computer gets its information.

Different parts of the brain receive the messages from different senses. One part of the brain interprets them as a 'picture' that we can 'see', another part converts them into 'sounds' that we 'hear', and yet a third part makes us aware of sensations called 'feeling' or 'touch'. Exactly how the brain functions is still not known.

Reflexes – rapid responses for staying alive

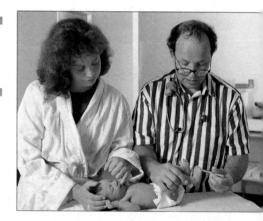

If something comes too near to your eyes, you blink. If you place your hand on something hot, you pull it away without even thinking. And if you take bad food into your stomach, you vomit.

All these responses are called *reflexes*. They are very rapid reactions to stimuli, and we have many reflexes to protect our bodies from harm. The eyelids come down to cover the eyes. The hand is moved away from the hot object before the skin is badly burnt. Food that could make you ill is passed out of the body by the quickest possible route.

One of the first things that happens to you when you are born is that the doctor or nurse will tickle the soles of your feet. If your toes curl up, the doctor knows that one of your important reflexes is working.

These reflex actions are automatic – this means that you don't have to think before you respond. Thinking would waste valuable time and you could be hurt before you can react.

But human beings can *think*. The 'thinking brain' can over-ride some reflexes. If you are stupid enough you can keep your hand on a hot object for as long as you can bear the pain! You can also 'train' yourself not to blink when something moves near your eyes.

Fright, fight or flight?

Have you ever been scared? Or frightened? Or even just a little bit nervous? A sudden noise. Footsteps behind you in a dark lane. A visit to the dentist – or having to make a speech or sit an exam.

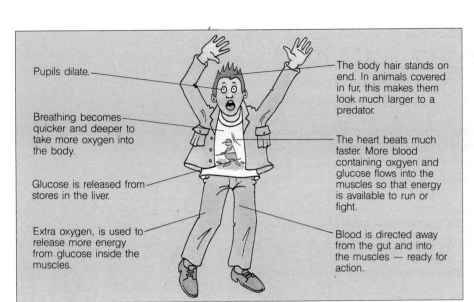

- Pupils dilate.
- Breathing becomes quicker and deeper to take more oxygen into the body.
- Glucose is released from stores in the liver.
- Extra oxygen, is used to release more energy from glucose inside the muscles.
- The body hair stands on end. In animals covered in fur, this makes them look much larger to a predator.
- The heart beats much faster. More blood containing oxgyen and glucose flows into the muscles so that energy is available to run or fight.
- Blood is directed away from the gut and into the muscles — ready for action.

◄ This is what adrenalin does to the body.

When you are scared or frightened you get 'butterflies in the stomach'. Your heart beats faster. These are automatic biological reactions – and are part of your human 'survival kit'. They are caused by the sudden release of a special chemical hormone called *adrenalin*. It's released into the blood from glands just above the kidneys, in response to danger and fear. This is the fright part of the response, and it's automatic — you don't have to think about it.

Adrenalin prepares your body for facing danger. All the effects it has are designed to help you stay alive.

In the wild, for most animals this will usually mean either a *fight* against an enemy, or *flight* – running away. For both activities, the changes that need to happen in the body are the same. And adrenalin makes them happen fast!

'Getting the adrenalin flowing' is a technique many athletes use to improve their performance. They 'psych themselves up' in a kind of controlled panic to tap otherwise hidden reserves of strength and speed. It's not surprising that this makes them aggressive and sometimes difficult to control.

Instinct and learning

Most animals, including humans, are born with instincts. These are types of behaviour that don't have to be learnt. Instincts are inborn. Instinctive behaviour can be very important in keeping animals alive, especially when they are very young.

A duckling pecks its way out of the shell by instinct. Young birds in a nest, unable to fly, stay silent and still when a hawk passes overhead. Human babies don't have to learn how to suckle at the breast. And new-born deer must be able to run with their mothers within an hour or so of birth if they are not to be attacked and killed by predators.

These patterns of behaviour are already 'programmed' into the young. They will obviously help them to survive in their normal habitat. But what happens if this changes? Instinct only really works well when conditions don't change. If things do change, it could make animals appear almost

▲ The instinct of this adult bird is to bring food when it sees the brightly coloured throats of its young.

7

suicidal in their behaviour! Young European salmon, for example, are driven by instinct to swim thousands of miles across the Atlantic ocean to the coast of North America. When fully grown and ready to breed, they swim all the way back again to find the *same* river in which they were born. If the river has become polluted or blocked, all the salmon will die before they get the chance to reproduce.

This journey of the salmon made sense in the past: they would always find the clean, fresh water where they were born, and could now safely breed. But the instinct to return is so strong that the salmon cannot learn how to find a clean river should the original be polluted.

Behaviour patterns for survival

Most animals have patterns of behaviour to cope with the most important aspects of staying alive and for ensuring that new animals are produced and stay alive in their turn. Behaviour covers all aspects of an animal's life.

- Courtship – finding a mate, e.g. a male peacock displays its fan of coloured tail feathers to attract a female bird.
- Territory – guarding the feeding area. A pair of robins will chase other pairs out of their territory.
- Parenthood – looking after the young.
- Feeding – catching, gathering, eating and storing food; e.g. a young squirrel learns the best way to open a hazel nut; predators learn to hunt.
- Aggression – frightening away other animals, especially predators.
- Communication – ways of passing on information to other individuals to aid survival, e.g. a human baby cries when it is hungry, cold or wet; animals give out warning cries and displays.
- Social – making contacts within the social group so that each animal becomes an accepted part of the group and learns how to co-operate to the benefit of all members. For example, young monkeys groom the fur of elders and neighbours.
- Play – young animals learn the main patterns of behaviour needed to survive as an adult, e.g. young chimpanzees learn through play how to use a stick to retrieve insects from inside tree trunks; animals often learn to fight by playing.

Some behaviour patterns may have to be learned, others seem to be inborn. In some cases, the general pattern is inborn but the finer points have to be learnt by trial and error. For example, a bird has an inborn set of reflexes that enable it to fly – but exactly *how* to fly (taking off, landing, etc.) has to be learnt by practising.

The human brain makes us very good at learning new skills, and new ways of behaving to cope with change. It gives us the edge when it comes to survival. This is just as well – because the modern world is changing faster than at any time in human history.

Changing and controlling behaviour

All behaviour depends on the brain and the rest of the nervous system. Any substance that affects or interferes with this system is likely to change the way a person behaves. Drugs are chemicals that do just this. Some drugs can bring relief from pain by stopping nerve endings working in a small area of the body. This is what happens when we have a local anaesthetic at the dentist.

More powerful *general anaesthetic* drugs can change the chemistry of the brain itself and send us into a very deep sleep. We can have a major operation and know nothing about it at all.

There are times when our brains seem to be overactive. The stress of everyday life may be difficult to bear, and the more we worry about our problems the more anxious we become.

Humans have been using sedative or tranquiliser drugs for thousands of years. This type of drug slows down the workings of the brain. They are called *depressants*. Alcohol is a depressant. This is why it can make people feel relaxed. The fumes from glues and solvents are depressants, except that the effect lasts for a much shorter time.

The main kinds of drugs and their uses

Type	Effect/uses	Examples
analgesics	pain killers	Aspirin Codeine Paracetamol morphine heroin
anaesthetics	cause loss of feeling or unconsciousness	cocaine nitrous oxide ether
tranquillisers (sedatives or 'downers')	slow down brain activity, have a calming effect	Valium barbiturates alcohol Librium morphine heroin
stimulants ('uppers' or 'pep pills')	increase brain activity, help depression	caffeine cocaine nicotine benzedrine amphetamines
hallucinogens	make people see or hear things that aren't there, or see things more vividly	LSD marijuana Mescalin

Hallucinogenic drugs affect the parts of the brain which control hearing and sight. Users see and hear things that are not really there. In this fantasy state they may behave in ways which are strange and unsafe, believing that they have super-human abilities.

Many of the drugs that change behaviour are obviously useful for human survival. But they have to be used with care. Most drugs also have serious side-effects. A side-effect is an extra thing that the drug does, which isn't wanted. One of the most dangerous of these is *addiction*.

Addiction

Drugs which have a powerful effect on the brain may create a strong craving by the body for more and more of the drug concerned. This is what is meant by being addicted to a drug. Addicts are driven to steal and kill to maintain the supply of their drug. Addiction can develop very quickly – with heroin in less than a week. Also, most drugs actually damage the brain. As addicts use more and more of the drug, so the brain becomes more and more damaged. Even legal drugs can be strongly addictive and extremely dangerous. One hundred thousand people in Britain each year are thought to die from the side-effects of smoking tobacco. Alcohol kills more people than any other drug – because so many people use it.

Drug addiction can happen to anyone. It can be cured if the reasons for taking drugs in the first place are fully understood and overcome.

There is a lot more detail about reflexes, the brain, drugs and learning in the 'Reference section'. You don't need to learn the details, but you will find it interesting and useful in helping you to answer the questions at the end of this Chapter.

Defence against disease

Behaviour helps animals to defend themselves against other animals that might attack them. But one of the biggest dangers we all face comes from tiny things that we cannot see – *microbes*. All living things, plants, animals, humans, and even bacteria, are under constant attack from microbes.

If harmful bacteria and viruses get inside our bodies they interfere with our life processes and release poisons which make us ill. In some cases, the diseases they cause can be fatal.

The human body has quite complicated defence systems against these enemy microbes, to stop them getting inside us in the first place, and to destroy them if they do manage to infect us.

Keeping microbes out

It helps if we can keep harmful microbes from getting inside out bodies. Our skin forms an almost complete barrier between the inside of our bodies and the outside world. As long as the skin is intact, it keeps harmful micro-organisms on the outside where they can do little harm.

But if the skin is damaged or cut this can let microbes in, so an emergency-repair system quickly comes into action. Once a blood vessel is damaged the blood starts to leak out. Small bodies in the blood called *platelets* begin to clot the blood as soon as they come into contact with

▼
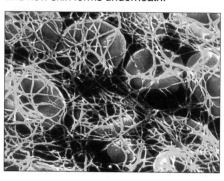
The yellow mesh is fibrin fibres starting to hold red blood cells in a clot. The clot dries and new skin forms underneath.

▼

The addiction to some drugs is more obvious than to others.

▼
This is a section through the human skin. You can see the surface skin cells that are continually worn away and the layers of growing cells underneath.

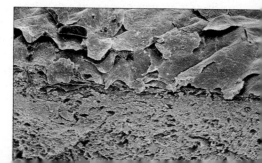

the air. The clotting process is described on page 211 in the 'Reference section'.

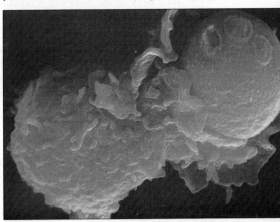
The phagocyte is engulfing the yeast cell that is almost as large as itself.

What happens when germs get inside your body?

Human blood contains two main types of white blood cell. These are called *phagocytes* and *lymphocytes*. Both work inside our bodies to keep us free from disease. You can see these white cells in the photographs.

Phagocytes

These cells pour out of blood vessels near any injury or wound. They surround and destroy any bacteria that enter the body before the wound can be healed. The damaged area becomes red, swollen, and painful. It's like the site of a battle, with the bacteria invading and the phagocytes in defence. Dead bacteria and white cells form the pus in a wound. This is removed from the skin surface as new tissue grows underneath it.

Lymphocytes

These white cells fight off bacteria and viruses in a quite different way. They make chemicals called antibodies which are released into the blood to kill the invading microbes.

It may take time for the lymphocytes to make the correct sort of antibodies. This is why we often fall ill for a few days from minor infections, and then recover. If the antibodies aren't made, or for some reason they cannot attack the disease-causing microbes, we may never recover at all.

Antibodies are *specific*, which means that they are made in exactly the right form to attack a particular type of virus or bacterium that is infecting the body. So antibodies that will kill the measles virus will not have any effect on the bacteria that cause cholera.

Antibodies destroy the invading germs by using a range of methods. They may make the microbes clump together so that the phagocyte white cells can engulf or ingest microbes more easily and in greater numbers.

Some antibodies dissolve the cell membranes of micro-organisms. This causes them to literally fall apart. Other types of antibody destroy the poisonous substances that bacteria release into our blood.

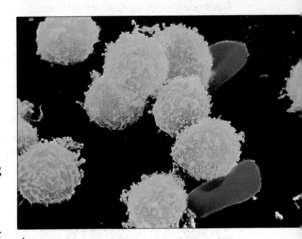
This lymphocyte produces antibodies: chemicals that protect the body from diseases.

Modern methods of staying alive

Two hundred years ago, doctors didn't know about microbes or that they caused disease. They certainly didn't know much about how such diseases might be cured. There were no anaesthetics to put you to sleep during surgery. The drugs were simple remedies made from herbs, and there were no injections to protect you against a host of fatal diseases. The first breakthrough for modern medicine was probably the discovery of *vaccination*.

Smallpox was once a deadly disease. In the eighteenth century, an English woman, Mary Wortley Montagu, was travelling in Turkey. She saw that the women there scratched the pus from the skin of a mildly infected smallpox victim into the skin of their children. They hoped that this would give their children a *mild* form of the disease, and protect them from the much worse form, which could kill them. Around 1722, this

Lady Mary Wortley Montagu.

method was widely used throughout Europe. It fell out of favour when it became clear that people treated in this way could develop the severe form of the disease, and die.

But the principles of vaccination can be found in use even earlier than 1722. The ancient Chinese had developed their own methods.

In 1796, Dr Edward Jenner took vaccination one stage further. He was very interested in curing smallpox. His treatment succeeded in making people immune from the disease. But how does this work?

Immunisation – helping the body defences

If you have measles, and survive, you are not likely to catch measles again. Why does this happen with some diseases, and how does it come to happen at all? The answer is to do with antibodies.

Once antibodies have been made against a microbe, they may stay in the blood for some time. The white cells which made these antibodies can also 'remember' exactly the sort of antibody they made. So if the same type of microbe enters your body again, you already have the design for a ready supply of antibodies to attack the microbe at once. This means that the microbes are wiped out before they have the chance to make you ill. You are said to be *immune* from the disease.

Jenner's discovery worked by making people immune from diseases by deliberately injecting them with a harmless form of the disease. This is called *immunisation*. The lymphocytes are stimulated to make the correct antibodies. They 'remember' how to do this. If the harmful form of the germ ever gets into your body, it is doomed from the start. You are safe from this disease, at least. For some diseases the immunity may last until the end of your life, but for others you need 'booster' injections.

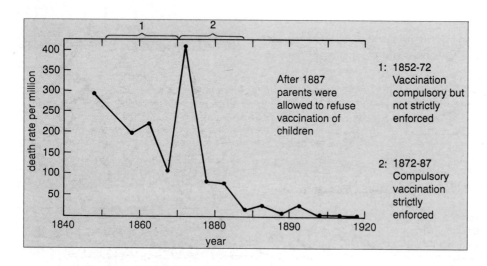

After 1887 parents were allowed to refuse vaccination of children

1: 1852-72 Vaccination compulsory but not strictly enforced

2: 1872-87 Compulsory vaccination strictly enforced

◄ Deaths from Smallpox in England and Wales 1848–1920.

The body as a machine

Many parts of the body are very similar to simple machines in the way that they work. The human heart, for example, is a four-chambered pump. The joystick on a computer game moves in just the same way as thigh and shoulder bones do at their joints.

Modern materials make it possible to replace various parts of our bodies if they get damaged or wear-out. Machines can be placed inside us by surgery, or they may be used outside the body to help a person stay alive, or overcome a disability.

This life-support technology can give people the chance for a better life. In some cases, it offers the only hope they have for life at all.

Life-support technology

- Many babies are born premature – they are born too soon and may die without special treatment. Incubators give warmth, oxygen, and careful monitoring to keep them alive until they are old enough and strong enough to survive under normal conditions.
- Pacemakers are fitted when a person's heart cannot beat to a normal rhythm. The heart stops and starts, and may stop beating altogether. The pacemaker sends electrical impulses to the heart to keep it beating regularly.
- Injured or diseased hip joints can be replaced with artificial ones. This allows a person who may have been completely crippled to walk again normally.
- Kidney (dialysis) machines carry out the same jobs as the human kidney. They filter the blood to remove poisonous wastes, and keep water and salts at the correct levels in the blood. Using a machine is an inconvenient and lengthy business. It takes many hours for the blood to be purified and the treatment must be repeated every two or three days. But without it, if your own kidneys had failed, you would soon die.

Activities

1 Imagine that you have been shipwrecked on a desert island with three of your friends. The island has animal and plant life, but no other human beings. On the beach you find a chest, washed up from the wreck of the ship. It contains *five* things, brought with you from civilization. You are not likely to be rescued for at least a year.

   What five things would it be best to have in the chest to help you 'stay alive' for that time? Discuss it with your friends, and decide what the things should be. Be ready to explain your choice to the rest of the class.

2 Imagine that you are a member of a mountain-climbing team responsible for taking out groups of climbers and walkers on expeditions into the Cairngorm mountains in Scotland. Unexpected storms, blizzards and mountain mists can occur with little or no warning. Every year people get lost or injured during these climbing and mountain-walking expeditions. Some of them die through exposure before they can be rescued. You have been asked to design a *survival kit* to be carried by every person participating in such expeditions. The kit should allow an injured or stranded member of the team to survive the low temperatures, heavy rainfall, and high winds for at least 24 hours. Follow the design brief below but you may add as many features to the survival kit as you think necessary and practical. You could make a 'mock-up' of your survival kit to show its design clearly.

Design brief for survival kit

(i) The kit must be light in weight, and compact so as to be carried easily.
(ii) It must deal with the need for the person to stay warm and dry.
(iii) It must contain some form of emergency food and drink.
(iv) It must contain some form of basic first aid equipment.
(v) It must contain some way of attracting the attention of rescuers.
Say why each item that you include would be useful.

Questions

1 Read about the stimulus–response model of behaviour in the story on page 4. Use this model to explain your response when you realised that the car was no longer a threat.

2 Write out the sentences below, matching the correct ending to each of the beginnings.

	Beginnings	*Endings*
(i)	The main types of microbes which cause disease are	by white blood cells.
(ii)	Small bodies in the blood called platelets	lymphocytes
(iii)	The skin	start the clotting process
(iv)	Antibodies are made by white blood cells called	stops microbes getting into the body.
(v)	Microbes inside the body are killed	bacteria and viruses

3 For each of the five examples of simple behaviour described below, copy and fill in the chart to give the *stimulus*, *receptor*, *response*, and *effectors* in each case. The first one has already been filled in.

Five examples of behaviour:
- leaping to your feet and shouting when your side scores a goal at a football match;
- dancing to a favourite record;
- trying to find out who is wearing a very pleasant-smelling perfume or aftershave in a room at a party;
- trying to locate the light switch in a very dark room;
- crying because you are peeling onions.

Stimulus	Receptor or sense	Response	Effector
Sight and sound of goal being scored	eyes and ears	leap to feet wave hands in air etc. shout	leg and trunk muscles arm and hand muscles vocal chords

4 One popular pastime in Sweden is to take a sauna bath and then run outside and roll about in the snow — naked!

Make a list of all the changes that would take place in the skin of a person doing this as they move from an extremely hot and humid situation (the sauna) into the much colder environment outdoors. Describe fully how each of the physiological changes in your list takes place. The 'Reference section' will help you.

Checklist

These are the facts and ideas you should have learned by studying this topic.

To succeed at Basic Level you should:

- know how important food is for life, and that we need carbohydrates and fats for energy, proteins for growth, and vitamins and minerals for health
- know the two main types of nerve: for sensing and for controlling muscles
- know about drugs or drinks that can harm you
- know how to look after your teeth
- know that we can get well without medicines because the body can defend itself against diseases
- be able to recognise some human cells: red blood cells, nerve cells, sperm cells
- know that the *heart* pumps blood and that the *kidneys* filter it

To succeed at Foundation Level you should:

- know what the body needs to keep healthy, i.e. a balanced diet of carbohydrates, fats, protein, minerals and vitamins (and which foods provide these); a healthy lifestyle (like not eating too much or too little; keeping fit, not using tobacco, alcohol and other drugs)
- understand how microbes can be harmful in causing diseases, know some examples (bacteria, viruses, fungi, protozoa), and know how the body defends itself
- know how to prevent tooth decay
- know that living things are made up of different kinds of cells and about the jobs they do – especially sperm cells, nerve cells and red blood cells
- know what happens to the blood when the heart or kidneys are failing

To succeed at Merit Level you should:

- be able to analyse data about diet and exercise and their effects on health
- be able to analyse behaviour in terms of *stimulus, receptor, co-ordinator and effector*
- understand the risks of alcohol, solvent and drug abuse, and know their effects on the body
- know how diseases are spread (by touch, through air, water or food, and by animals such as insects)
- know how microbes cause tooth decay
- know how living things can protect themselves against disease (e.g. by white blood cells and antibodies)
- know the basic structure of a living cell
- know about organ transplants and the problem of rejection
- know about the discovery of germs and the causes of diseases (e.g. the work of Louis Pasteur)

To succeed at Special Level you should:

- be able to analyse data on diet and lifestyles and draw conclusions about how they affect health
- understand the idea of a *conditioned reflex*
- know about the social effects of drug abuse and the meanings of *withdrawal symptom* and *addiction*
- know what is likely to cause the rapid growth of populations of microbes and the consequences for infection
- understand the effects of disease microbes on the body, and how immunisation and medicines can help in cure or prevention
- know how the structure of different cells is related to the jobs they do (e.g. sperm cells, red blood cells, nerve cells)
- be able to explain how modern technology is used in life-support systems (e.g. pacemakers, kidney machines, incubators), and evaluate the effects of their use

15

CHAPTER TWO

sound and music

We sense sound through our ears. The ear picks up sound waves from the outside world and changes them into electrical signals that go to our brains.

The brain can then sort out the sounds. It can tell between high and low notes, how loud the sounds are and what direction the sounds are coming from.

A good sense of hearing is very important. Animals need to be able to hear predators coming and to be able to warn each other. Many animals communicate by using sound. People listen to music.

This chapter will tell you what sound is. It tells you how different musical instruments work. What do we mean by *loudness*? What is the difference between a high and a low note? It also explains how sound is recorded and stored on a disc or tape so that it can be played back later — music for your ears!

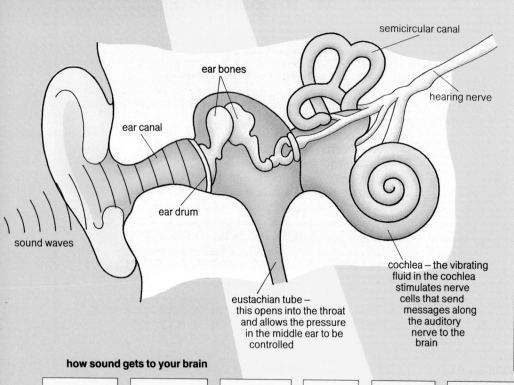

semicircular canal

ear bones

hearing nerve

ear canal

ear drum

sound waves

cochlea – the vibrating fluid in the cochlea stimulates nerve cells that send messages along the auditory nerve to the brain

eustachian tube – this opens into the throat and allows the pressure in the middle ear to be controlled

how sound gets to your brain

| 1. Vibration produces sound waves | 2. Sound waves in air – longitudinal waves | 3. The eardrum changes the waves into transverse waves | 4. The ear bones vibrate | 5. The oval window has transverse vibrations | 6. Longitudinal waves travel along the fluid of the inner ear | 7. Nerve endings are stimulated, which send electrical signals to the brain |

outer ear   middle ear   inner ear

the bones of the ear

hammer anvil stirrup

oval window

④

⑤

round window

② air ③

air

⑦

①

⑥

fluid-filled canal

Making sound

When any object vibrates, sound is produced. The sound travels as a wave, carrying energy. Light also travels as waves, but sound waves behave differently from light waves. Light waves move up and down, or from side to side. They are called *transverse* waves. Water waves are examples of transverse waves.

▼
Transverse and longitudinal waves are made by different types of vibrations.

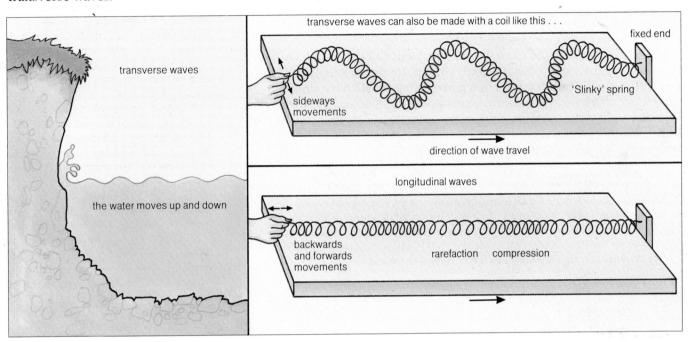

Sound waves move to-and-fro. You can see this kind of movement with a long spring. You have to move the end of the spring to-and-fro instead of up and down. Sound waves are *longitudinal* waves.

If you watch the paper cone of a loudspeaker, you can see that it is bouncing in and out. As the cone *vibrates*, it affects the air in front of it. It pushes and pulls the air. This movement squeezes and stretches the air. You can feel the air in front of a loudspeaker vibrating.

When the air is squeezed, the molecules in the air are pushed closer together. This increases the pressure in the air, creating a *compression*. When air is stretched the molecules are pulled further apart. The pressure is less. This low pressure area is called a *rarefaction*.

As the air molecules vibrate to-and-fro, they pass their energy on to the next lot of molecules. The 'sound' energy spreads as a pressure wave through the air. This is shown in the drawing (right).

The distance from the peak of one pressure wave to the next is its *wavelength*. The maximum difference in the pressure of the sound wave is called its *amplitude*. These are shown on the graph in the drawing.

The pressure amplitude of an everyday sound wave is very small. It is about one millionth of ordinary air pressure! A healthy human ear can detect sounds where the pressure differences are a billionth of normal air pressure. If a sound has a pressure amplitude of just one hundredth atmospheric pressure you feel pain, and the ear may be permanently damaged.

▼
Sound travels as a pressure wave. The pressure changes are very small compared with the normal pressure of air.

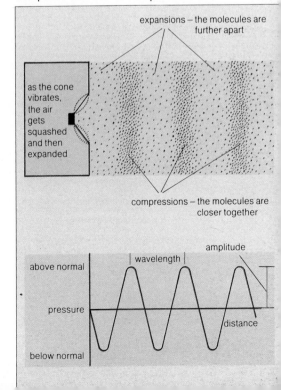

How sounds are different

We tell one sound from another by hearing three main differences:
- in loudness,
- in pitch – how high or low the note is,
- in quality – the tone of the sound, e.g. whether it is made by guitar or a whistle.

We've already seen that differences in loudness are due to the size of the pressure variations in the sound wave. Sounds carry energy, and louder sounds carry more energy than quieter ones.

Differences in pitch are caused by the frequency of the sound. Ordinary sounds are usually quite complicated. To start, think of a simple sound, like the one made by a recorder or a guitar string. It will have simple waves, like those shown in the diagram opposite. These are the waves the sounds would make if it were shown on a cathode ray oscilloscope screen.

The number of sound waves produced in 1 second is called the *frequency*. We measure this frequency in hertz (Hz).

Think of a sound made by an instrument vibrating 512 times a second. It will produce a note at Middle C, 512 Hz. The speed of sound in air is about 340 m/s. At the end of 1 second the first compression will be 340 metres away from the instrument that made the sound. There will be 512 waves in this distance. So we can work out the length of the wave:

$$\text{wavelength in air} = \frac{340 \text{ metres}}{512 \text{ waves}} = 0.66 \text{ metres.}$$

Of course, the speed of sound is different in different media. In water, the speed is about 1400 metres a second. This means that an underwater note at 512 Hz would have a larger wavelength – the same number of waves are spread over a greater distance:

$$\text{wavelength in water} = \frac{1410 \text{ metres}}{512 \text{ waves}} = 2.75 \text{ metres}$$

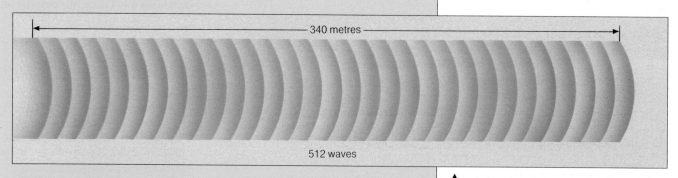

340 metres

512 waves

▲
In one second's worth of the sound there are 512 waves.

Wavelength, speed and frequency are related by a formula:

$$\text{wavelength} = \frac{\text{speed}}{\text{frequency}}, \quad \text{or } \lambda = v/f,$$

(λ is the Greek letter *lamda*)

The formula is usually written: speed = frequency × wavelength,

$$\text{or } v = f\lambda.$$

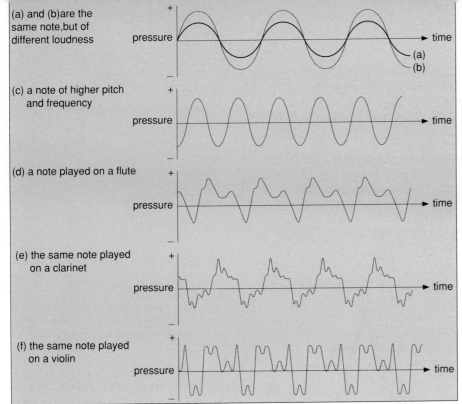

(a) and (b) are the same note, but of different loudness

pressure → time

(a)
(b)

(c) a note of higher pitch and frequency

pressure → time

(d) a note played on a flute

pressure → time

(e) the same note played on a clarinet

pressure → time

(f) the same note played on a violin

pressure → time

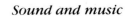

◄
Air pressure varies with different types of sound.

The more waves per second the greater the frequency – and the higher the pitch of the note we hear. The figure at the top of this page shows the wave patterns produced by notes of different amplitudes and frequencies. Very low notes will have a typical frequency of about 20 Hz (20 waves would go past you in 1 second). The lowest note that we can hear is about 16 Hz. Babies cry at about a 1000 Hz – the human ear is most sensitive to sounds of this frequency. Babies aren't fools! The highest frequency that we can hear is about 22 000 Hz for young people. As we get older our ears get less sensitive to high-frequency sounds. A 50-year old might only hear sounds up to about 12 000 Hz.

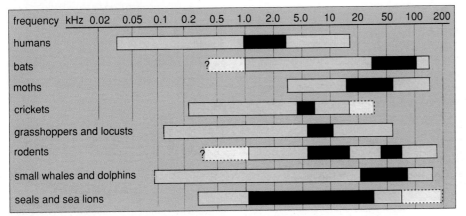

| frequency kHz | 0.02 | 0.05 | 0.1 | 0.2 | 0.5 | 1.0 | 2.0 | 5.0 | 10 | 20 | 50 | 100 | 200 |

humans
bats
moths
crickets
grasshoppers and locusts
rodents
small whales and dolphins
seals and sea lions

◄
The hearing ranges of different animals are very different. The darkest areas show the frequencies that the animals hear best.

The quality of a sound is decided by the way the source vibrates. Trumpets and flutes have different shapes, and are made of different materials. The sounds that they make sound different even when they play the same note at the same loudness. Voices are different because the sound box in the throat, the tongue and the mouth are different in different people.

These differences mean that the sound waves produced by different instruments have different shapes. The sound patterns made by a violin and clarinet, both playing a note of the same pitch and frequency, are very different.

RESONANCE

A vibrating object has energy. It can give some of the energy to another object and so make it vibrate as well. The energy transfer works best when the two objects are vibrating with the same frequency. When this happens, it is called *resonance*.

The simplest example of resonance happens when you push a child on a swing. A swing is a simple pendulum. It will swing backwards and forwards at the same rate all the time. In other words, it has a definite frequency of vibration (or oscillation). To make the swinging get larger and larger you have to inject energy at the same rate as it swings. You do this by giving it a push in time with its swinging. The energy of the swing builds up. It *resonates* at the same frequency as your pushes.

◄
To build up the height of swing, you have to put the energy into the swing at the right point – when the swing is at its highest.

▼
Gusts of wind made the Tacoma Narrows Bridge resonate just like the swing. A wave built up along the bridge, which shook itself to pieces.

The frequency of a swing is very low, about 0.5 hZ. You can see and feel what is happening. But the same kind of thing is happening all the time in many musical instruments, but at much higher frequencies.

When you pluck a stretched string it vibrates at its natural frequency. The sound it makes is not very loud, but it will last quite a long time. The energy can't get into the air very easily – the string is simply too small to move much air and to build up the pressure waves.

But if the string is fixed to a piece of wood the energy can go from the vibrating string into the wood. A well-designed piece of wood will be able to vibrate, quite naturally, at a whole range of frequencies. It will pick up the energy from the string very efficiently and start vibrating at the same frequency. It will *resonate*, just like the swing, but at a much higher frequency.

The 'piece of wood' could be a guitar, a violin or a cello. The strange shapes of these instruments has been developed by trial and error over hundreds of years to make sure that they resonate properly at the frequencies used in music.

Resonance happens in other things as well. Soldiers marching over a small bridge have to 'break step', in case the regular stamp of their feet makes the bridge resonate. Wind eddies can make tall buildings resonate. The slow vibrations can build up and might strain the building, and make the people in it feel seasick! Earthquakes cause most of their damage to buildings when the buildings resonate to the frequency of the Earthquake waves. The most famous example of resonance is the complete destruction of the Tacoma Narrows Bridge in Washington State, USA, in 1940.

Activity 5 is about resonance.

The speed of sound

The speed of sound in different materials

Material (medium)	Speed in m/s
air	331
hydrogen	1286
carbon dioxide	260
wood	4200 (varies)
copper	3813
iron	5000
rubber	1600 (varies)
cork	500
water	1480

How fast a sound moves depends on what it is moving through. In dry air, at 0 °C, sound travels at a speed of about 340 metres per second. But sound can travel through liquids and solids as well. In water at 0 °C, sound travels at 1400 m/s. In steel, the speed of sound waves is near 6000 m/s.

Some aircraft can go faster than the speed of sound in air. As they reach the speed of sound they meet the 'sound barrier'. This makes a shock wave. Think of a pile of sound waves building up in front of the plane. When the plane 'overtakes' these waves, a shock wave is free to travel behind the plane, down to the grand. Buildings have been damaged by these shock waves.

Transmitting and recording sound

Sound doesn't usually travel very far. This is because its energy is absorbed by the air it is travelling through. To send messages further we use telephones, radio or television or record sounds on to tape or disc.

Before you can transmit or record a sound it must first be changed. First, the wave pattern of the sound is changed to an electrical pattern. In its new form it can be sent over long distances, or stored so that you can hear it again. The device that changes sound signals to electrical signals is called a *microphone*.

There are many sorts of microphone. For high quality recording the *moving-coil microphone* is used. This has a thin plate, or *diaphragm*. The diaphragm vibrates up and down when someone speaks into the microphone. There is a coil of very thin wire attached to the diaphragm. This also moves up and down. It moves between the poles of a magnet. As a result of this movement, electrical signals are generated in the coil. These vary in strength and shape with the loudness and pitch of the sounds. The electrical signals travel along wires to an amplifier. From here they can be recorded, or sent to a transmitter.

To get the signals to travel through space they have to be changed to radio waves. These can be transmitted over very long distances. At the other end the waves can be received by a radio. This has an aerial which collects the radio waves and changes them back to electrical signals. They need to be decoded and amplified before going to a loudspeaker to be changed back to sound.

The final part of any sound-transmission chain is the loudspeaker. It converts the electrical signals back into sound. A speaker may look very different from a microphone, but in fact they are very alike. Both have a diaphragm, a moving coil and a magnet. When electrical signals pass through the coil, they create changing magnetic fields. These react with the magnetic field of the magnet. Sometimes the coil is attracted one way, other times it is pushed the other. This changes as the current in the coil changes. The coil moves in and out, very quickly. The moving coil makes the diaphragm vibrate, creating sound. In a loudspeaker the diaphragm is a paper cone.

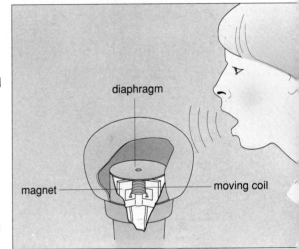

▲
The moving coil microphone is used for high-quality recording. It copes well with the same range of sounds as the human ear.

▼
The moving coil loudspeaker. Large speakers are used to make low notes. Small speakers are better at making high notes.

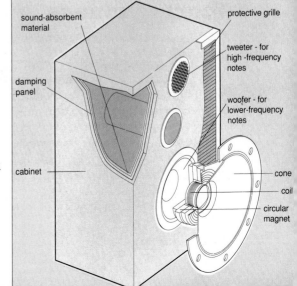

Microphones and loudspeakers change information from one kind of energy carrier to another.

- microphone : sound → electricity
- loudspeaker : electricity → sound

Devices that do this are called *transducers*.

Telephones

These photographs show the microphone and earpiece of a telephone. Older telephones use carbon microphones. Modern ones use moving-coil or *electret* microphones. Signals are carried short distances (e.g. local calls) in the form of changing electric currents in copper wires. Long-distance phone calls travel through optical fibres. First, the signal is coded into an 'on-off' digital signal. This is then carried by a beam of infrared laser light down a thin plastic fibre. There is more about digital coding of signals on page 24.

▼
The electret microphone is much smaller than the old carbon microphones. This means that the telephone has been made much smaller as well.

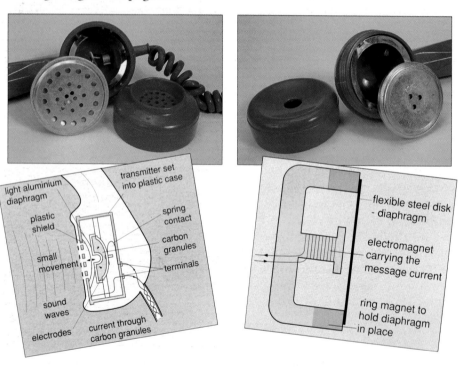

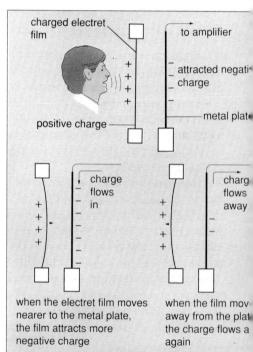

Storing sounds

Thomas Edison invented the world's first sound-recording machine in 1877. He named it a 'sound writer', or *phonograph*. His phonograph had a small horn to catch sound. At one end of the horn was a needle. This vibrated when he shouted down the horn. The needle was pressed onto some tin foil wrapped around a brass cylinder. The cylinder had a spiral groove in it. As Edison turned the handle he shouted 'Mary had a little lamb'. The needle vibrated, making wiggly grooves in the foil. Edison put the needle back to the beginning, and swapped the horn for a much larger one. He turned the handle. As the cylinder turned he heard the ghostly sound of his own voice, very faint and scratchy.

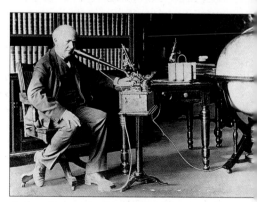

▲
Thomas Edison sitting beside his first phonograph.

In the groove

The sound on a 'vinyl' record is stored as a wiggly groove. This is a kind of copy of the sound wave and so the groove is called an *analogue* of the wave. As the record turns, a stylus (a needle point) travels along the groove. The wiggles make the stylus vibrate. The vibrations are then used to re-create the sound. If you listen very carefully to a stylus travelling on a record, you can hear, very faintly, musical sounds. The sounds need amplifying to be heard properly. Early gramophones had a large horn to make the sounds louder. Later the vibrations were converted to electrical signals so that they could be amplified electronically.

Two into one

Listening to sounds coming from a single loudspeaker is not a very natural way of hearing things. In the real world sounds are spread out. You hear them with two ears. Stereo sound is an attempt to make recorded sounds seem the way they are in real life. Two sets of signals are recorded and then played back through two speakers. This creates the illusion that the sound is spread out, just like the real thing. Early recordings were all 'mono' – meaning that they were designed to come from one loudspeaker.

The trick was to record both sets of signals into the single groove. If you look at the picture of the mono groove you can see that the two sides of the groove are the same. The stereo groove is different. The two sides of the groove carry different sets of signals. These are called tracks. As the stylus travels along the groove, one track makes it vibrate in a direction at right angles to the first. So there are two separate sets of vibrations.

The two sets of vibrations have to be changed into electrical signals so that they can be amplified. This is done by the *cartridge*. Inside the cartridge the stylus is connected to two small coils of wire, one for each set of vibrations. These vibrate as the stylus does. They vibrate in the magnetic field of a strong permanent magnet. This induces an alternating voltage in each of the coils. Slow vibrations produce a voltage which alternates slowly. Fast vibrations make the voltage alternate quickly. This gives low and high notes. Big vibrations make larger voltages, which make louder notes. Small vibrations result in quieter sounds. The two sets of varying voltages are amplified before going to the two speakers.

Taping it

The stereo LP gives you excellent quality sound reproduction, providing you look after it. But it does have serious drawbacks. It cannot be used on a portable system. The slightest movement of the record player makes the stylus bounce all over the record. The disc is also very large and is easily scratched.

The search for portable sound gave us the *cassette* tape. This is simple and cheap. Used with the microchip the result is the personal stereo.

Magnetic tape recording

Magnetic recording tape is a long strip of plastic. This is coated on one side with a brown material. The chemical name for this is ferric oxide. It is actually a form of rust! The tiny particles of ferric oxide can be made to behave like millions of tiny magnets. These magnets are usually all jumbled up. This means they cancel out each others magnetism. If you bring a magnetic field near to the tape this all changes. The particles

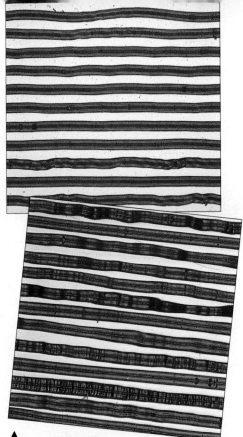

Top, a mono record groove on a vinyl LP, and below that of a stereo groove at very high magnification.

▼

A diamond stylus sitting in a groove on a vinyl record.

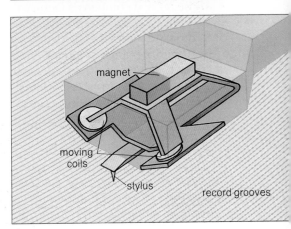

▲
The stereo cartridge that 'reads' the patterns in the groove of the record and converts them into electrical signals.

23

rearrange themselves into a magnetic pattern. The pattern will remain when the magnetic field is removed.

If you move the tape past a rapidly changing magnetic field, a copy of the field is left recorded on the tape. This changing field can be made by a rapidly changing electric current from a microphone. So the pattern on the tape will be a record of the sounds that went into the microphone. Again we have a 'wavy' copy (or *analogue*) of the original sound waves.

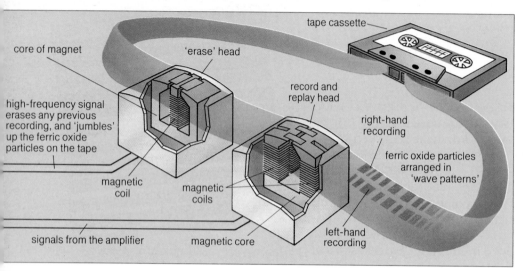

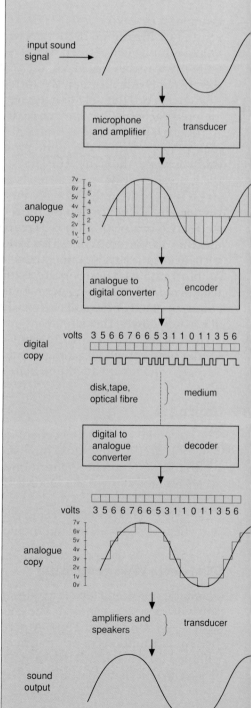

◄ Patterns of sound waves are turned into patterns on magnetic tape. There are four tracks on the tape – two for when the tape is played in one direction and two for the other side.

▼ In digital recording, sound waves are stored as numbers by using a code developed for computers – the binary code. Most sound is now recorded and transmitted digitally.

Playing it back

Getting your sound back is just the opposite of recording. The tape moves past a playback head. Inside this is a coil of wire. As the tape with its magnetic pattern moves past, a changing voltage is created in the coil of wire. This changing voltage is then amplified and sent to a loudspeaker, which converts the electical signals into sound.

Digital recording

To get rid of crackles and hiss from master tapes and to improve the final quality of what we hear, *digital* recording is used. The sound made in the recording studio is changed into a digital code. The code is made of 0s and 1s. It is this *code* which is recorded onto the master tape. The code is exactly like the code used in computers. It uses *binary* numbers.

At the record company's factory the master tape is replayed. The digital signals are converted to normal analogue signals. It is these that are copied onto the tapes and vinyl discs that you buy.

In 1983 the Philips company introduced the compact disc, or CD. The idea was to get rid of the problems that go with discs and cassettes. The digital information from the original master tape is stored directly on the CD. This is done by pressing a series of pits into one side of a plastic disc. The other side of the disc is given a reflective aluminium coating. It is this reflective side that is read by a laser in the disc player. The laser actually reads the series of bumps on the disc. Each bump is only 0.6 of a micrometre across. They start at the centre of the disc and spiral out as a track towards the edge. The track is very narrow – it winds around six hundred times for each millimetre across the disc.

In digital language, a bump means a 1, and no bump means a 0. So the track is still a set of *binary* codes. As the laser reads the track it is reflected only where there is a bump. No bump means no reflected laser light. A

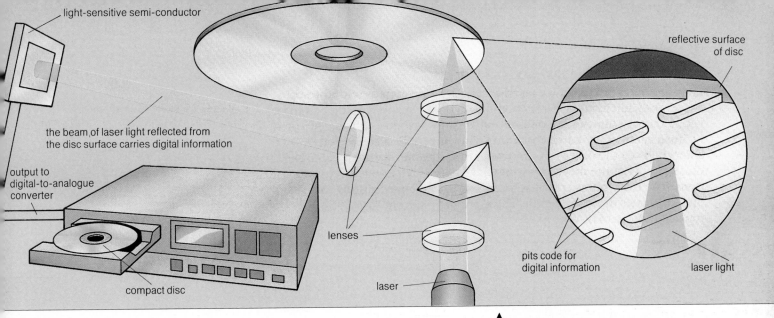

light-sensitive semi-conductor

the beam of laser light reflected from
the disc surface carries digital information

output to
digital-to-analogue
converter

compact disc

lenses

laser

reflective surface
of disc

pits code for
digital information

laser light

special device called a photodiode detects the light from the laser. It
converts the pulses of light into electrical signals. The digital electrical
signals are then changed into analogue signals. These are amplified and go
to the loudspeakers to be converted into sound.

▲
The binary code stores sound information
on the surface of a compact disc. Laser
light is reflected from the bumps on the
surface of the disc.

Making music

In science we need to measure and record what we are studying
accurately. Composers and players have to be just as accurate with music.
Musical notes are defined precisely by their *frequencies*.

The way notes are linked is called a musical scale. The scientific scale
for music starts with a note called middle C. It has a frequency of 256
hertz. At double this frequency, 512 hertz, is another note, called C. It has
a higher pitch. In between are the notes D to B. There are *eight* notes in
all, so they form an *octave*.

C	D	E	F	G	A	B	C	
256	288	320	341	384	426	480	512	Hertz

Musical scales were invented thousands of years before anybody could
measure frequencies. It was all done by 'ear'. People decided which notes
were in 'harmony' with each other. Some notes clash when played
together. They just do not sound right. Others blend together to make a
pleasant sound. The most pleasing sounds are made when one note is
twice the frequency of the other.

The whole family of notes called 'C' are:

			'middle'					
C	C	C	C	C	C	C	C	
32	64	128	256	512	1024	1028	4096	Hertz

A piano tuned like this would sound fine as long as you only wanted to
play scales based on the note C. But musicians want to play scales based

on other notes as well. If we use the same relationships as with the scale based on C, life would get very complicated. The piano would need to be retuned every time, or it would sound wrong.

Musicians already know about this. They invented systems that smoothed out the differences between the scales. In standard, 'classical' music, for example they simply divided each octave into twelve equal units. The extra notes are called sharps and flats. Together they can make musical scales that sound right. These are the different 'keys' that musicians have to be able to use.

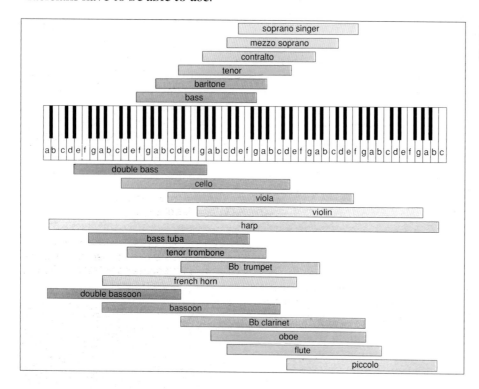

◄
Different instruments can play different parts of the whole musical scale.

Harmonics

When an object vibrates, it is unusual to find it vibrating at just one frequency. However, a tuning fork is made to do just that. It vibrates producing a very pure sound. The sound can be converted to electricity by a microphone. The electrical signals can be fed into an oscilloscope. This will draw a graph of their shape. The graph shape for the tuning fork is a very smooth wave shape called a sine wave. Musical instruments usually produce more complicated patterns. (See page 19).

A French mathematician called Fourier discovered that these patterns followed some rules. Each has a basic frequency, just like the sine wave. It is called its *fundamental*. Joined with the fundamental are other frequencies. Their frequencies are usually simple multiples of the fundamental. That is, they could be twice, three times, four times the fundamental, say. Each multiple is called a *harmonic*. Some harmonics may have a higher sound level than others. It is the pattern of harmonics which gives the sound of each musical instrument its own special *quality*. This quality is called tone or timbre.

You can get several instruments to play the same note while you record them separately. The instruments produce very different versions of this one note. But when you filter out the harmonics electronically, you cannot tell which instrument is which.

▲
Tuning forks vibrate at a very accurate frequency. It looks blurred because the prongs of the fork are moving very fast.

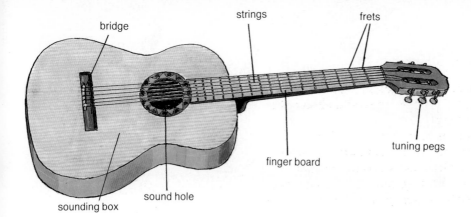

bridge · strings · frets · tuning pegs · finger board · sound hole · sounding box

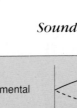

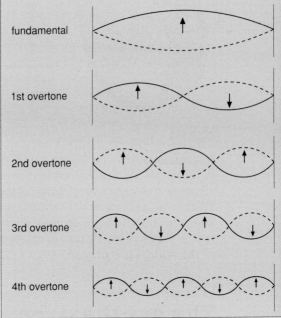

fundamental

1st overtone

2nd overtone

3rd overtone

4th overtone

▲
The fundamental and harmonic frequencies of a string.

▼
The strings on a violin can be of very different thicknesses so that the strings are all the same length and yet many different notes can be played.

How musical instruments work

Vibrating strings

Guitars, pianos, violins and harps all work by having strings that vibrate. The vibration is amplified so that you can hear the sound.

If you look at a vibrating string on a guitar you just see a blur. You can see it better if you use a flashing light, called a *stroboscope*. It doesn't look like a 'wave', but in fact waves are speeding along the string from one end to the other and back again. These waves are called *standing waves*. The way a string can vibrate is shown in the picture. In practice, the string might have all these waves – and more – going along it at the same time. The longest wave makes the lowest frequency, or fundamental. The other waves make the higher-pitched harmonics.

The pitch of the note depends on three things. They are:

- the length of the string;
- the tightness of the string;
- the 'thickness' of the string.

Long strings vibrate more slowly than short ones. Long strings give low-frequency notes. Short strings give high frequencies. The tighter the string, the higher the note it makes. Most string instruments are tuned by slightly changing the string tension.

Thin strings vibrate faster than thicker ones of the same material. So thin strings can produce higher-pitched notes. Strictly, it is the *mass per centimetre* of the string that counts.

By using these three rules you can arrange to have all the strings on your instrument the same length, like in violins and guitars, and yet still get a full range of notes. Compare this with the strings in a piano.

To *amplify* the sound, most instruments have a sound box. The vibrations from the string cause the sound box to vibrate. The effect is called resonance. The sound box has a large surface area to make the air around it vibrate, making the sound louder.

Blow it!

All wind instruments are pipes. They contain a column of air. When the air column is made to vibrate, sound is produced. These vibrations can be created by vibrating your lips, as in a bugle or trumpet. In a recorder, the air vibrates as it passes over a sharp edge. Oboes and clarinets use a vibrating reed.

The longer the column of air in the pipe, the more slowly it vibrates. The pitch of a note from long pipes is low. If you look at the pipes in an organ, you can see that there is a tremendous range of sizes. This means that the organ can make a wide range of notes.

Some wind instruments have holes or valves. This allows you to change the length of the air column. You can then play a wide range of notes on a single pipe.

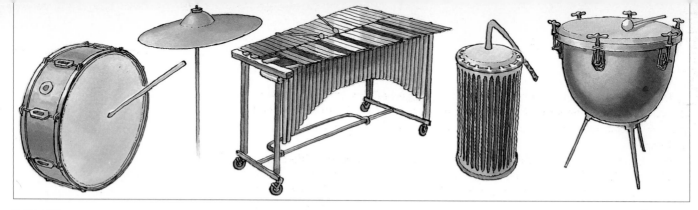

Hit it!

Instruments that you hit are called percussion instruments. Some of them work by having a skin stretched over a frame. When you hit the skin it vibrates, making a sound. Large skins, like bass drums, mean slow vibrations and low notes. Drums can usually only produce a singly note. In an orchestra, the large drums called tympani sometimes have a pedal fitted. This lets the drummer change the skin tension, changing the pitch of the note as it is played.

The synthesizer

Most pop groups have a *synthesizer* in their line up. It lets them create a whole range of sounds and notes. Some of these sounds could not be created in any other way.

The heart of a synthesizer is a system of microelectronic circuits called *oscillators*. An oscillator produces electrical vibrations. Each oscillator is tuned to give a particular frequency. In the mid 1960s Dr Robert Moog linked a piano-type keyboard to a set of oscillators. The synthesizer was born.

To produce a musical sound, the synthesizer must produce the fundamental and the harmonics, each at the right sound level. This is done by tuning one oscillator to the fundamental. This gives the note its *pitch*. Other oscillators are tuned to produce the harmonics. By creating the right set of harmonics, the synthesizer can be made to sound like any instrument you want. You can even invent your own sounds.

Too much sound

Measuring the loudness of sound

When you talk about the loudness of a sound, you mean the effect that the sound has on your ears. Soft, quiet sounds are difficult to hear. Loud ones are easy to hear. Very loud sounds can actually hurt. The loudness of a sound is also affected by how far away its source is. Finally, how you hear a sound depends upon how good your hearing is.

To investigate all this we need a scientific way of describing the loudness of a sound. Scientists use a scale of loudness measurements which works by comparing one sound with another. When one sound is 10-times louder than another, its sound level is 1 bel higher. The bel is a big unit and so it is divided up into units called decibels, or dB.

Loudness is often measured by using *sound-level meter*. The meter is designed to be most sensitive to frequencies of 1 or 2 kilohertz. This is the range for which your ears are most sensitive. The scale is marked in decibels.

At a sound level of 140 decibels, you may feel pain. You may also go deaf for a while after the noise. A longer exposure to much lower sound levels can be even more damaging. Sound at 90 decibels will permanently damage your hearing if you are regularly exposed to it. There is growing evidence that personal stereos can have these effects if you play them too loud and for too long. The table, below, gives the levels of some everyday sounds.

Loudness	Sound you hear	Soundlevel (dB)
Silence	Limit of your hearing	0
Quiet	Ordinary breathing Faint whisper Turning newspaper page	10 20 30
Moderate	Inside a car, windows shut Ordinary conversation Normal TV listening level Television adverts	40 50 60 70
Loud	Busy street traffic Pneumatic drill Underground train	80 90 100
Extremely loud	Thunder, jet taking off Tickling feeling in ears Thunder directly overhead	110 120 130
Dangerous to hearing	Near speakers at rock concert Military jet taking off Space rocket at lift off	140 150 160

Sound pollution

You could think of pollution as anything in the wrong place. This could be litter in a park instead of a bin, or chemicals in a river.

Sound can be polluting. It is then called noise. You may cause noise by playing your records too loud. Aircraft and traffic noise cause many problems.

You can learn to live with some noise. The background rumble of motorway traffic becomes less noticeable with time. Other sounds disturb you. A dog barking, or a car alarm, can be very annoying, especially at night. The sound is broken up into separate bits. There is no pattern for you to get used to.

Protection from noise — soundproofing

Noise can be reduced by soundproofing. Some materials are very good at soundproofing. They are often made of fibres or foam. These materials

▲ It is important that we monitor noise pollution as well as the more obvious types of pollution, like litter and smog.

have air trapped in them. They work by absorbing the energy of the sound wave.

Most of the soft furnishings in your home are good sound absorbers. Carpet and underlay stops sound from travelling through floors. Curtains and the soft fabrics on chairs also absorb sound. You must have noticed the difference between the sound in an empty room and in a furnished room.

The right design

If a machine or building is designed properly, all sorts of noise pollution can be reduced.

If you look carefully at the inside of a car, you will see that it is soundproofed. Designers of cars go to a lot of trouble to reduce the noise inside. A car is basically a metal box. The metal panels could create a lot of noise if they were allowed to resonate. Moving parts can also make a lot of noise. The moving parts are separated from the passengers by blocks of rubber that obsorb the vibration. The passenger compartment is also lined with sound-absorbing materials. Look at the floor, and the lining of the roof. If you could see inside the doors you would see they too are lined with vibration-absorbing panels. The doors have soft rubber seals to stop wind noise getting in.

Modern jet aircraft can be very noisy. This causes serious noise problems. The jet engine works by forcing a powerful stream of air backwards.

The problem is that the faster the air leaves the engine the more noise it makes. However, if you slow down the air to reduce the noise, you get less thrust from the jet. Civil airliners use quieter versions of jet engines called turbofans.

A modern design of pneumatic road drill has much lower noise levels than older types. This has been done by using plastics and foams to replace metal parts. A redesigned exhaust system completed the job. These changes also made the drill twenty-five per cent cheaper to build!

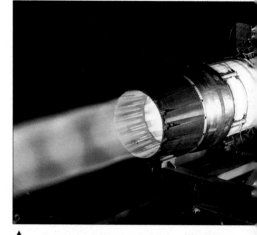

▲
Jet engines force planes through the air by forcing large amounts of air behind them. This is just like creating massive sound waves. You can see the 'waves' in the exhaust of this engine.

▼
Ultrasound can be used to look at sections through our bodies. This woman is having an ultrasound scan that shows her baby just before it is born.

Sounds that you can't hear!

Ultrasound

Some vibrations have frequencies of several *million* hertz – megahertz. These vibrations produce *ultrasonic* waves, or ultrasound. One very useful property of ultrasound is that the waves can travel through solid objects. Ultrasound can be used to look inside objects without damaging them.

Jane is pregnant. She has an appointment at the hospital for her 'scan'. A very narrow beam of ultrasound is passed through her womb. Some of it is

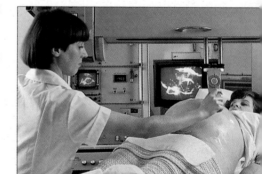

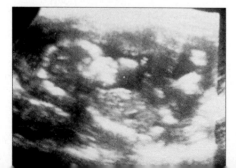

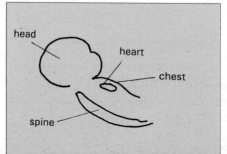

head
heart
chest
spine

◄
This is an ultrasound scan of an 18-week old foetus. The drawing helps to show what the scan reveals.

reflected back. This depends on the type of tissue it is passing through. The more solid the tissue the more ultrasound is reflected. The reflections are used to build up a computer picture of the unborn child. The doctor can tell from the picture whether the child is developing properly.

Ultrasound can clean!

If an intense beam of ultrasound is passed through a liquid, millions of tiny bubbles may form. These bubbles grow and collapse very quickly and violently. The bubbles can be used to shake dirt out of washing, or to clean dirt or rust from any object placed in the liquid.

Because ultrasound can pass through solid objects, it can be used to check how fast liquids are flowing through pipes, and even how blood is flowing through blood vessels.

Sonar: **So**und **Na**vigation and **R**anging

A ship can send out pulses of ultrasound into the water beneath it. The pulses go straight down to the seabed and are reflected back. The time it takes for this to happen is measured. From this the depth of water can be worked out.

The crew of a trawler can use the same method to find shoals of fish. They can then decide when it is the best time to put out his nets.

More sophisticated SONAR systems can be used to detect submarines, and can also find wrecks on the seabed.

The ultrasonic bat

Bats are mammals. They hunt for food at night. Flying at speed in the dark is a risky business, but the bats manage very well. Not only do they avoid flying into things, they can also catch their food as they go.

The bat sends out pulses of ultrasonic sound at regular intervals. These have frequencies of about 50 kHz. The pulses of sound bounce off things and are reflected back to the bat. The bat can tell not only what is in its way, but how far away it is. It can even tell if it is food. It is just like 'pulsed radar' systems used to detect aircraft.

If the bat detects a possible prey, it can send out shorter pulses of sound. Bats can then produce one hundred and seventy pulses a second. The pulses reflect from the prey and the bat homes in on it. Objects as small as a gnat can be detected. The bat's system of using ultrasound is called echo location.

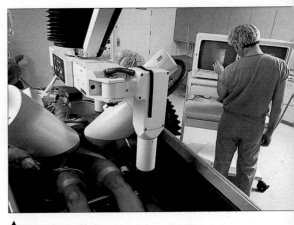

▲
Kidney stones cause a lot of pain. They can be removed by focusing ultrasound waves onto the kidney. These shatter the stones into smaller pieces that can then be excreted in the urine.

◄
This bat is using ultrasound to find and chase its prey. You can see the bat's large ears designed to pick up as much of the ultrasound as possible that is reflected from the insect.

Activities

1 You have to find the best material for keeping noise out. You have a small buzzer and a cardboard tube about 0.5 metres long. If you put your ear to the end of the tube when the buzzer is at the other end you can hear the sound very clearly. You also have some materials like foam rubber, cotton wool, polystyrene ceiling tiles, and a blanket. Design an experiment that would let you find out which material is best at absorbing sound. Explain how you would make sure that your test was fair. Say what other materials you might use in your experiment. Check you plan with your teacher.

2 You need a stringed instrument such as a guitar. Try to find the harmonics (see page 26).

Just plucking a string gives mostly the fundamental note. To sound the first harmonic, lightly touch the string at its mid-point and pluck it on one of the halves. The string will vibrate in two halves. The next harmonic is quieter but can be heard by touching the string one third along and then plucking it. Can you find any more harmonics? Repeat the experiment with a different string. Explain what you have found out. How does the word 'octave' fit into your findings?

3 A decibel meter is a special meter that measures sound levels.

You are going to design an experiment using a decibel meter to measure sound levels from the traffic on a road. Some of the things that you might like to think about are:
- would you get different results from different kinds of traffic?
- would the time and date be useful?
- how could you do the experiment safely?
- where would be the best place to stand to make the measurements?
- how would you sort out and display your measurements?
Now write your plan, then check it with your teacher.

4 Make a simple musical instrument that can play a tune.
Ideas: 1 8 milk bottles with different levels of water;
2 8 bits of wood on two rails (a xylophone);
3 8 bits of metal hanging from a string;
4 a length of hosepipe (easy to make – tricky to play!)
Look at the sounds that you make, by using a microphone and an oscilloscope.

5 (a) Strike a tuning fork and hold it near to your ear. You will just be able to hear its sound. Strike it again and hold the bottom of it against an upturned empty drawer, or a wooden box. Explain what is happening.
(b) Use this apparatus (below) to hear what happens to the sound of the tuning fork when you change the length of the air column in the tube. Explain your results.
(c) In (b), resonance first occurs when the length of the air column is almost exactly a quarter of the wavelength of that sound in air. Use the formula speed = frequency × wavelenth ($v = f\lambda$) to calculate the speed of sound in air.

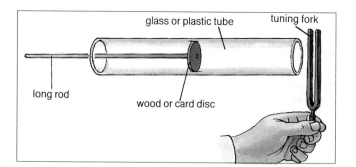

glass or plastic tube   tuning fork

long rod

wood or card disc

Questions

1 A girl holds her ruler on the edge of her desk. She flicks the end to make a sound. She discovers that if she slides the ruler so that less hangs over the edge, then the sound changes.
(a) How does the ruler make a sound?
(b) Why does moving the ruler change the sound?
(c) What happens to the pitch of the sound as the girl moves the ruler?
(d) How does the sound get from the ruler to the girl's ears?

2 A guitar has all its strings roughly the same length. They have different thicknesses. Explain how can the guitarist make so many different notes?

3 A boy is sitting on a beach. Suddenly he sees the flash from a lifeboat maroon. This is a rocket which calls out the lifeboat crew.Three seconds later he hears the bang. How far was he from where the rocket exploded?
Remember that sound travels at about 340 m/s in air.

4 The fundamental of a certain note on an instrument has a frequency of 320 Hz. Harmonics are 'simple multiples' of the fundamental.
(a) Work out the frequencies of the first five possible harmonics of this note.
(b) What note has a frequency of 320 Hz?

5 On page 29 is some information about the effect of sound levels on your hearing. Use it, or any other information you have, to answer these questions.
(a) What is the difference in hearing level between ages 40 and 65 for people with normal hearing?
(b) What sound level has caused the most damage to peoples' hearing?
(c) What sorts of sounds might cause this damage?
(d) What are the symptoms of the hearing problem called tinnitus?
(e) Why do you think that many doctors are worried about the increasing use of personal stereos?

6 On page 19 there is a diagram showing the frequency range of hearing of some animals.
(a) Which animals have hearing which is most sensitive to ultrasonic sound?
(b) Suggest some reasons why humans have not developed the ability to hear ultrasonic sound?
(c) Try to find out why dolphins and other small whales use ultrasonic sound.

Checklist

These are the facts and ideas you should have learned by studying this topic.

To succeed at Basic Level you should:

- know that sounds are produced by vibrating objects and can travel through different materials
- be able to explain how musical sounds are produced in simple musical instruments
- know how you hear sounds and how your ear can be harmed by loud sounds

To succeed at Foundation Level you should:

- know that it takes time for sound to travel (e.g. thunder and lightning, echoes, etc.)
- know how vibrating objects produce sound waves in air
- know about transducers and what they do
- know how frequency affects the pitch of a sound, and how the amplitude of a sound wave affects its loudness
- understand the importance of noise control in the environment (e.g. loud machines in the workplace, traffic noise in town centres, discos)

To succeed at Merit Level you should:

- know the meaning of wavelength
- know that high-frequency waves have short wavelengths
- understand the difference between longitudinal and transverse waves
- be able to describe the working of audio devices, e.g. the microphone, loudspeaker and telephone
- know how sound can be changed so that information it carries can be recorded and/or sent over long distances
- know that the loudness of a sound can be increased by using a sounding board, e.g. a tuning fork on a table, a string on a guitar and a loudspeaker cone
- know that the shape of a sound waveform (e.g. as displayed on a CRO) affects the quality of the note
- be able to explain the working of the human ear and some common defects in hearing

To succeed at Special Level you should:

- be able to use the relationship: velocity = frequency × wavelength
- be able to work out the wavelength of sound produced by standing waves in string and wind instruments
- understand the use of electronic sound technology in industrial, medical and social applications (e.g. in cleaning, flaw detection and prenatal scanning by ultrasound), musical production by using electronic instruments
- be able to explain resonance in sound or mechanical systems
- understand the use of electronic sound technology in industrial, medical and social applications (e.g. the use of decibel meters to monitor sound levels)

CHAPTER THREE

PHYSICS AT HOME

Frank was late for work. But he just had time for breakfast — if he was quick. He switched on the electricity to his halogen ceramic hob, placed a sauce-

pan on top, and dropped in two eggs. While they were boiling, he put some beans in the microwave cooker, set the timer and switched it on. Water was boiling in his automatic jug kettle, and toast popped out of the automatic toaster — done to perfection. Frank did not take the time to think about how all these appliances used materials effectively in their designs. He didn't think about how he was using energy. He was just happy to have a speedy and satisfying breakfast.

How many ways to boil an egg?

Boiling an egg involves some very complicated physics. If you were designing an electric cooker, what would you have to think about? The aim must be to use materials that allow energy to be transferred to the food being cooked, but not the surroundings. It is impossible to achieve this perfectly, but designers make very good use of the properties of materials. *Strength, thermal conductivity, electrical conductivity* and cost are important.

In an electricity showroom you will find a range of different hobs and cookers. A *ceramic* hob is made of a smooth sheet of ceramic glass, which is easy to clean and resistant to high temperatures. It is very strong and does not conduct electricity. The *heating elements* are underneath the hob. There are different types of heating element. *Radiant-ring elements* are *resistance* wires, like those in an electric bar fire, sealed in a spiral metal tube. They radiate thermal energy through the hob. Several energy transfers later, the energy reaches the egg, and cooks it.

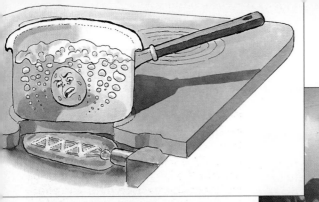

Modern ceramic hobs may actually be heated by a lamp. This is a special *tungsten halogen* lamp under each cooking area. The lamp has a very fine element that reaches a high temperature more quickly than the thinner radiant-ring element. It also cools down more quickly than a radiant-ring element.

Other types of hob may have the radiant rings exposed so that you can see them glow. Others are sealed in a solid cast-iron plate.

The most modern design is an *induction* hob. This hob doesn't get hot. It doesn't transfer energy by thermal conduction, but uses the magnetic properties of materials. A special generator supplies *alternating current* to a coil beneath a ceramic hob. The current alternates (changes direction) many times a second. A steel or iron pan placed on the hob becomes hot. This is because the changing current produces a changing *magnetic field*. This in its turn produces a changing current in the iron pan, which makes it hot – so the water gets hot and the egg gets cooked. The hob only gets hot by thermal conduction from the pan. As soon as the pan is removed, the hob cools down very quickly.

All hobs are designed so that the maximum energy is transferred upwards into the food. To stop energy going the other way, thermal *insulating material* or shiny reflectors are sealed in the underside of the hob.

Cooking with radar

The *microwave* cooker is now a familiar sight. In the top of the microwave cooker is a magnetron. This was first used to make radar signals. The microwaves carry energy. This is absorbed by the food, which then gets hot.

A *convection* oven has large heating elements, like those in radiant rings, at the top or sides of the oven. These heat the air in the oven – starting, of course, with the air closest to them. This air expands and rises, moving around the food in convection currents.

A combination oven has both a magnetron and radiant-heating elements in it.

You can plug a microwave cooker into a normal electrical socket, but a convection or combination oven must be wired separately into the mains supply. This is because they have a much higher *power rating* than the microwave cooker – they need a bigger *current* to operate.

The temperature inside an oven has to be controlled. In a convection oven, this is done by a *thermostat*, which operates according to the temperature set by the controls. In a microwave cooker, the temperature of the food is controlled by the length of time the cooker is on and the *power output* of the cooker.

Both a microwave and a convection cooker may have a fan at the top, but they are used in different ways. In a microwave cooker, this is used to reflect the microwaves evenly round the cooker. In a convection oven, the fan circulates the hot air evenly – this is more efficient than unassisted convection.

Some convection ovens have liners that are impregnated with a *catalyst*. Any food that splashes on to this catalytic liner reacts with air to form a gas in a reaction helped by the catalyst. This makes it easier to keep the oven clean.

A good thermal *insulator* is needed in the space between the heating elements and the outer casing of the oven to keep energy in. Ceramic wool is often used.

Well-designed ovens make very good use of modern materials – and many different physical principles. The key ideas are in italics on these pages. This chapter will deal with most of these. It will show you how much science there is in our everyday lives – even when just boiling an egg.

Energy in the home

The energy we use to run our homes gets there in two main ways: as fuels, or carried by electricity.

The fuels are likely to be coal, oil or gas – the fossil fuels. We burn these in grates, stoves or boilers, combining them with the oxygen in the air in a process called *combustion*. We mostly use the energy from this to *heat* things – to keep us warm, heat water and to cook food.

Using electricity to carry the energy is easier and often cleaner than using fuels that have to be burnt. And we can use the energy in many more different ways. We don't use electricity just for heating and cooking. We use it to make motors work (like hair dryers and vacuum cleaners). We use it to help us store information, in computers, tape and video recordings. We use it to send and receive messages, – in telephones, television and radio, and we use it to light our homes.

You can learn more about *fuels* in Chapter 12, *Fuels and the environment*, and there is more about electricity in book 2.

Energy is expensive. One of the most important decisions in life that you might have to make is about which kind of energy source to use in your home. But whichever you choose, you must try to make sure that you don't waste energy. Wasting energy usually means letting it go to places where you don't want it to be. This is where the use of modern materials comes in.

The pie chart shows what we do with the energy we take into our homes: 94% of it is used for heating!

Think about what happens to this energy. Quite a lot of it goes down the drain! After washing up, having a bath and doing the laundry, we pour hot water away. Just as much energy escapes from a warm house – through the floor, the walls, the windows and the roof.

▼
What the average UK household uses energy for.

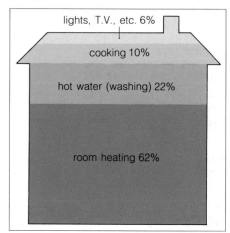

lights, T.V., etc. 6%

cooking 10%

hot water (washing) 22%

room heating 62%

Energy transfer

How does energy move? Let's begin with what we call 'heat' energy. A hot object can lose its energy in three ways: by *conduction*, *convection* and *radiation*.

Conduction

In conduction, energy travels from particle to particle through a substance. In a hot object the particles are moving fast. They have more kinetic energy than the particles in a colder object. In a solid, the particles vibrate about a fixed point. When the solid gets hotter the particles vibrate further and move faster. In a liquid or a gas the particles can move more freely, even when an object is cold. Their particles only just move faster when the object is heated.

When a hot object touches a colder one, the fast-moving particles bump into the particles in the cold object and make them move about more. In turn, these bump into their neighbours and the extra energy of movement spreads through the colder object – it gets hotter. We can feel this, and measure the temperature rising. The hot object has now lost some energy and so gets cooler.

Convection

Convection only works in a gas or a liquid (a *fluid*). In convection, the hot object warms the fluid touching it. The energy makes the particles in the fluid move faster and they also move further apart, on average. So the warmed part of the fluid gets bigger – it *expands*. This makes it less dense. It is now lighter than the colder fluid surrounding it and floats upwards. As the warm fluid floats away it takes its increased energy with it. Cooler fluid moves in to take its place, and this now gets warmed.

This is a continuous process. Warmed fluid floats up and is continually replaced by cooler fluid. This flow is called a *convection current*.

▲ Convection currents in a fluid.

▼ A special photograph to show the currents of hot air moving around a man's body.

Radiation

Radiation is completely different. Every object sends out energy in the form of radiation. This is infrared radiation. This is part of the electromagnetic spectrum beyond where our eyes can detect it. Hot objects give out more of this radiation than colder ones.

You can feel the radiation from a hot object. Your skin warms up when it absorbs the radiated energy. You can feel the infrared radiation from your own forehead if you have been exercising, or 'have a temperature'.

Infrared radiation travels at the speed of light. Like all parts of the electromagnetic spectrum, it can pass through transparent materials and through a vacuum. It is reflected by shiny surfaces, and is absorbed by black and rough surfaces.

Moving energy usefully

The drawings show how some cookers use these ways of transferring energy to help cooking. They rely on using materials that are:

- good conductors (usually metals),
- good convectors (all liquids and gases),
- good insulators (bad conductors: rock wool, most plastics and wood),
- good absorbers of radiation (water is very good at absorbing microwave radiation),
- good reflectors of radiation (shiny metal surfaces),
- materials that let radiation through (glass for infrared, ceramic, glass and plastic for microwaves).

◄ Conduction and convection.

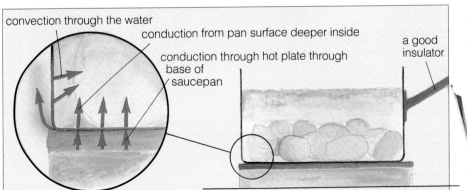

convection through the water

conduction from pan surface deeper inside

conduction through hot plate through base of saucepan

a good insulator

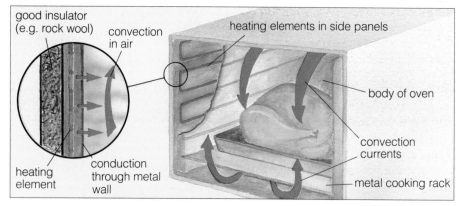

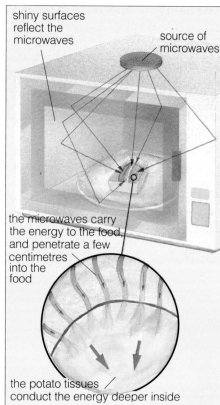

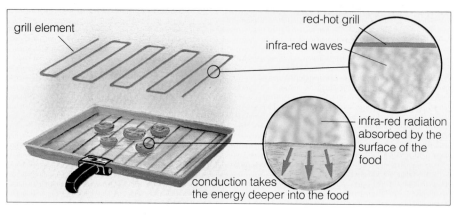

Microwaves are a kind of radiation that is very similar to infrared, but infrared is a lot easier to produce. A hot grill is a very good source of infrared radiation, and cheaper than the special magnetron needed to make microwaves. But microwaves can travel more deeply into food, and use less energy. A microwave oven cooks much more quickly than a hot grill. It is also much quicker than cooking in an oven or boiling water. This means that it saves a lot of energy. The table shows the energy needed to cook a chicken by using different methods.

Method	*Power used* (W)	*Time taken* (minutes)	*Energy supplied* (kJ)
microwave	650	8	312
boiling	about 100	120	720
conventional oven	about 700	90	4000
pressure cooker	about 50	20	60

How much energy does it take to make something hot?

The short answer is 'More than you might think!' For example, it takes about 336 kJ of energy to bring a litre of water to its boiling point. Suppose you gave it the same amount of energy, but as kinetic energy (movement energy)? You could do this by, say, throwing it. If you could, it would break the sound barrier! It would have a speed of over 800 m/s which is more than twice the speed of sound.

Specific heat capacity

The energy needed to raise the temperature of 1 kilogram of a substance through 1 °C is called its *specific heat capacity*. For water, this is 4200 joules. So, to heat a kilogram of water from room temperature (about 20 °C) to its boiling point of 100 °C takes 4200 J for every degree rise. This means that:

energy needed to heat the water = 80 × 4200 = 336 000 J.

Water is a special material. It takes more energy to heat water than any other material we use at home. The table (right) gives the specific heat capacities of several everyday materials. Scientists use the *kelvin* scale of temperature rather than degrees Celsius for this. A kelvin is the same size as a degree celsius. To convert a Celsius temperature to a kelvin, add 273.

As so much of the energy we use at home is for heating things, we should think very carefully about ways of making the best use of the energy we buy for doing this.

Material	Specific heat capacity (J/kg K)
water	4200
aluminium	886
copper	380
iron (steel)	500
glass	500

The pressure, temperature and volume of a gas

Pressure cooking

Vegetables cook more quickly in a pressure cooker than in a saucepan of boiling water. The diagram shows the design of a pressure cooker. Once the food has been placed in the cooker, the lid is sealed. The water becomes steam as it receives energy from the hot hob. Particles of steam hit the sides and lid of the pressure cooker. The pressure of the steam within the vessel increases. The moving particles have a great deal of energy – so much that the temperature inside the pressure cooker rises to above 100 °C. This means that the particles can give even more energy to the food than in an open-top saucepan, and so the food cooks more quickly.

There is a safety valve to ensure that the pressure inside the vessel does not get too high. If the valve is opened while there is still pressurised steam inside the cooker, the steam rushes out through the hole until the pressure inside the cooker is the same as that outside.

The pressure cooker is a useful application of the relationship between the volume of a gas and its pressure and temperature. If the volume of a gas is kept constant (the space inside the pressure cooker), increasing the temperature of the gas will increase its pressure.

If a gas is free to do so, it will expand when heated. For example, bubbles of carbon dioxide trapped in bread dough expand when the dough is placed in a hot oven. The dough isn't strong enough to keep the bubbles the same size. If you look at a slice of bread, you can see the holes where the bubbles were.

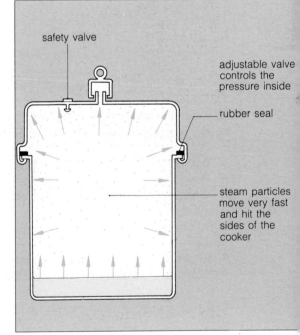

▲ A cross section through a pressure cooker.

safety valve

adjustable valve controls the pressure inside

rubber seal

steam particles move very fast and hit the sides of the cooker

The gas laws

The molecules (particles) in a gas are free to move. The molecules are very small compared with the amount of space between them. In fact, a gas is mostly empty space. This is what makes gases fairly easy to squash. But they are not *that* easy to squash, which means that we can use gases (like air) in cushions and tyres. When you feel a tyre or an air cushion you can feel the pressure exerted by the gas. This pressure is caused by the bombardment of the billions upon billions of molecules against the walls of the container. In air, the molecules are moving at an average speed of about 500 m/s. This is faster than the speed of sound. When you squash a gas its pressure increases. This is caused by the fact that when the gas fills a smaller space, the molecules of the gas can hit the sides more often. They haven't got so far to go between collisions.

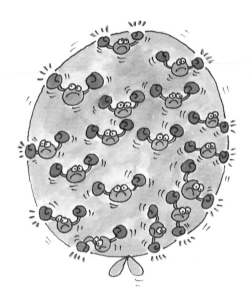

You can also increase the pressure of a gas by making the gas hotter. The extra energy you give to the gas makes its molecules move faster. They not only hit the sides of the container more often, but harder as well.

If the container is able to expand freely so that the pressure stays the same, then obviously the gas has expanded – its volume has increased. Look at page 145, and page 241 in the 'Reference section' for lots more about the gas laws.

Using electricity to deliver energy

Quite a lot of the energy we use in the home is delivered as electricity. How this is done, and how electricity is controlled, is dealt with in book 2. This section deals with how much energy electricity can supply, and how it is measured.

Imagine that you want to buy an electric kettle. You will find that there are many different designs in the shops – although they all do the same basic job. Some kettles are made from plastic, others have a metal body. They all have a metallic electric element inside. Some switch themselves off when the water boils. Eventually, you decide on a rather smart plastic kettle; you buy a plug and take the kettle home.

- What does the label mean, with all the words about volts and watts?
- How do you wire up the plug correctly?
- What is the fuse in the plug for, and how do you know if you have put the right one in?
- The kettle switches itself off when the water boils – how does it do this?
- How can you be sure that the kettle is safe to use?
- How much electricity will the kettle use, and how much will this cost?

Can you answer all of these questions correctly?

Electrical power

If you look on a kettle, a television, or any other electrical appliance, you will see a label very much like this one.

There are two very important pieces of information here: these are the *supply voltage* and the *power* that the appliance uses.

The power requirement appears on the label as the number of *watts*. The power rating is a measure of the *rate* at which energy is being used. An electric toaster rated at 1400 watts uses more energy per second than a television rated at 70 watts.

Power, voltage and current

We can use the power rating to calculate how much electric current is taken by an appliance when it is switched on.

Electrical power is the voltage across the appliance (as measured with a voltmeter) multiplied by the current going through it:

power (watts) = voltage (volts) × current (amps).

$$W = VI$$

This can be re-arranged as:

$$\text{current} = \frac{\text{power}}{\text{voltage}}$$

Look at the label for the kettle. It has a power rating of 2400 W. The current through the kettle element can be calculated:

$$\text{current} = \frac{\text{power}}{\text{voltage}} = \frac{2400}{240} = 10\,\text{A}.$$

The fuse

A current of 10 A will flow through the kettle element in normal use.

The kettle could be damaged if more current than 10 A went through the element. Sometimes the wiring inside an appliance can break or move so that there is a 'short-circuit'. In a short-circuit the electric current by-passes some of the wiring. A larger current than normal flows because of the short-circuit. This can damage the appliance or cause it to overheat.

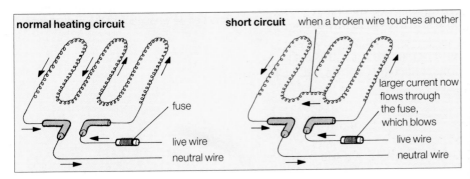

normal heating circuit | short circuit — when a broken wire touches another

fuse
live wire
neutral wire

larger current now flows through the fuse, which blows
live wire
neutral wire

◀ This is how a short circuit can happen.

▼ A selection of common fuses.

This could be very dangerous, but can be prevented by putting a fuse of the correct size in the plug.

An electric plug is wired so that the current coming into the appliance along the 'live' wire travels through a fuse. If too much current travels through the fuse wire, it gets hot and melts. This breaks the circuit and prevents electricity flowing through the appliance.

You have to make sure that the correct fuse is in the plug. In the plug connected to the kettle you would put a 13A fuse. The normal current of 10A would have no effect on the fuse. The 13A fuse would 'blow' only if there was a short circuit. How to wire a plug correctly is shown in the 'Reference section'.

There are other safety features of electrical appliances. An *earth wire* connects the appliance to the Earth. If the appliance is damaged, electricity passes along this wire and safely away to 'earth' rather than through a person.

▼ A fuse wire that has 'blown'.

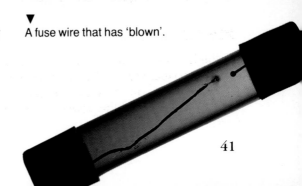

41

Watts, joules and kilowatt-hours

A *watt* is the unit we use to measure how quickly we are using energy. 1 watt means that we are using energy at the rate of 1 joule every second. A 1 kilowatt electric fire uses 1 kJ every second. (When we say 'using energy' we mean transferring it to somewhere else. The fire transfers the energy from moving electrons in its element to make the air particles in the room move faster – in other words, it heats the air.)

If we run the fire for 1 hour, we transfer 1000 joules every second for 3600 seconds. This means we transfer a total of 3 600 000 J or 3.6 megajoules (MJ) of energy. A joule isn't very much energy, so the electricity companies prefer to use a larger unit, which, logically enough, they call a 'unit' of energy. This is the energy supplied when an appliance rated at 1000 W is used for an hour – hence its other name of the 'kilowatt-hour (kWh).

Energy delivered electrically = watts × seconds (answer in joules)
or,   = kilowatts × hours (answer in 'units')

Buying electricity

How much will the kettle cost to use? How does the electricity board work out the electricity bill?

An electricity meter measures the energy used in the house that has been delivered electrically. This energy is measured in kilowatt-hours or *units*. A 1 kW bar fire used for 1 hour will use 1 kilowatt-hour (unit) of electrical energy.

The electricity board decides the cost of a unit of electricity. You are sent an electricity bill every three months. The meter readings at the beginning and end of each three-month period are used to work out how many units of electricity have been used, and you pay for the number of units you have used.

For example, the new kettle, rated at 2.4 kW, takes 5 minutes (1/12 of an hour) to boil some water. In this time the kettle uses 0.2 kilowatt-hours (2.4 × 1/12) of energy.

The electricity bill gives the cost of a unit of electricity. If this is 6p, then boiling a kettle of water using 0.2 units will cost 0.2 × 6p, i.e. 1.2p.

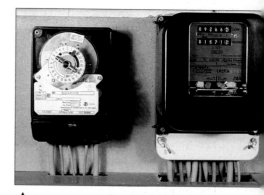

▲
Try to find your electricity meter at home and decide what each of the dials means.

To summarise . . .

- Power = voltage × current,
  (Watts = volts × amps)
- 1000 W is 1 kilowatt (kW),
- Energy = power × time,
- Electrical energy transfers can be measured in joules or kilowatt-hours,
- Joules = watts × seconds,
- Kilowatt-hour = kilowatts × hours,
- 1 unit of electricity is 1 kilowatt-hour.

Useful materials

Like most modern cooking equipment, this non-stick pan is made from more than one material. Designers have to be aware of all the properties of materials they use. The important physical properties of a material are:

- strength – a strong material needs a large force to break it,
- flexibility – a flexible material bends easily under a force,
- hardness – a hard material is not easily scratched,
- toughness – a tough material bends rather than breaks when a force is applied,
- density – a small volume of a dense material is very heavy,
- electrical conductivity – electricity passes easily through a good electrical conductor,
- thermal conductivity – energy is transferred easily through a good conductor,
- melting point – a material with a high melting point changes from a solid to a liquid at a high temperature,
- appearance – a material may be shiny, smooth, coloured, and so on.

Designers normally choose a material because of its combination of properties. Most of the pan is made of metal not just because metal is a good thermal conductor, but it also has a high melting point, is tough, strong and can be shaped easily. The cost is also important.

You wouldn't want to burn your hands on the handles so they have to be made from a material that is a good thermal insulator. In this case, a rigid plastic is used.

The inside surface of the pan is coated with polytetrafluoroethene (PTFE). PTFE is a material which is very slippery. It can be used where we want to reduce friction. PTFE is used to lubricate moving parts in machines and by plumbers in threaded joints in copper pipes. You will know it by its common name – Teflon.

Blu-tack would be totally unsuitable for a non-stick surface. It has opposite properties to PTFE but this makes it useful in other ways. Its high coefficient of friction and 'stretchiness' make it very useful for sticking posters to walls.

Which material for the job?

How do you think that a manufacturer decides which material a kettle should be made from? The designer has to consider all of the properties needed in a material to be used:

◀
Objects that have the same function can be made from very different materials. Designers have to suit the material to the exact purpose.

- high melting point,
- tough – won't break easily,
- easily shaped or moulded – to help the manufacture,
- a good thermal insulator – energy is not lost to the surroundings and the water inside stays hot.

Metals have most of these properties, but they are not good insulators. Metal kettles have very shiny surfaces. These are good reflectors, and poor radiators of radiation. So making the surface of the metal kettle shiny reduces the energy radiated as infrared waves to the surroundings. But this doesn't reduce the energy transferred by *conduction* to the outside of the kettle.

Metals were the only suitable materials for making kettles until suitable plastics were developed. The metals that were used, like iron, copper and aluminium, can withstand the high temperatures generated by flames and red-hot heating elements. Some plastics, like PVC, have all of the desirable properties for a kettle, but they cannot withstand direct heating. The heating element must therefore be *inside* the kettle and stay under the water level.

Many other objects that we use in our everyday lives have been designed to make good use of the properties of materials.

Energy saving

In any process, we want to make the energy transfers efficient. Thermal insulators are often used to reduce the amount of energy that is 'lost'. Air is a very good insulator, but it is only effective when it is confined. (You should be able to explain why from your knowledge of convection currents.) Cavity walls, double glazing and ceramic wool all make use of this property of air.

Temperature control

Controlling the temperature inside an oven is not only a useful way of saving energy, but it also ensures that food is cooked correctly. Central heating systems, electric irons and convection ovens all have *thermostats* that control temperature.

▲
A layer of air trapped between the panes of glass insulates the cold outside from the hotter air inside.

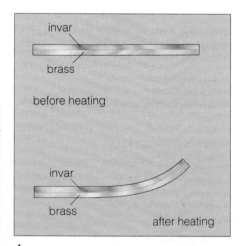

▲
The principle of the bimetallic strip.

◄

Bimetallic strips are used as thermostats in irons and kettles.

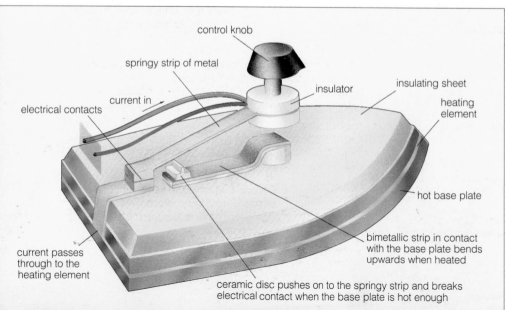

control knob

springy strip of metal

current in

electrical contacts

insulator

insulating sheet

heating element

hot base plate

current passes through to the heating element

bimetallic strip in contact with the base plate bends upwards when heated

ceramic disc pushes on to the springy strip and breaks electrical contact when the base plate is hot enough

Thermostats use bimetallic strips to control the current in a heating element. When a metal is heated, it expands. Some metals expand at different rates to others. A bimetallic strip is made from two different metals sandwiched together. When a bimetallic strip is heated, it bends because of the different expansion rates. Automatic kettles have thermal cut-outs that use these strips to cut off the power when the water boils.

Activities

1 Do a survey of your class to find out what type of kettle each person has in their home. What is good and bad about each type of kettle? Plan an experiment that each member of the class could do to compare the cost of using each kettle. Remember to make it a fair test. You could display your results as a poster.

2 Produce a leaflet to encourage energy saving in the home. Illustrate it with diagrams that show the major energy losses from a house.

3 Find out what 'Economy 7' ('Cheap-rate electricity') means for

costing electricity. How many of the class use 'Economy 7' electricity in their homes? Why is electricity cheaper at night?

4 Examine the labels on five electrical appliances in your home. Draw up a table to show the power rating in watts of each appliance. Work out how much it would cost to run each of them for an hour. Find out the cost of a 'unit' (kilowatt-hour) from an electricity bill.

5 Find out what forms of radiation make up the electromagnetic spectrum. Find out the different uses of the different radiations.

Questions

1 Here is a list of power ratings of some common electrical appliances.

Appliance	Power rating
bar fire	2500 watts (2.5 kilowatts)
light bulb	100 watts
kettle	2000 watts (2 kilowatts)
washing machine	250 watts
drill	360 watts
colour TV	340 watts
iron	720 watts

(a) Which appliance will have the most current running through it when it is switched on?
(b) Which appliance would cost the least to operate for an hour?
(c) Which appliance would need the lowest value fuse connected in its circuit?

2 Tara says that it uses less electricity to microwave a potato than to bake it in an electric oven. Michael disagrees and says that baking is cheaper. What information would you need to decide who is correct?

3 You have been asked to design each of the following:
 • a dinner plate,
 • a bicycle frame, and
 • a hot-water bottle.
(a) What important properties would you want in each of the materials you use to make each object?
(b) Suggest a material for each object.
(c) Are there any objects that would use a combination of materials? If so, explain what materials you would use, and why.

4 (a) Work out the power rating in watts for each of the appliances in the following table.
(b) Work out what size of fuse you should put in the circuit of each appliance. Fuses are available in the following sizes only: 1 A, 3 A, 5 A, 13 A and 30 A.

Appliance	Mains voltage (V)	Current taken (A)
kettle	240	9.0
iron	240	4.2
lamp	240	0.2
hair dryer	240	2.0
shower	240	26.0

5 In a certain district, electricity costs 6p for a kilowatt-hour (or unit). How much would it cost to use the following appliances?
(a) A kettle, rated at 2 kW, for one hour
(b) A microwave cooker, rated at 1.5 kW, for 30 minutes
(c) A radio, rated at 10 W, for 6 hours
(d) An electric blanket, rated at 200 W, for 4 hours
(e) A vacuum cleaner, rated at 500 W, for 30 minutes.

6 The manufacturers of ceramic hobs recommend that only flat-bottomed pans should be used on the hob. Pans that are 'ridged' or 'bow out' are not suitable. Why do you think they make this recommendation?

7 Radio waves are a form of electromagnetic radiation – like microwaves and visible light. Describe some of the properties that you would expect these three forms of radiation to have in common.

Checklist

These are the facts and ideas you should have learned by studying this topic.

To succeed at Basic Level you should:

- know that if you heat materials they may melt or change into something else
- know the temperature is a measure of how hot or cold something is
- be able to list the ways in which some everyday materials are the same, or are different
- know that water freezes and boils at definite fixed temperatures (freezing point, boiling point)
- know that many things at home work off electricity, and that misusing them can be dangerous
- understand how earthing and fuses help to make it safer to use electricity
- know about conductors and insulators, and why we need a complete circuit to make electrical devices work
- know that for things to work they need a source of energy

To succeed at Foundation Level you should:

- be able to compare and classify materials in terms of their main properties and so explain why they are useful for different jobs (i.e. solid, liquid or gas; their strength, hardness, flexibility, and if they dissolve or not)
- understand what happens when we heat or cool everyday substances (i.e. they melt or freeze; boil or condense)
- know that gases can be weighed
- know that we can use the idea of very small particles called atoms to help us understand that happens when things melt, boil, evaporate or dissolve
- know how important energy is in everyday life, and that we need to use it wisely (e.g. off-peak electricity, house insulation, etc.)

To succeed at Merit Level you should:

- know about the main types of everyday materials (metals, ceramics, glass, plastics, fibres) in terms of their different properties and uses
- recognise the main energy sources supplying the home, and be able to trace the energy transfers when we use them

- be able to use the particle theory to explain the differences between solids, liquids and gases, and what happens when things change state, evaporate, diffuse or dissolve
- know that the volume of a gas depends upon both pressure and temperature
- know that energy is involved when substances change state or expand or contract
- be able to calculate electricity costs given the basic data in simple cases
- understand that although energy isn't destroyed it often spreads out to become less usable
- understand how energy is transferred from one place to another by thermal processes (conduction, convection) and by radiation, and how to control this by using the right materials and design
- know the meaning of efficiency and relate it to the everyday use of energy in the home
- know about using electromagnetic radiations in the home (infrared heaters, microwaves, grills)

To succeed at Special Level you should:

- be able to select and analyse quantitative data about materials and relate these to their domestic use
- know that the boiling point of a liquid depends on the pressure exerted on it (e.g. in a pressure cooker)
- be able to use the gas formula: $(P_1V_1)/T_1 = (P_2V_2)/T_2$
- be able to use the ideas of specific heat capacity and latent heat to explain everyday effects, and make calculations using them
- know about thermal expansion and its effects and applications
- be able to make calculations involving current, voltage, energy and power and understand the relations between these quantities
- be able to calculate electricity consumption and costs in the home
- understand and use the principle of the conservation of energy
- understand that, in the end, all energy transfers dissipate energy to heat the environment
- understand the ideas of cost-effectiveness and pay-back time in making decisions about home insulation
- know about the effects of electromagnetic radiations and be able to describe their use in the home

CHAPTER FOUR

Growing and Changing

What is growth?

Growth is a permanent increase in the size of an organism. When living things grow, they do so by making new, extra, cells. These then increase in size. The whole organism then becomes larger – its height, length and mass all increase.

Single-celled plants and animals simply grow in size until the cell is large enough to split into two.

One parent cell then becomes two identical daughter cells. These cells in turn feed, grow and divide in exactly the same way as their parent cells did. *Cell division* like this is the basis of how all living things grow.

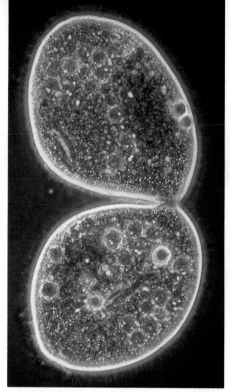

▲ A single-celled animal, a *Paramecium*, dividing into two cells. Each will be a complete new animal.

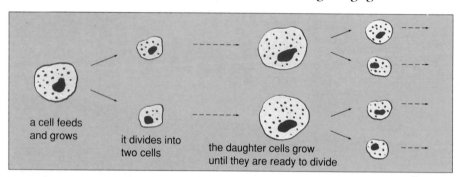

a cell feeds and grows

it divides into two cells

the daughter cells grow until they are ready to divide

Plants

Plant cells grow and divide in the same way, but only with cells in special tissues. These special growth tissues, or *meristems*, are found near the tips of shoots and roots and inside buds. New cells are only formed at these meristem areas. The cells then swell and elongate, making the whole plant bigger.

Bushes and trees are *woody* plants. Their stems have a huge outer layer of bark that protects the more delicate tissues inside. Tree trunks of course grow in diameter, as well as height. Each year of the tree's life a new layer of the cells that carry the water from the roots to the leaves is laid down. These cells are called xylem cells. Each year's new growth can therefore be seen as a ring of xylem cells. The age of the plant can easily be worked out by counting the number of rings.

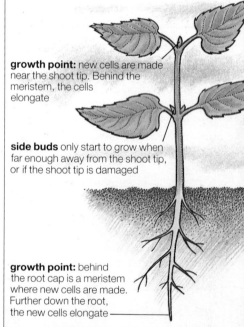

growth point: new cells are made near the shoot tip. Behind the meristem, the cells elongate

side buds only start to grow when far enough away from the shoot tip, or if the shoot tip is damaged

growth point: behind the root cap is a meristem where new cells are made. Further down the root, the new cells elongate

▲ In plants, growth only occurs in certain special areas of cells called *meristems*.

Animals

Animals do not have special growth tissues. Cells divide and grow throughout the body of a young animal. Different organs and tissues grow at different rates, which is why young mammals often seem to have large heads, or especially long legs. The different growth rates also mean that the shape of the body – the body's proportions – change a great deal as we get older.

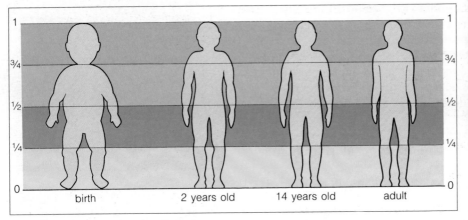

◀◀
Because different parts of the body grow at different rates, the overall shape, or proportions, of the body changes as we get older.

The *rate* at which new cells are formed also changes throughout the life of an animal. Once you reach the age of 13, there are more cells dying in your body than you are actually making. You could literally be described as being 'past your prime'. But our bodies continue to grow because the development of new cells is concentrated into key areas. Bones continue to grow longer and other tissues still increase in size and mass despite the overall slow-down in cell division.

Animals continue to grow until they reach their adult size. This depends on their growth being controlled properly and there being no hindrance to growth.

An external skeleton

Insects and shore crabs are a part of the largest group of animals on Earth – the arthropods. These animals have their skeletons on the outside of their bodies – an *exoskeleton*. Once the animal's body has filled their tough outer covering, further growth is impossible. So, insects and crabs have to lose this 'skin' and then grow very quickly before a new covering forms. These sudden, regular growth spurts can be seen very clearly in the locust.

Once the exoskeleton has been lost, the locust puffs up its body so that the new skeleton that forms is larger than the old one. There is then room for the locust body to grow.

The control of growth

Plants and animals use 'messenger' chemicals to control many parts of their lives, but especially growth and development. These chemicals are called *hormones*. Growth is controlled by *growth hormones*. The more growth hormone produced, the faster an animal or plant will grow.

Growth hormones affect our bodies in different ways according to our age. When we are young, they have a great effect – we grow fastest at this time. But although these hormones are still produced in the adult body, adult tissues and organs no longer respond to them. Children's bones

▼
The growth stages in a locust.

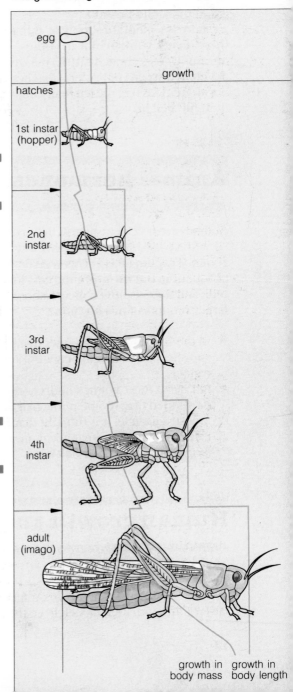

egg

growth

hatches

1st instar (hopper)

2nd instar

3rd instar

4th instar

adult (imago)

growth in body mass   growth in body length

grow if children are injected with extra human growth hormone, but there is no effect on adult bones. The reason is that the bone cells have changed. The growth regions at the tips of the bones are no longer active and the bone cells are no longer receptive to the hormone.

But some people do go on growing longer for longer than they should. Others grow unusually fast. This is because their bodies produce too much growth hormone, or their cells don't stop responding to it. Such people can become 'giants'.

If a person cannot produce enough growth hormone, they do not grow to a full height. This condition is called *achondroplasia*, more commonly known as dwarfism.

Human growth hormone is one of the most valuable medical substances. It is made by the pituitary gland, which is at the base of the brain, just behind your eyes. This gland is the only part of the body that the law allows to be collected and kept after a post-mortem examination. The growth hormone is then extracted and used to treat children who do not produce enough of the hormone themselves. This condition affects about one child in 5000.

There is a plentiful supply of animal growth hormones. Unfortunately, these do not work in human bodies. Treating a child with human growth hormone costs about £10000 per year. But now biotechnology has developed strains of bacteria that actually produce the human growth hormone. This means that many more children can be helped to grow to their full height.

▲ Both of these hands are of three year-old children. One of the children has a hormone imbalance and has grown to giant size.

Animal hormones: use and abuse

Animals are given extra growth hormones to make them grow faster. But should we use hormones in this way? One example is **B**ovine **S**omato**T**rophin (BST). This is given to cattle to boost growth and milk production. But the hormone gets into the human food chain through milk and there is now concern about the effects of eating and drinking large amounts of this hormone.

- In the United States, another hormone, DES, was given to beef cattle and sheep. DES had to be withdrawn when it was found to cause cancer.
- In Puerto Rico, young children – some only 18 months old – have developed breasts and pubic hair, and very young girls started their menstrual cycle. It is thought that this has been caused by the children eating too many animal hormones, which were used by local poultry farmers to fatten their chickens.

Human growth and development

Where it all began

Your life began at *fertilisation*. At fertilisation, a single sperm cell from the father joins with a single cell from the mother – the *egg* cell.

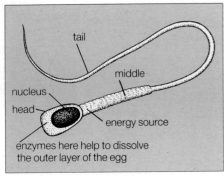

A human sperm cell.

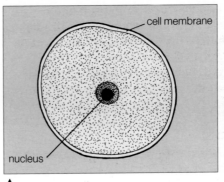

A human egg cell.

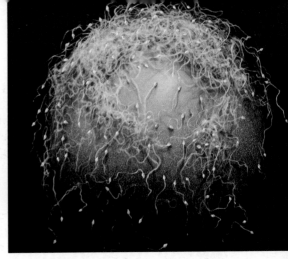

Human sperms crowding around an egg cell. You can see how much bigger the egg is. Why do you think this is?

The fertile egg, or *ovum*, starts to divide straight away, but *growth* can only start when the fertilised ovum buries itself in the lining of the mother's womb. To grow, the ovum needs new materials. These must all come from the mother, and are all supplied through a special tissue that develops between the mother and ovum – the *placenta*. The ovum can now develop into an *embryo*.

The embryo takes all its food and oxygen from the mother's blood and passes wastes and carbon dioxide back the same way. As soon as the embryo is joined to the womb, the woman is *pregnant*. The embryo is nourished, kept warm and protected. It grows and becomes a *foetus* – the name for the developing baby.

A human embryo at one month old, three months old and six months old.

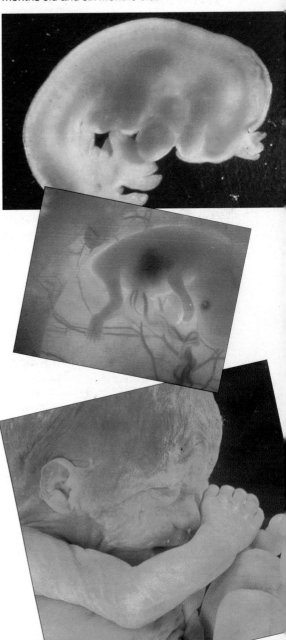

Things that can go wrong

The placenta is a superb biological filter, but like many filters, some unwelcome substances can cross it and affect the development of the embryo. (These include poisons like nicotine, alcohol, and other drugs, like heroin.) Most dangerous germs (bacteria and viruses) are dealt with by the mother's defence system and so do not reach the baby's body. But the *Rubella* virus, which causes German Measles, can cross the placenta and harm the developing baby.

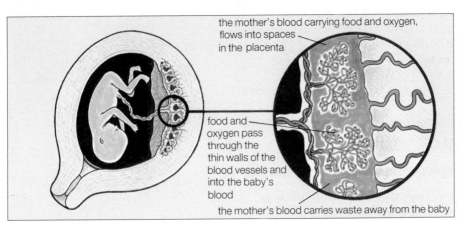

the mother's blood carrying food and oxygen, flows into spaces in the placenta

food and oxygen pass through the thin walls of the blood vessels and into the baby's blood

the mother's blood carries waste away from the baby

This shows how the blood supplies of the mother and the developing baby are very closely associated through the placenta.

In some cases, the mixing of *genetic information* from each of the parents is unsuccessful. The fertilised egg may not develop at all, or vital parts of the body may not grow. The embryo may be damaged or harmed, or the placenta itself may not form properly. These things can result in a *miscarriage*. This is how the body stops the pregnancy. There are many factors that can lead to a miscarriage, but the precise causes seem to be varied and difficult to define.

Being new to the world

When it is born, the human baby depends on its parents for everything. It is helpless, unlike the young of many other animals, which can, and often have to, look after themselves. Young horses are able to walk soon after they are born. Young chickens can peck up food almost as soon as they have hatched. Young wildebeest have to keep up with their migrating parents or they may be killed by lions. Newly hatched turtles race for the sea, running a great risk of being eaten on the way!

What babies need

The human baby, or a puppy, or a kitten needs the care and attention of it's parents whilst it learns to take care of itself. *Parental care* makes sure that the newborn receives food, air, warmth, and shelter. Drinking mother's milk also gives young mammals protection against some of the diseases that the mother may have suffered from.

Human company is very important to the baby. The contact with its mother and family stimulates the developing mind. We continue to learn from our surroundings and fellow humans throughout our lives, but we learn especially quickly in our early years.

We learn the important *rules* of our society and of our culture from our contact with other people. This takes a very long time in humans, because we have so much to learn. We have the longest 'childhood' of any animal species.

The helpless baby soon becomes the *infant* or 'toddler'. *Childhood* is the time for more learning; we learn from our experiences of trying and doing, and also from older people. Family, friends, teachers, and many other people help us to develop our skills and to form opinions and values.

Boys' and girls' bodies are very similar during childhood. As the child nears adulthood, however, the differences between the sexes become much more noticeable.

Puberty and reproduction

Adult animals are capable of *reproduction*. They can make more of their own kind from sex cells (gametes). These cells are brought together in sexual reproduction. Children, or juveniles, are not capable of producing sex cells.

At puberty, children start the transition into adults. The changes do not happen overnight, and they happen at different times in different people, so there is no 'normal', only an average of what the changes are and when they happen. Puberty is triggered by hormones that are released from the pituitary gland. These cause other hormones to be released. These *sex hormones* then make our bodies change.

In both sexes	Body size increases dramatically Body hair starts to grow – armpit and pubic hair Sexual 'drive' develops

In the male	Beard starts to grow; and chest broadens
	Body becomes more muscular and changes shape –
	    becomes 'squarer'
	The voice breaks
	Penis, testes and scrotum enlarge and start to
	    produce sperm and semen

In the female	Breasts develop (humans are the only species where this occurs before pregnancy) Hips get wider and the body shape rounder Vagina, uterus and oviducts grow and develop The menstrual cycle begins

Leaving childhood

Girls usually begin puberty when they are 11–13 years old. Puberty in boys is usually two or three years later. Puberty takes several years to complete. During this time, young people are called *adolescents*.

Adolescence brings many changes. One of the changes is a rapid increase in growth, a *growth spurt*.

Human growth rates

The table on page 217 of the 'Reference section' shows the *average* mass and height for boys and girls of different ages. Can you see where the growth spurt begins?

A six year old girl has achieved one third of her final adult mass. By eighteen years old she will almost have stopped increasing in mass. Bones grow faster than muscles, which is why adolescents often seem 'gangly' and 'clumsy'. It is also very common to arrive at adulthood with feet of different sizes, showing just how complicated the whole process of growth is!

The sex hormones cause our bodies to change in size and shape – inside and out!

These changes to our bodies are called the *secondary sexual characteristics*. They are the outward signs of adulthood.

The male and female reproductive systems

During puberty, the growth hormones literally 'turn on' the reproductive systems. In boys, the penis and testes enlarge and the testes start to produce sperm. In girls, their menstrual cycle begins.

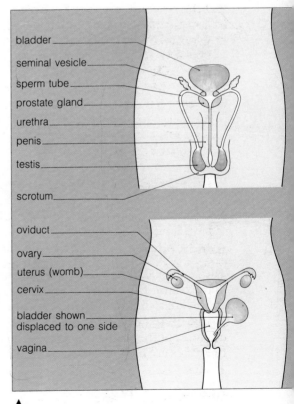

bladder
seminal vesicle
sperm tube
prostate gland
urethra
penis
testis
scrotum

oviduct
ovary
uterus (womb)
cervix
bladder shown
displayed to one side
vagina

▲
The human male and female reproductive systems.

The menstrual cycle

Girls start to have periods as their menstrual cycle begins. This is a series of events that take about 28 days in most women. It is controlled by two hormones – oestrogen and progesterone, which are produced by the ovaries.

First, the pituitary gland produces a hormone which causes a part of the ovary to become a *follicle*, whose job is to grow around a developing egg cell and carry it to the edge of the ovary. When the egg cell is ready, it is released into the egg tube, and it travels down this to the uterus. While this has been going on, the follicle itself has produced a hormone (oestrogen) to make the lining of the womb repair itself after the previous menstruation.

Then, when the egg is released into the egg tube, the pituitary gland goes into action again, to make the follicle do another job. It changes the follicle into a kind of temporary gland which produces yet another hormone called *progesterone*. This makes the womb lining grow into the thick wall that can receive the fertile egg that would grow into a baby. If the egg is not fertilised, the temporary gland (the ex-follicle) stops working and fades away. The thickened lining to the uterus breaks down and is shed through the woman's vagina. This is called menstruation. But if there is a developing baby present the gland keeps working to produce the progesterone hormone that keeps the womb lining growing. This means, of course, that menstruation doesn't happen. Often the first sign of pregnancy is a 'missed period'. Progesterone has another effect too – it stops the ovaries from releasing another egg.

▼
The menstrual cycle.

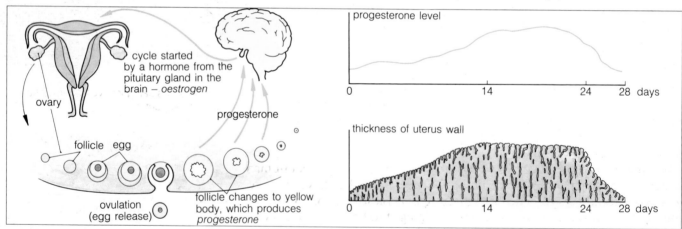

And in boys . . .

The boy's body is influenced by the male sex hormone, *testosterone*, made in the testes. This causes a boy's testes to mature and produce sperm. Sperm are also produced in a continuous cycle. But whereas the human female produces a single egg every 28 days, sperm cells are made by the million. Sperm production is very sensitive to temperature. This is why the testes are held outside a boy's body where the temperature is lower.

Emotional changes

The hormones and changes can make puberty a confusing and often worrying time. Young people become aware of sexual feelings and are sometimes uncomfortable with the strong emotions that they experience as they change from being children into responsible adults.

Continuing the line

The changes of adolescence signal that young people are becoming capable of sexual reproduction. The secondary sexual characteristics are signals: voices change, hair grows, girls' bodies become more curved and boys' become more muscular. The emotional and physical changes allow people to become sexually aroused and to have sexual intercourse.

The growing sexual drive is an important part of our emotional development. It is so strong that humans are the only species to have sexual intercourse for pleasure. They may not actually want to have a child. (See *Using hormones*, below)

▲ Fish fertilise their eggs outside the body of the mother. This is why the fish has to produce so many eggs, to ensure that at least some of them meet sperm from the father.

Infertility

One of the strongest behavioural urges in animals is that to reproduce – to produce offspring. Humans are no exception. But some people are unable to have children. One of the many possible causes of would-be parents not being able to have children is that the woman's ovary is not able to begin the cycle by producing the egg follicle. *Fertility drugs* act like hormones in stimulating the production of follicles – doing it so well sometimes that several follicles start working at the same time, leading to several eggs and multiple births.

Sometimes it is the man who is infertile. His testes may not produce enough sperm, or the sperm may be too weak to reach and fertilise the egg cell.

Using hormones

The best known use of artificial hormones is the *birth pill* or oral contraceptive. When taken regularly at the correct time of the female menstrual cycle it can stop the ovaries from releasing an egg. It does this by introducing artificial progesterone into the body, so that the ovaries behave as though the body is already pregnant.

Hormones are very powerful chemicals and can seriously affect human beings. Growth hormones are also called *steroids*, and they have come to be used by some athletes to improve strength by building more muscle. They are now banned, partly because it is thought to be unfair, but mainly because the 'side effects' of using powerful chemicals like these have been shown to be harmful! The natural balance of the body is upset – male athletes may develop breasts, for example.

▲ Fertility drugs can give even better results than you expected.

Plant growth

Just like a human, a plant needs water, oxygen and food. But plants have one major advantage – they can make their own food.

By using *photosynthesis*, plants take energy from sunlight to change simple chemicals into food:

sunlight energy

carbon dioxide and water ——————→ glucose (sugar) and oxygen.

Many people think that plants get their food from the ground. This is not true! They 'feed' on air! There is more about this in Chapter 9, *The green world*.

The food made by a plant can be used for growth, and for making the energy its cells need. The food can also be stored in special *food-storage organs*, such as the root of a carrot, an onion bulb, or a potato tuber. Plants also store food in seeds. This ensures that the offspring are guaranteed some food as they start their lives.

Because photosynthesis is the basis for all plant life, plants have some basic needs that are different to those of animals. A plant must collect *light* and *carbon dioxide*. With these as raw materials, the plant can make the starch and sugars that it needs for energy and growth. All animal life depends on plants for their foods at some stage.

From the starch and sugars, and using minerals taken up from the soil, the plant can make other useful chemicals. One of the most important is *chlorophyll*. This is the green chemical that the plant uses to capture light energy.

Plant growth conditions

Keen gardeners know that different sorts of plants grow better in different conditions. The growing conditions that a plant receives will affect how well it can grow, and for how long it can continue to grow.

Plants need minerals

A range of different minerals is essential to produce a healthy plant. Without its minerals a plant will not be able to grow and develop correctly. There is more information about plants and minerals in the 'Reference section' of this book.

Plants get *mineral deficiency diseases* if they cannot get enough of particular minerals. These diseases can be avoided by feeding *artificial fertilizers* to the plants that we grow. Fertilizers supply the minerals required by the plants. See Chapter 9, *The green world*.

Climate and vegetation

Some plants can only grow in tropical conditions, some in deserts. Others manage to grow in bitter cold high up on mountains, or near the Arctic Circle. The plants that grow naturally in Britain are not the same as those in the warm, dry, lands around the Mediterranean. The plants that grow there are not the same as those in the South American rain forest; or the African Savannah or the Australian Bush. The amount of rainfall and the annual temperature variation (in other words, the *climate*) largely determines which plants will grow.

But the plants that we find in one place today may not have always been there. For example, it is surprising how many of the plants found in Britain today have originated from all over the world. This map gives some well-known examples.

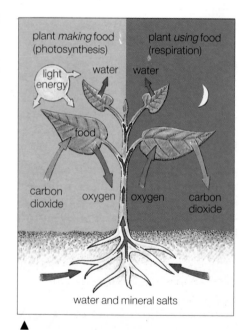

▲
A plant's needs are different when it is photosynthesising as well as respiring. Plants are always respiring.

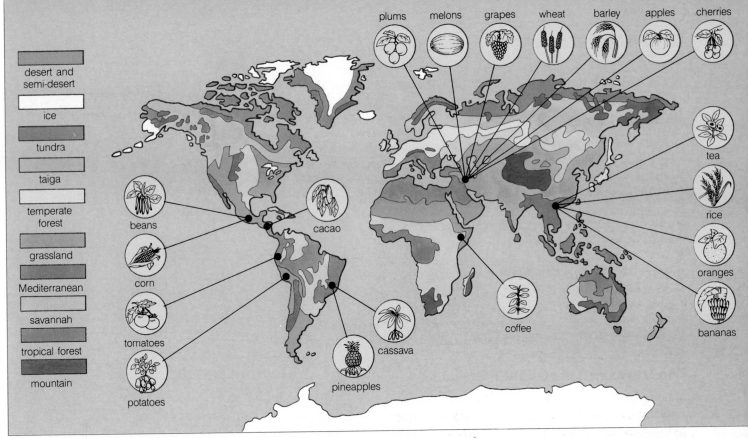

Some plants grow well in their new environments. Others need some help. To satisfy our needs for a varied diet and raw materials, plant breeders have produced 'improved' plants. They do this through careful *breeding*. Plants are selected to give higher crop yields, and to produce larger fruits. They can also be made more resistant to disease, frost and drought. The best specimens are bred with each other to give better and better varieties.

▲
World vegetation zones and the origins of some of our most important cultivated plants.

◄
Sexual reproduction produces variation. Here, an orange plant and a grapefruit plant have been *cross fertilised* to make an entirely new fruit.

▼
We can create entirely artificial environments for plants and animals, where all of their needs are provided for.

Promoting plant growth

Plant growers can supply extra minerals to a plant by using fertilisers. Warmth, and water can be provided. The strength and length of sunlight, and carbon dioxide levels can all be controlled in computer-controlled greenhouses. The conditions can be adjusted to produce plants, fruits and seeds, when we want them and in exactly the size and shape that we want.

Plant hormones

Growth and development in plants is controlled by chemicals that are very much like the hormones found in animals. We call these chemicals *plant growth substances* – plant hormones.

Plant hormones control every aspect of the plants' life:

- shoots grow 'upwards' and bend towards the light
- roots grow 'downwards'
- seed germination
- growth of fruits and flowers
- opening and growth of buds
- healing of wounds
- ripening of fruits
- dormancy in the winter (the plant's leaves fall and it becomes inactive).

Can we make use of plant hormones?

When plant hormones were first discovered it was thought that they might solve all of the world's food problems by allowing us to grow enormous vegetables and other plants, in huge amounts. This didn't work out! The hormones simply made giant plants that were weak-stemmed and did not live for very long. However, our knowledge of different types of plant hormones has been useful in some ways:

- preventing spoiling of cereal foods and potatoes to enable them to be stored for longer periods of time. This is done by keeping them dormant or inactive;
- making sure that barley seeds all germinate at the same time. This is for use in the malting industry;
- making 'selective' weedkillers such as 2, 4–D. These do not affect grasses, but make weeds outgrow themselves and die;
- fruit ripening can be accelerated or delayed by using plant hormones. This is especially important where machines harvest the fruit crop, as in grapes. Unripe fruit is tougher and easier to pick without bruising. It

▲
Plants have been bred to be exactly what we want them to be. These carrots are very different from their wild counterparts – and shops want fruit and vegetables that actually fit the packaging!

▼
The dangers and uses of plant hormones.

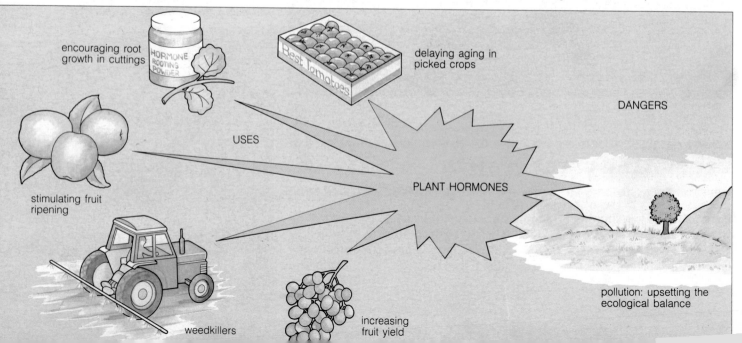

encouraging root growth in cuttings

HORMONE ROOTING POWDER

Best Tomatoes

delaying aging in picked crops

DANGERS

USES

stimulating fruit ripening

PLANT HORMONES

pollution: upsetting the ecological balance

weedkillers

increasing fruit yield

can be transported with less damage, and then ripened before being sold in shops;

- rooting hormones help in the propagation of plants through taking cuttings. When a cutting is dipped in a rooting preparation it is stimulated to make roots and grow.

Plant growth responses

Plants react to light, gravity, temperature, chemical substances, water, and touch. There are two types of responses: *nastic* responses, and *tropic* responses.

Nastic responses do not have a direction. For example, when flowers close their petals at night, or when a venus flytrap snaps shut on an insect.

Tropic responses, or *tropisms*, have a definite direction of movement that is determined by the direction of the stimulus causing the response. The plant may move or grow *towards* the stimulus, a positive tropism; or it may move away, a negative tropism.

A root is *positively geotropic*: it grows towards the centre of the earth, 'towards gravity'. A shoot is *negatively geotropic*, it grows away from the centre of the earth, against the pull of gravity.

The shoot of a plant is positively phototropic. It bends towards the light. Extension task 4 on page 189 is about these responses.

Activities

1 Carry out some surveys measuring growth and development in animals. Present your information in an interesting way. You could find out about one of the following (remember: people are also animals!):
- the average height of boys and girls of *different ages* in your school;
- whether girls have broader hips than boys, and boys have wider shoulders than girls, *before* and *after* the start of puberty;
- how other animals change in size or mass as they grow — you could study small mammals such as mice or gerbils, or insects.

Think very carefully about what you are going to measure and how you could measure it. How many times will you take measurements? Could you draw graphs of your results? Can averages be worked out for the different measurements that you take? And be *very* polite to the human 'animals' that you are investigating!

2 (a) Look carefully at the diagrams of bean plants. Can you decide which mineral might be missing to cause the symptoms shown? Use the data in the 'Reference section' about plant nutrients to help you make a list of what you feel is wrong with each plant and your reasons for deciding this.
(b) Collect information from some fertiliser packets. What are the commonest minerals that are supplied to plants? You could find the packets at home or in a garden centre or DIY store.

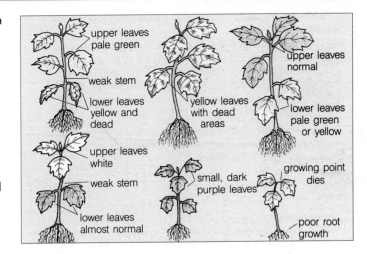

Do fertilisers for different sorts of plants such as rose fertilisers, grass feeds and tomato fertilisers contain the same mineral nutrients.
(c) Use gardening books and the data from the 'Reference section' to find out why these minerals are needed by plants. Try to explain some of the claims made on the fertiliser packets, e.g. 'makes greener lawns'; 'for bigger blooms'; 'increases fruit yields'.

3 Plan and carry out an investigation to see if seeds germinate better (or if seedlings grow more quickly) under glass or out in the open. You could use fast-growing seeds like cress, or you could use peas or beans (which would take a little longer). Clear-plastic bottles can be cut to make small greenhouses. You could grow the seeds outside if it is Spring or Summer, otherwise grow them indoors.

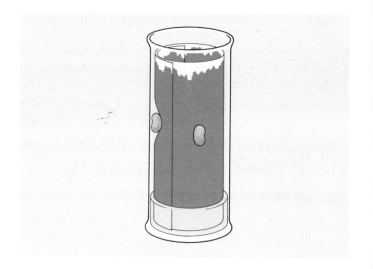

4 Plant some runner bean or pea seeds in a jam jar. If you put in a tube of absorbent paper you should be able to trap the seeds, between the paper and the sides of the jar, about halfway up. You can set several seeds in one jar and you can observe their growth. Put water in the bottom of the jar, but do not let the seeds fall into it.

Measure and plot the growth of your plants over a few weeks. Are there any other changes you could record or measure apart from the height?

What is the result if you do the same for a plant grown in the dark, or one grown in continual shade?

Questions

1 (a) Make a list of what a plant needs to grow. For each need, say how the plant obtains what it requires.
(b) How could you make sure that a tomato plant grew as well as possible?
(c) At the end of the summer, a tomato plant weighed 5 kg. It started as a seed weighing less than 0.1 g. Where has all this extra material mostly come from?

2 (a) By using the data on page 217 draw graphs showing the growth of boys and girls up to the age of 18 years. Plot the information for boys and girls on the same graph so that you can compare them. (The age should be along the bottom of the graph.)

What can you decide about the growth of boys and girls from your graphs?
(b) On your graphs mark where you think that the boys and girls reach puberty. Explain how the shape of the graph helps you decide. Label your graphs to show the stages of birth, infancy, childhood, adolescence, and the beginnings of adulthood. Show the 'beginning of life', i.e. conception, on your graph.

3 You have just got a job as a reporter for your local newspaper and have been put in charge of the *Gardening Section*. How would you reply to this letter?

4 These plants have been grown in different light conditions. Suggest for each what sort of light condition might have caused the plant to grow in that way.

Dear Theresa Green,

I have recently moved to a new flat and the plants in the windowbox do not seem to be growing properly. They are small and some of the leaves are turning yellow. They get plenty of sunlight because the window faces South and I water them regularly. We do not have a cat.

How can I find out what might be wrong with them?

Yours sincerely,
Ivor Duffplant

Checklist

These are the facts and ideas that you should have learned by studying this topic.

To succeed at Basic Level you should:

- be able to describe the main stages of human life
- understand the idea of life span, the need for living things to reproduce themselves and that young children need a lot of care from their parents
- know that children, young animals and even plants are never exactly the same as their parents

To succeed at Foundation Level you should:

- know about the changes that take place in young people (adolescents)
- understand how mammals reproduce
- know at least two important things that young children need if they are to grow and develop properly
- know the differences between the ways in which animals and plants grow
- know that hormones control how children grow and change

To succeed at Merit Level you should:

- know about the range of physical and emotional changes that takes place during adolescence and the need to have a responsible attitude to sexual behaviour
- understand what happens when babies are conceived and born
- understand what young children need to develop properly and what might happen if they are neglected
- be able to analyse and use data about growth in both animals and plants
- know how hormones affect growth and development in animals and plants

To succeed at Special Level you should:

- know about the role of the pituitary gland and the gonads in controlling sexual development
- know about the implications for health of promiscuous sexual behaviour
- know why some parents are unable to have children, and how they can be helped
- know that growth rates in plants and animals are not constant
- know enough about the use of hormones in controlling growth and fertility to be able to make informed judgements about it
- show an understanding of how scientific ideas about growth and reproduction have changed and developed over time

CHAPTER FIVE

◄ Dmitri Ivanovich Mendeleev.

In the 'Reference section', there is a rock key that allows us to classify some common rocks into groups. Biologists also place the organisms that they are studying into groups — plants and animals being the most obvious ones. Chemists use the properties of the substances that they are studying to order them into groups.

Scientists have been trying to group the chemical elements for over two hundred years. The most important event was in 1869 when Dmitri Mendeléev published the first *periodic table*.

CHEMICAL PATTERNS

The periodic table

Mendeléev was Professor of Chemistry at St Petersburg University in Russia. His table contained only 64 elements — all the elements known at the time. Mendeléev grouped the elements using his knowledge of their properties. He also compared the compounds they made.

Mendeléev arranged the elements in a grid. He did this by using two main facts about each element.

First, he put the elements in order of 'atomic weight' starting with the lightest. ('Atomic weight' is now known as relative atomic mass.) Then he put elements with similar properties in the same vertical column.

When Mendeléev drew up his periodic table he found that he had to leave blank spaces to fit the elements with similar properties in the same columns. The 'next' element didn't seem to fit in that column. The gaps, he claimed, would be filled by elements that had not yet been discovered. Mendeléev went one stage further. He actually predicted what some of these undiscovered elements should be like. For example, he described what an element in the fourth column between silicon and tin would be like.

It is a brave scientist who risks their name and reputation by predicting the future. If you get it wrong other scientists can be extremely rude! But Mendeléev got it right. The table shows some of Mendeléev's predictions about the unknown element. When the element, now called germanium (Ge), was discovered 15 years later, most of his predictions were found to be correct.

	Group I	Group II	Group III	Group IV	Group V	Group VI	Group VII	Group VIII
Period 1	H							
Period 2	Li	Be	B	C	N	O	F	
Period 3	Na	Mg	Al	Si	P	S	Cl	
Period 4	K Cu	Ca Zn	* Y	Ti Zr	V Nb	Cr Mo	Mn Br	Fe Co Ni
Period 5	Rb Ag	Sr Cd	In	Sn	Sb	Te	I	Ru Rh Pd

▲ Mendeléev's first periodic table.

Mendeléev's predictions	Observed properties
Light grey metal	Dark grey metal
Relative atomic mass 72	Relative atomic mass 72.6
Density 5.5 g/cm³	Density 5.47 g/cm³
Each atom will combine with two atoms of oxygen to form a white oxide which will have a high melting point.	A white oxide, formula GeO_2 is formed. The melting point is 1112 °C.
The chloride will be a liquid, with a low boiling point.	The boiling point of the chloride ($GeCl_4$) is 83 °C.

Since Mendeléev's time more elements have been discovered. The modern periodic table lists 103 elements. We also know what Mendeléev's couldn't even guess at: the detailed structure of the atoms. Slowly the reasons why groups of elements are similar has become understood. The key to this understanding is the way the atoms are built up from sub-atomic particles called protons, neutrons and electrons. Chemists are particularly interested in the electrons because these are the outside part of the atom. When one element reacts with another, the atoms from the two elements come very close together. The electrons on the outside of each atom meet. Electrons can then swap from one atom to another. These electrons swaps are what make chemical reactions take place.

The reactive metals are on the left-hand side of the table. The most reactive metals are at the bottom left.

The non-metals are all towards the right-hand side. There are 22 elements classified as non-metals.

The change from metallic to non-metallic character is very gradual across the table, starting surprisingly close to the left-hand side. But, in the recent past, a 'staircase' has been drawn on the table to show the rough position of the change. Elements next to the staircase have both metallic and non-metallic properties.

Vertical *groups* are given Roman numerals I to VII.

The horizontal rows are called *periods*. They are numbered 1, 2, 3, etc.

Some groups are given names. The elements in these groups have very similar properties – 'a group chemistry'. Group I is the alkali metals, Group II is the alkaline earth metals; Group VII is called the halogens and Group O the inert gases, or noble gases (these are extremely unreactive).

Another large group at the very centre of the periodic table is called the transition elements. These are very dense and unreactive metals. Compounds of transition metals are all coloured. This group is made of two families. First, the lanthanides, or rare earths, which are all fairly similar metals, and secondly, the Actinides. These are all radioactive. Elements in this family to the right of uranium do not occur naturally, they are made in nuclear reactions.

Apart from the noble gases, there are five other elements that are gases. They are chlorine, fluorine, hydrogen, nitrogen and oxygen. Note where these elements are grouped in the table.

Only two elements are liquids at room temperature. These are mercury and bromine.

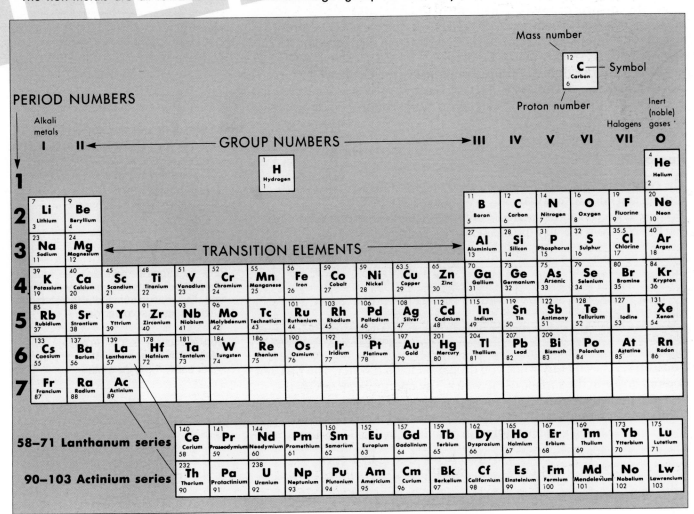

Patterns in the periodic table

The periodic table makes it easier to understand a lot of chemical behaviour, but it still isn't that simple. First, you can see that there are eight groups, labelled Group I to Group 0. Group 0? Why not call it Group VIII? The reason is partly because the elements in the Group were discovered very late after most of the periodic table had been drawn up. Another is that it was first thought they ought to be in front of Group I. We now know that it makes better sense to put them after Group VII, on the far right (see page 63).

You will also notice that there are a lot of very useful looking elements, all metals, that aren't put in a Group at all. These are in the block between Groups II and III. We can forget about this for a while and look at some of the simpler patterns of elements that are put into the Groups.

Up, down and sideways

The left-hand side of the periodic table contains the very reactive metals. As you move sideways the metals become generally less reactive. Then come the non-metals, like silicon, sulphur and chlorine. Finally, on the far right, are the Noble gases, like neon and argon. These are chemically inert – they do not form compounds naturally.

As you move down a Group with metals in it, the metals get more reactive. In Group I, potassium (K) is more reactive than sodium (Na), and caesium (Cs) is very reactive indeed.

But as you move down a Group of non-metals, the elements get *less* reactive. Fluorine, in Group VII, is a very reactive (and deadly poisonous) gas. Iodine is quite reactive – it kills germs, for example – but is quite safe to touch.

Period 3

The rows in the periodic table are called *periods*. Period 3 starts with sodium and ends with argon.

There is a trend across period 3 of metal changing to non-metal. This can be seen from the way the elements react with water.

group I	II	III	IV	V	VI	VII	VIII
Na	Mg	Al	Si	P	S	Cl	Ar
sodium	magnesium	aluminium	silicon	phosphorus	sulphur	chlorine	argon
metals				non-metals			

◀

Patterns across the periodic table. Metallic properties decrease as you move to the right. The change from metal to non-metal is not always easy to decide.

▼

Sodium melts at 98°C. The energy released by the reaction of the sodium with water easily melts the metal.

Sodium reacts violently when you drop it on to cold water. The piece of sodium floats on the surface of the water. The energy given out by the reaction immediately melts the sodium. A shiny grey ball is seen whizzing about across the surface of the water. Often the reaction ends in an explosion. A strongly alkaline solution of sodium hydroxide is left:

$$\text{sodium} + \text{water} \rightarrow \text{sodium hydroxide} + \text{hydrogen,}$$
$$2\text{Na} + 2\text{H}_2\text{O} \rightarrow 2\text{NaOH} + \text{H}_2.$$

The explosion is caused by hydrogen reacting with oxygen in the air.

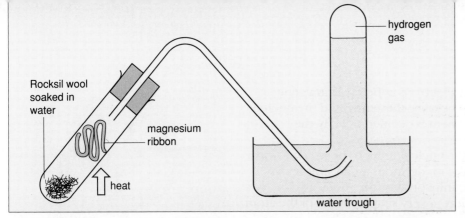

◄
Rocksil wool at the bottom of the test tube soaks up the water and keeps it at the bottom of the tube. The water is heated by conduction through the glass of the test tube. The water in the Rocksil wool starts to boil some time after the magnesium has been heated. This ensures that the steam meets hot magnesium.

Magnesium reacts rapidly if heated in steam, but reacts very, very slowly with cold water. Magnesium oxide doesn't dissolve in water so we get:

$$\text{magnesium} + \text{water} \rightarrow \text{magnesium oxide} + \text{hydrogen,}$$
$$\text{Mg} + \text{H}_2\text{O} \rightarrow \text{MgO} + \text{H}_2.$$

Aluminium will only react with water if the protective oxide layer on its surface is first removed. This has to be done chemically by using a solution of mercury chloride. The aluminium will then react in the same pattern, giving aluminium oxide and hydrogen:

$$\text{aluminium} + \text{water} \rightarrow \text{aluminium oxide} + \text{hydrogen,}$$
$$4\text{Al} + 6\text{H}_2\text{O} \rightarrow 2\text{Al}_2\text{O}_3 + 3\text{H}_2.$$

Silicon, phosphorus and **sulphur** do not react with water. Phosphorus does react very easily with oxygen and so has to be stored away from the air – under a layer of water.

Sulphur used to be mined by pumping super-heated steam under high pressure, down bore holes into underground deposits of sulphur. Sulphur melts at 119°C and so was pushed up to the surface of the Earth by the pressure of steam.

Chlorine does react with water, it forms an acidic, bleaching solution:

$$\text{chlorine} + \text{water} \rightarrow \text{bleach} + \text{hydrochloric acid}$$
$$\text{Cl}_2 + \text{H}_2\text{O} \rightarrow \text{HOCl} + \text{HCl}$$

Argon does not react with water, or indeed with anything else!

▲
White phosphorus burning in air.

The secret of the periodic table

Atomic structure

The patterns of the periodic table are decided by the structure of the atom itself. An atom has two main parts. The central part is the *nucleus*. It is made up of smaller, 'sub-atomic' particles called *protons* and *neutrons*. The outer part, around the nucleus, contains *electrons*. There is more about this in Chapter 10, *Atoms, molecules and materials*.

We now know that the atom is a lot more complicated than this very simple picture. But we can still explain a lot of chemistry with this simple model. First of all, the chemical properties of an element are decided by its electrons. Especially important is how the electrons are arranged in the atom.

It makes a lot of sense to think of the electrons as being arranged in groups. These groups are called *shells*, because they surround the nucleus like a nutshell! The chemistry of an element is decided only by the electrons in its outermost shell.

The electrons are whirling around the nucleus at high speed. They form the *electron cloud*. But we can make the model atom much simpler by pretending that the electrons are in definite orbits – the shells. By 'stopping' the electrons we can then draw a very simple model of the atom like this.

In many of the diagrams in this chapter we use different symbols to represent the electrons, but, of course, all the electrons are really the same.

The number of electrons in each shell is decided by some very advanced laws of physics. You must remember that the shells are only part of a model that helps us to understand how the atom fits together. The electrons do not orbit in the nucleus in neat circles.

So, there is a strong link between the periodic table and the structure of the atoms of elements. This link is between the number of electrons in the outside shell of the atoms and the Group number – they are the same. For example, all Group I elements have *one* electron in the outside shell of their atoms. All Group IV elements have four electrons in the outside shell of their atoms.

Electrons have almost no mass. It takes 1836 electrons to equal the mass of a proton. So practically all of the mass of an atom is concentrated in the nucleus. When two elements react, the electrons from the outside shells of their atoms move from one atom to another. The masses of the atoms do not alter. The nucleus is quite unaffected by the chemical reaction.

Atomic number and mass number

You can work out the number of electrons, protons and neutrons in the atom of an element by using two pieces of data: the *atomic number* and the *mass number*.

- The atomic number of an element gives the number of protons in an atom. In a neutral atom there is the same number of protons and electrons.
- The mass number gives the total number of protons and neutrons in the nucleus.

Fluorine, for example, has an atomic number 9 and a mass number 19. It contains nine protons and ten neutrons in the nucleus. Round the nucleus are nine electrons. The electrons are arranged to leave seven electrons in the outside shell and two electrons in the inside shell. Each electron shell is able to hold a certain maximum number of electrons. The innermost one can hold two, and the next shell, eight. The table on the next page shows how the electrons are arranged in the first eighteen elements in the periodic table.

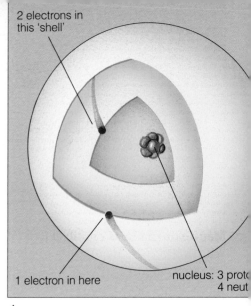

2 electrons in this 'shell'

1 electron in here

nucleus: 3 proto 4 neut

▲
The electrons orbit an atom in 'shells'. The shells are not real things. They are regions where you are most likely to find an electron.

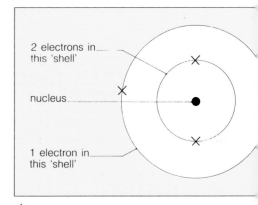

2 electrons in this 'shell'

nucleus

1 electron in this 'shell'

▲
This is the same atom, but drawn in a different way. Scientists use many different ways to show what atoms are like.

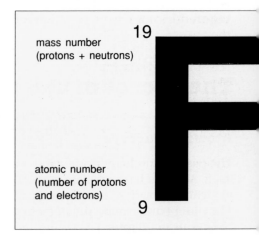

mass number (protons + neutrons)

19

F

atomic number (number of protons and electrons)

9

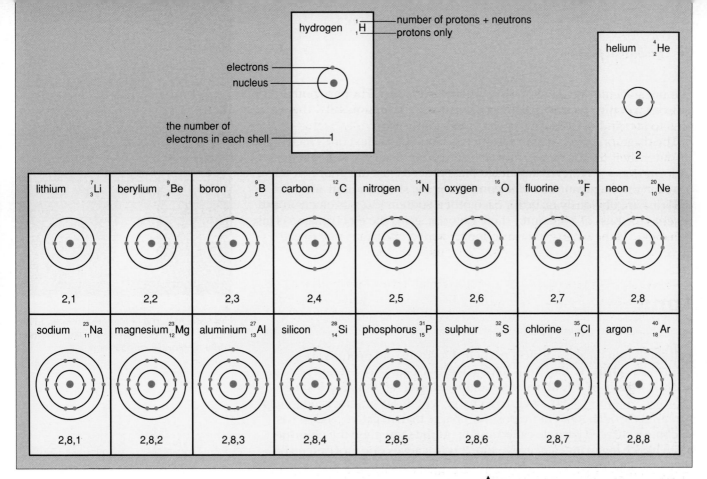

hydrogen $^1_1$H — number of protons + neutrons — protons only

electrons
nucleus

the number of electrons in each shell — 1

helium $^4_2$He

2

lithium $^7_3$Li	berylium $^9_4$Be	boron $^9_5$B	carbon $^{12}_6$C	nitrogen $^{14}_7$N	oxygen $^{16}_8$O	fluorine $^{19}_9$F	neon $^{20}_{10}$Ne
2,1	2,2	2,3	2,4	2,5	2,6	2,7	2,8
sodium $^{23}_{11}$Na	magnesium $^{23}_{12}$Mg	aluminium $^{27}_{13}$Al	silicon $^{28}_{14}$Si	phosphorus $^{31}_{15}$P	sulphur $^{32}_{16}$S	chlorine $^{35}_{17}$Cl	argon $^{40}_{18}$Ar
2,8,1	2,8,2	2,8,3	2,8,4	2,8,5	2,8,6	2,8,7	2,8,8

▲ How electrons are arranged in the first 18 elements in the periodic table.

Why atoms react

The noble gases do not react because they have a very stable arrangement of electrons. Look at helium, neon and argon in the table. They all have a full outer shell of electrons. When any element reacts, the atoms of the element try to end up just like this, with a full outer shell of electrons. This is as natural as water flowing downhill, and happens for the same reason – the atom can lose energy by doing this. For an atom, a low-energy state is the most desirable. This could apply to some people too. This process explains why elements react to form compounds, and why energy is released when they do. Metals lose their partly filled outer shell of electrons to leave the full shell underneath. Non-metals do the opposite. They try to fill up their outer shells. When a metal reacts with a non-metal, electrons go from the metal to the non-metal. This leaves *both* with full outer shells. The result is a pair of particles which are like the noble gases and so do not react further. Just think about the well-known reaction between sodium and chlorine.

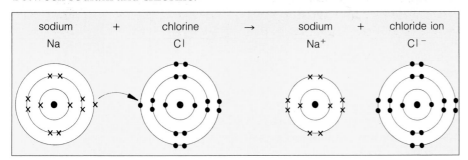

sodium + chlorine → sodium + chloride ion
Na   Cl   Na⁺   Cl⁻

◄ When elements combine to form compounds, electrons are exchanged as the elements try to gain complete outer shells.

67

Sodium and chlorine are both very reactive elements. They are both nasty poisons. Yet the reaction produces a substance – common salt – that is vital to life. And all because one electron has moved.

The diagram shows what has happened. Sodium has just one electron in its outer shell. This is easy to move, making sodium an active element. Chlorine has a very nearly full outer shell. It needs just one more electron to reach the magic number of 8, completing the shell. Sodium and chlorine are obviously made for each other. Sodium loses its electron and reaches the bliss of a full outer shell. Chlorine gains the electron and is just as happy. The new particles are no longer active, and salt is safe to eat!

▲ Hot sodium burns fiercely in chlorine gas. It gives off clouds of white smoke. This is sodium chloride, or common salt.

Ions

Full shells don't make a perfect particle. Electrons and protons are electrically charged. Electrons have a negative charge of -1 and protons a positive charge of $+1$. In making sodium chloride, sodium has lost one electron, and this takes its negative charge with it. So sodium is no longer a neutral particle. It has more positive charge than negative, and so has become a charged particle called an *ion*. At the same time the chlorine atom has changed into a negative ion. It now carries one more electron than it should.

This is an example of a reaction that has produced an *ionic compound*. There is more about ions on page 231.

Two important groups
Group I: The alkali metals

A group in the periodic table contains elements with similar properties. But these properties change as you move down the group.

This is a summary of the properties of the elements in Group I.

All of the elements are:

- metals
- low-density solids;
- very good conductors of electricity;
- very good conductors of heat;
- soft and easily cut with a knife;
- light grey and shiny when freshly cut.
- They rapidly lose their shine as the metal reacts with both oxygen and water in the atmosphere.
- They are stored in oil to protect them.
- They react with cold water to form hydrogen and an alkaline solution.
- The reactivity increases down the group.

Atoms of the elements in Group I all have one electron in the outer shell of their atoms. When they react with other elements or water, they lose this outer electron. This leaves behind a 'stale', complete shell of electrons. Thus their atoms form positive ions. Each ion has a charge of $+1$.

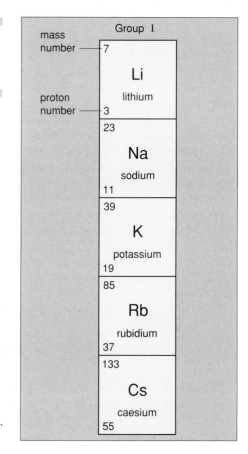

Group I

mass number	7
proton number	Li lithium
	3
	23
	Na sodium
	11
	39
	K potassium
	19
	85
	Rb rubidium
	37
	133
	Cs caesium
	55

The reactivity increases down Group I because the atoms get larger. The outer electron further away from the attraction of the nucleus and is more easily lost from the larger atoms.

Compounds of Group I elements

The compounds containing Group I elements also have similar properties. For example, they are all soluble solids that dissolve easily in water. They are also white, unless the negative ion that makes up the other part of the compound is coloured.

When compounds containing metal ions are heated they give out light. Each metal ion gives out a different colour. This is used to test for the presence of these metal ions. This test is known as a *flame test*.

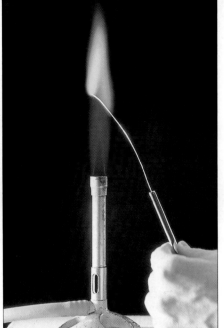

▲
The flame tests for sodium (top) and rubidium.

Metal ion	Flame colour
Li⁺	scarlet red
Na⁺	orange-yellow
K⁺	lilac pink
Rb⁺	red

◄
The colours of fireworks can tell you what metals are burning.

The bright red of fireworks is due to either lithium or strontium compounds mixed in with the gunpowder.

The orange glow of street lights comes from sodium ions that have been energised electrically.

Two important groups
Group VII: The halogens

'Halogen' means 'salt-maker'. The halogens react easily with metals to form salts such as chlorides, fluorides, iodides, etc.

The elements in Group VII show a number of similarities in their reactions. They also show a steady change in their properties down the group. This table gives a summary of their properties.

All these elements:

- are coloured;
- do not conduct electricity;
- are diatomic molecules;
- They have increasing melting and boiling points down the group.
- At room temperature:
  Fluorine, F_2 is a yellowish gas,
  Chlorine, Cl_2 is a greenish gas,
  Bromine, Br_2 is a dark red liquid. (It has a low boiling point, and the vapour is deep red.)
  Iodine, I_2 is a black solid. (It forms a purple vapour.)
- They become less reactive down the group.
- The halogens react with hot metals to form ionic compounds called metal halides.
- The halides are fluoride, chloride, bromide and iodide.
- With metals, the halides always form negative ions. F^-, Cl^-, Br^-, I^-.
- Ionic halides are white, unless the positive ion that makes up the other half of the compound is coloured.
- The halogens react with heated non-metals to form compounds that are molecules. These molecules are held together by covalent bonds. They are called non-metal halides. Many of these molecular, non-metal halides are coloured.

How do the halogens make compounds?

These diagrams show the electron structures of the halogen's outer shells. They are all one electron short of a complete outer shell. When these atoms react with metals, they gain an electron. This extra electron completes the outer shell. The ion then formed has a charge of $+1$ because of this extra, negatively charged electron.

However, when the halogen reacts with another non-metal element, there is no gain or loss of electrons. Instead, the two non-metal atoms *share* their outer electrons. In this way, *both* atoms are able to have complete outer shells. Bonds between atoms formed by sharing electrons are called *covalent bonds*. Water is formed this way.

Halogens bond with each other

The 'energetic pressure' to complete the outer electron shell is so high that the halogen atoms bond to themselves in pairs.

The diagram shows how all halogen molecules exist as *diatomic molecules*. That is, each halogen molecule is found as two joined halogen atoms.

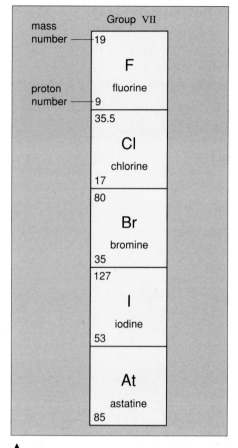

▲
The Group VII elements.

▼
Fluorine is a diatomic molecule. Two fluorine atoms join together to form a molecule of fluorine.

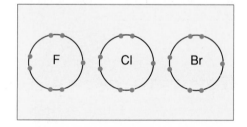

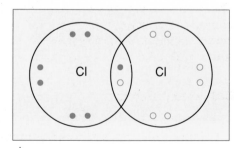

▲
The two atoms share electrons to fill their outer shells.

Reactivity

The reactivity increases up Group VII because the atoms are smaller towards the top of the group. This allows the positive nucleus to attract extra electrons more strongly.

The everyday metals are electronically confused

The transition elements

Most of the metals we use for making things appear in the block in the middle of the periodic table diagram on page 63. These are metals like iron (Fe), copper (Cu), zinc (Zn), silver (Ag) and gold (Au). They are not put into a group because their properties don't have a simple pattern like, say, the metals in Groups I and II. This is because they have more complicated electron patterns in their shells.

You need to be a really expert chemist to understand how these elements get their properties from their electron patterns. What causes the complication is that electrons that are 'officially' meant to be in the inner shells can move in orbits that are further away from the nucleus than electrons in outer shells!

This gives the strange effect that as we go from left to right, say from scandium (Sc) to zinc (Zn) in period 4, electrons start to fill the outer shell before an inner shell is complete. We only get back to normal when we reach gadolinium (Ga). The metals affected by this strange confusion amongst the electrons are called *transition elements*. The electron patterns are 'in between' the normal patterns found in Groups II and III. These elements represent the *transition* between metals and non-metals. There is no sharp change from metallic to non-metallic properties.

This makes the chemistry of these elements very difficult to explain. Nearly all the metals in this block are fairly stable and quite strong. This is why we find them so useful.

Understanding formulae

The formula for a compound is a shorthand way of describing what the compound is made from. Symbols are used for the elements present. Numbers tell how many particles of each element are there. This may sound very complicated but an example or two should make it clear.

Calcium chloride

The formula for calcium chloride is $CaCl_2$.

Calcium chloride is an ionic compound. In calcium chloride there are twice as many chloride ions as there are calcium ions. Put another way, one calcium ion combines with two chloride ions.

$$Ca^{2+} + 2Cl^- \rightarrow CaCl_2$$

Aluminium oxide

The formula for aluminium oxide is Al_2O_3.

In aluminium oxide, two aluminium ions combine with three oxide ions.

$$2Al^{3+} + 3O^{2-} \rightarrow Al_2O_3$$

A simple rule

It is always possible to work out the formula for a compound if you know the charges on the ions that make the compound. Overall a compound has no charge, it is electrically *neutral*, so the total amount of positive charge must always balance out the total negative charges.

In aluminium oxide this is:

- two aluminium ions $2 \times (3+) = 6+$,
- three oxide ions $\quad 3 \times (2-) = 6-$.

A copy of the periodic table is very useful, because the charges on many ions can be found by seeing which group the element is in.

Group 1 elements form 1+ ions
Group 2 elements form 2+ ions
Group 3 elements form 3+ ions
Group 4 elements form 2− ions
Group 5 elements form 1− ions

Ion	Formula and charge
ammonium	NH_4^+
hydroxide	OH^-
nitrate	NO_3^-
carbonate	CO_3^{2-}
sulphate	SO_4^{2-}

Writing formulae – made easy

1 Write down the two ions, using the information in this chapter, e.g. Al^{3+} and O^{2-}.
2 Lightly draw a bracket around any 'complicated ion, e.g. $(CO_3)^{2-}$.
3 'Swap and drop' the numbers for the ion charges, e.g. Al_2O_3.
4 Check to see if the formula can be made simpler. See if the bracket is still needed. (Where you now have a molecule with more than one complicated ion in it, the bracket will stay.)
5 Finally, check that the positive and negative charges balance.
Try this method to find the formula for ammonium sulphate.

The simple rule gets more complicated!

Elements in Groups IV and V often do not form ions. Instead they form compounds by sharing electrons. The group numbers are still useful though, because they give information about the number of electrons that can be shared. Compounds in which electrons are shared, rather than swapped, are called covalent compounds. (See *'How do the halogens make compounds?'*) The transition elements have no simple rules, often they form more than one ion. Iron, for example, forms Fe^{2+} and Fe^{3+} ions.

There is one other group of ions that you need to know about. They are ions made from a group of atoms. You have probably met them already. Each of these complicated ions is very common.

Electrolysis

Metals are good conductors. They conduct energy both electrically and thermally (as 'heat'). Nearly all non-metal elements are insulators. Solid compounds are also insulators. However, some compounds will conduct electricity when they are molten or dissolved in water.

The compounds that conduct electricity when they are molten or dissolved are known as *electrolytes*. Electrolytes conduct electricity because they are ionic compounds. They contain charged particles, as ions. It is the movement of these particles that makes the current of electricity.

Semi-conductors

The boundary between metals and non-metals is around Groups III and IV of the periodic table. But this boundary is very hazy. For example, two elements, silicon and germanium sometimes act as conductors and sometimes as insulators. Carbon is a non-metal but it conducts electricity. The elements that are not very good conductors are called semi-conductors.

The unusual properties of silicon and germanium are why these elelments are used to make micro-chips and components for the electronic and microelectronics industries.

▼
This large silicon wafer has circuits etched onto its surface.

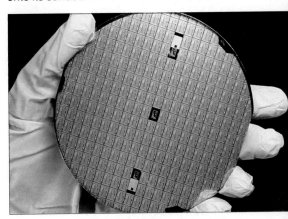

Electrolysis of molten ionic compounds

The ions in solid compounds are arranged in neat rows. The positive ions alternate with negative ions to form a huge fixed structure. It is an insulator. But when it is heated so that it melts the ions are free to move. They become all jumbled up.

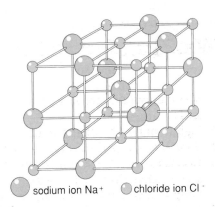

○ sodium ion Na⁺   ○ chloride ion Cl⁻

▲
The giant structure of sodium chloride.

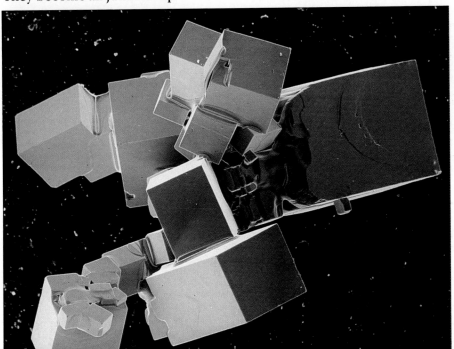

◀
A group of sodium chloride crystals. You can see the sharp corners of the crystals. Compare this with its particle structure.

73

When a simple compound is electrolysed it splits up into the elements it is made from. The positive ions are attracted towards the negative electrode. The negative ions move in the opposite direction, towards the positive electrode. Metal ions are always positive so a metal is formed at the cathode. Likewise non-metal ions are always negative. They go to the anode, where the non-metal is given off. High temperatures are needed for all this to happen. Common salt ($NaCl$) melts at $801\,°C$.

Electrolysis in solutions

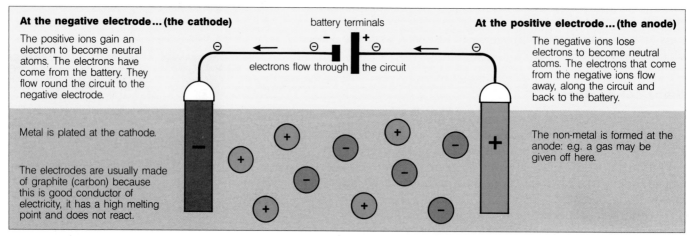

At the negative electrode... (the cathode)

The positive ions gain an electron to become neutral atoms. The electrons have come from the battery. They flow round the circuit to the negative electrode.

Metal is plated at the cathode.

The electrodes are usually made of graphite (carbon) because this is good conductor of electricity, it has a high melting point and does not react.

battery terminals

electrons flow through the circuit

At the positive electrode... (the anode)

The negative ions lose electrons to become neutral atoms. The electrons that come from the negative ions flow away, along the circuit and back to the battery.

The non-metal is formed at the anode: e.g. a gas may be given off here.

Electrolysis is a lot easier if the ionic compound dissolves in water. When the ionic compound dissolves the ions become free to move. The solution formed is thus a good electrolyte. During electrolysis the dissolved positive ions go to the negative ion or *cathode*, and the dissolved negative ions go to the *anode*. However, in some electrolysis experiments the elements formed at the anode and cathode do not come from the dissolved compound. Sometimes they come from the water instead.

▲ Particles move through the solution during electrolysis.

This happens because water is very slightly ionic. About one water molecule in a billion breaks up into a hydrogen ion (H^+) and a hydroxide ion (OH^-) during electrolysis.

The metal ion in the dissolved compound may come from a reactive metal. If this is so then the metal will not form on the cathode. Instead, hydrogen is given off. All the metals in Groups I, II and III of the periodic table are classed as 'reactive'. So too are zinc and iron.

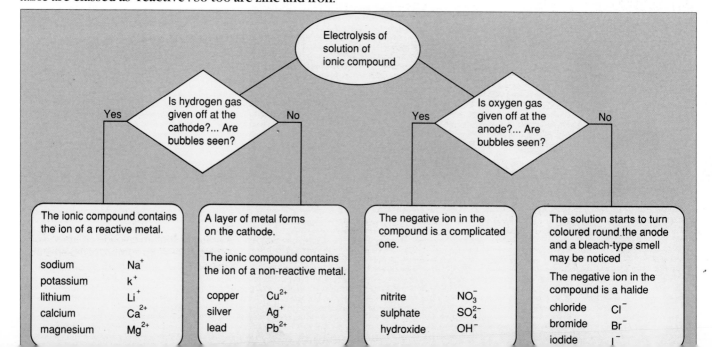

Electrolysis of solution of ionic compound

Yes — Is hydrogen gas given off at the cathode?... Are bubbles seen? — No

Yes — Is oxygen gas given off at the anode?... Are bubbles seen? — No

The ionic compound contains the ion of a reactive metal.

sodium	Na^+
potassium	k^+
lithium	Li^+
calcium	Ca^{2+}
magnesium	Mg^{2+}

A layer of metal forms on the cathode.

The ionic compound contains the ion of a non-reactive metal.

copper	Cu^{2+}
silver	Ag^+
lead	Pb^{2+}

The negative ion in the compound is a complicated one.

nitrite	NO_3^-
sulphate	SO_4^{2-}
hydroxide	OH^-

The solution starts to turn coloured round the anode and a bleach-type smell may be noticed

The negative ion in the compound is a halide

chloride	Cl^-
bromide	Br^-
iodide	I^-

Electrolysis of an aqueous solution

If the non-metal part of the compound is a complicated ion then oxygen is given off at the anode.

This table gives information about the electrolysis of a number of water-soluble ionic compounds.

Dissolved compound	Formula	At the cathode	At the anode
copper chloride	$CuCl_2$	copper	chlorine
copper sulphate	$CuSO_4$	copper	oxygen
silver nitrate	$AgNO_3$	silver	oxygen
potassium iodide	KI	hydrogen	iodine
sodium bromide	NaBr	hydrogen	bromine
sodium hydroxide	NaOH	hydrogen	oxygen
calcium chloride	$CaCl_2$	hydrogen	chlorine
magnesium sulphate	$MgSO_4$	hydrogen	oxygen
lead nitrate	$Pb(NO_3)_2$	lead	oxygen

A useful apparatus for electrolysis is shown here. Any gases given off will be collected in the up-turned test tubes. Any metal forming on the cathode will be seen as a shiny coat on the carbon electrode.

Chlorine, bromine and iodine are easy to detect. Bromine and iodine turn the solution around the anode a brown colour. Chlorine gas bubbles off, which has the unmistakeable smell of bleach and cannot be confused with oxygen.

Electrolysis is a very useful process. It is used to produce pure metals like sodium and aluminium from their compounds. It is also used to purify copper that has been made chemically from its ore.

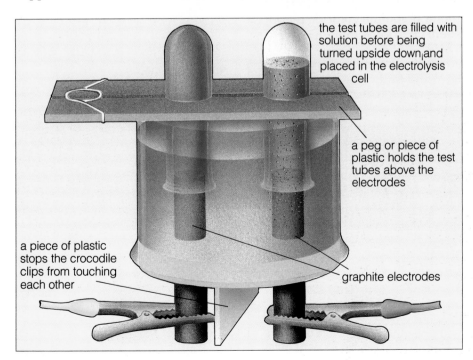

the test tubes are filled with solution before being turned upside down and placed in the electrolysis cell

a peg or piece of plastic holds the test tubes above the electrodes

a piece of plastic stops the crocodile clips from touching each other

graphite electrodes

◄

This is the sort of apparatus that you might use in a laboratory when investigating electrolysis.

Electroplating

Electrolysis is widely used in *electroplating*. This means putting a thin layer of metal on to another substance. This is done to make it look better, or to protect it from corrosion.

Electrolysis in industry

The electrolysis of molten ionic compounds is useful in industry. Reactive metals can best be obtained from their ores by electrolysis of a molten compound of the metal. Two important examples are described below.

Sodium

Sodium is obtained by electrolysing molten sodium chloride. Sodium ions go to the cathode and form molten sodium. The chloride ions go to the anode, where chlorine gas is given off. If these two elements came into contact in the electrolysis cell they would recombine to form salt. In the right conditions, there would be an explosion. The diagram of the industrial cell shows how the two products are kept apart.

Reaction at the cathode:

$$Na^+ + electron\ (e^-) \rightarrow Na$$

Reaction at the anode:

$$2Cl^- \rightarrow Cl_2^+\ 2\ electrons\ (2e^-)$$

The raw material for making sodium is sodium chloride, or common salt. There are large amounts of common salt in underground deposits.

In the electrolysis cell a molten mixture of sodium chloride and calcium chloride is used as the electrolyte. This has a lower melting point than pure sodium chloride. The lower temperature is important because it keeps energy costs down. (The melting point of sodium chloride is 800 °C. The mixture of calcium chloride and sodium chloride is molten above 600 °C.)

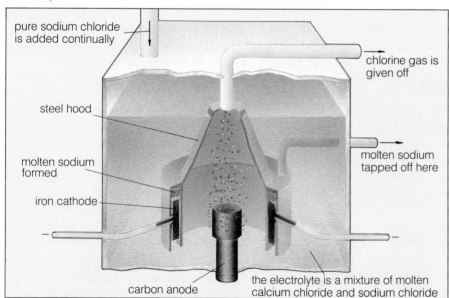

◄
The production of sodium.

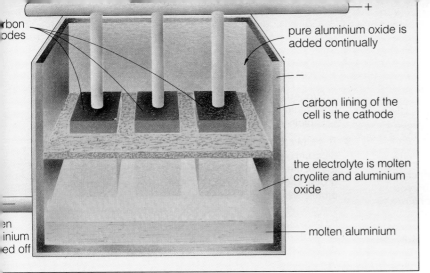

carbon
odes

pure aluminium oxide is
added continually

carbon lining of the
cell is the cathode

the electrolyte is molten
cryolite and aluminium
oxide

molten aluminium

en
inium
ed off

◀
The extraction of aluminium.

Aluminium

Aluminium is obtained by electrolysing molten aluminium oxide. *Bauxite* is an ore containing aluminium oxide. The first step in the extraction process is to get pure aluminium oxide from bauxite. This is done by using hot sodium hydroxide solution to dissolve the aluminium oxide from the ore. When this solution cools, the sodium hydroxide is neutralised with carbon dioxide and the pure aluminium oxide is released.

In the electrolysis cell is a mixture of aluminium oxide and an aluminium compound called cryolite. This mixture has a much lower melting temperature than pure aluminium oxide. It can be kept molten at a temperature of 950°C instead of over 2000°C for the pure oxide. During electrolysis molten aluminium is formed at the cathode. It sinks to the bottom and is run off. Oxygen is given off at the carbon anodes. These have to be replaced quite often because the oxygen reacts with them to form carbon dioxide.

Reaction at the cathode:
$$Al^{3+} + 3 \text{ electrons } (3e^-) \rightarrow Al$$

Reaction at the anode:
$$2O^{2-} \rightarrow O_2 + 4 \text{ electrons } (4e^-)$$

The world-wide production of aluminium is 15 million tonnes each year. The sites where aluminium is extracted are nearly always near large hydroelectric stations because these give enormous amounts of cheap electricity. To get some idea of the amount of electricity used, the following may help.

It takes 18 kilowatts of electricity flowing for 1 hour to obtain 1 kilogram of aluminium. A one-bar electric fire uses 1 kilowatt per hour. So to make one tonne of aluminium uses the same amount of energy as 1800 small electric fires each running for 1 hour. Put another way, the energy used in extracting aluminium each day would keep three million small electric fires burning all day long!

Activities

1 The table on page 227 of the 'Reference section' shows the names and symbols for all 103 elements. They are arranged in order of when they were discovered.
(a) Get a copy of a blank periodic table, and refer to the full periodic table on page 63. Write into each box in your blank table the symbol for each element and the rough date of its

discovery. Colour or shade the boxes so that you can tell in which timespan the element was discovered. As you do this a number of patterns will begin to emerge. (Sometimes the patterns will not be completely perfect. Perhaps one or more elements don't fit into any pattern.)
(b) Study your periodic table to see what patterns emerge for:

(i) the inert gases,
(ii) the alkali metals,
(iii) the actinides,
(iv) the transition elements,
(v) the gases, apart from the inert gases, and
(vi) the lanthanides.
Where you can, try to explain why a pattern is not perfect.
(c) Find out when current electricity was discovered. Can you link the discovery of electric currents to the discovery of a group of elements?
(d) Look at the dates of discovery of the elements in the reactivity series. How do the dates relate to the reactivities? Why do you think this is so?

2 Use a copy of a blank periodic table. Put into the table the elements known to Mendeléev in 1869. (Refer to the list on page 227 of the 'Reference section'.) There will be a number of gaps. Mendeléev predicted the properties of some of these missing elements.

Suggest two elements, other than germanium, that he might have been able to make some predictions about.
Explain why he could make fairly accurate predictions.

3 This table shows the type of information Mendeléev had about different elements. Put the information on small pieces of card (about the size of a playing card). Share this task amongst your group. These 24 cards should then be laid out in order of their atomic weight (relative atomic mass). You may immediately see a repeating pattern that you can form. If you do not, then try placing the cards in rows. In the first row you could try, say, six cards then lay another six in a second row beneath the first and so on. If six does not work, try seven and then eight in a row.

Eventually you should spot a repeating pattern appear. Similar elements will be underneath each other.

There will be two 'problems' left when you get to this stage. What are these elements? Where should these two problem elements go?

Element		Melting point (°C)	Boiling point (°C)	Shiny	Conducts electricity?	Reactive
Aluminium	27	660	2400	yes	yes	fairly
Argon	40	−189	−186	no	no	no
Arsenic	75		615	no	a little	no
Beryllium	9	1280	2500	yes	yes	fairly
Boron	11	2030	3700	no	a little	no
Bromine	80	−7	58	no	no	yes
Calcium	40	850	1440	yes	yes	yes
Carbon (diamond)	12	3500	3900	no	no	no
Chlorine	35.5	−101	−34	no	no	yes
Fluorine	19	−220	−188	no	no	yes
Gallium	70	30	2000	yes	yes	no
Germanium	73	958	2800	yes	a little	no
Krypton	84	−157	−153	no	no	no
Lithium	7	180	1340	yes	yes	yes
Magnesium	24	650	1110	yes	yes	fairly
Neon	20	−249	−246	no	no	no
Nitrogen	14	−210	−196	no	no	no
Oxygen	16	−219	−183	no	no	fairly
Phosphorus	31	44	280	no	no	yes
Potassium	39	63	760	yes	yes	yes
Selenium	79	217	688	no	no	no
Silicon	28	1410	2500	no	no	no
Sodium	23	98	843	yes	yes	yes
Sulphur	32	119	445	no	no	no

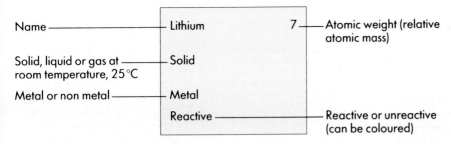

Name ——————— Lithium   7 —— Atomic weight (relative atomic mass)

Solid, liquid or gas at —— Solid
room temperature, 25°C

Metal or non metal ——— Metal

Reactive ——————— Reactive or unreactive (can be coloured)

Lay out your cards for activity 3 like this.

Questions

1 Give the names of:
(a) three active metals,
(b) four transition metals,
(c) four non-metals,
(d) two elements that are normally liquid,
(e) four elements that are normally gases.

								1 H 1								4 He 2
Li	9 Be 4			11 B 5	12 C 6	14 N 7	16 O 8	19 F 9	20 Ne 10
a	24 Mg 12			27 Al 13	28 Si 14	31 P 15	32 S 16	35.5 Cl 17	40 Ar 18

2 This question is about the first 18 elements in the periodic table.
(a) Which element has the smallest atom?
(b) Which element has the largest atom? (Look back to pages 63 and 67 if you need help.)
(c) Which is larger, a sodium atom or a sodium ion?
(d) Name the unreactive elements.
(e) Which element is chlorine most like?
(f) How many of the elements are gases?

3 Latin was once the language used by scientists. The list below gives the Latin names for a number of elements. What are the English names? You may be able to guess many of them. Write out a table of the Latin and modern names.
● Natrium
● Kalium
● Ferrum
● Cuprum
● Argentum
● Aurum
● Stannum
● Plumbum

Most symbols for elements are based on the first letter of the element's name and a second letter. The first letter is always in capitals, but the second letter is not.
Which other elements in the periodic table have symbols that are likely to be based on their Latin names?

4 The short way to describe the electrons around a sodium atom is 2,8,1. The electrons around a sodium *ion* are written 2,8. Use this short way to describe the electrons around:
(a) magnesium atoms and magnesium ions,
(b) calcium atoms and calcium ions,
(c) potassium atoms and potassium ions,
(d) fluorine atoms and fluorine ions,
(e) chlorine atoms and chloride ions.
(f) What do sodium, magnesium and fluoride ions have in common?

5 Write the formulae for the following compounds:
● magnesium oxide
● sodium oxide
● magnesium chloride
● aluminium chloride
● lithium fluorine
● calcium bromide

● ammonium chloride
● sodium nitrate
● sodium sulphate
● magnesium carbonate
● aluminium sulphate
● calcium nitrate

6 Look around you. Name as many transition elements as you can see. Explain why you aren't likely to be able to see any Group I metals.

Checklist

These are the facts and ideas that you should have learned by studying this topic.

To succeed at Basic Level you should:

- know that all things are made from about 100 chemical elements
- know that these elements can be arranged in a useful pattern called the periodic table
- be able to recognise important differences and similarities between different elements
- know that we often show the elements using symbols, like H for hydrogen etc.
- know that everything is made up of very small particles

To succeed at Foundation Level you should:

- be able to classify elements into solids, liquids and gases
- know that most elements aren't found on their own but joined with other elements in compounds
- know that everything is made up of atoms
- be able to recognise the following symbols for important elements: C, H, O, N, Cl, Br, Na and K
- know that when a chemical reaction occurs it makes new chemicals
- be able to talk or write about what your experiments prove, and realise that there could be more than one 'right answer'

To succeed at Merit Level you should:

- know that the periodic table puts elements with similar properties into 'groups'
- be able to make predictions using the reactivity series of metals
- be able to use data and observation to describe and sort materials as elements, compounds and mixtures
- understand the difference between elements and simple compounds in terms of atoms, ions and molecules, and can interpret symbols, models and diagrams of these
- be able to identify the elements represented by: H, O, C, N, Br, I, Na, K, Li, He, Ne, Ar
- be able to explain what happens in electrolysis
- be able to describe and explain how a new idea in science could predict new discoveries – for example, Mendeléev's idea for a periodic table

To succeed at Special Level you should:

- be able to describe a pattern of properties of some important compounds of metals and non-metals, e.g. their oxides, or carbonates
- be able to describe the structure of atoms in terms of the nucleus (protons and neutrons) and electrons, and explain how ions are formed
- understand how the structure of atoms decides where the first 20 elements fit into the periodic table, and relate this to the trends in the properties of elements in Groups I and VII
- be able to use symbolic equations to describe reactions
- know how ions are involved in electrolysis and precipitation reactions

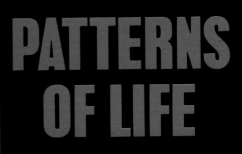

PATTERNS OF LIFE

Rabbit Population Explosion

...sh rabbits are living up to their ...utation. They are certainly breed-...like rabbits! Reports are coming in ...t their numbers have started to ...crease dramatically over the past few ...ars. The rabbit population is now ...bout a quarter of their 'pre-...yxomatosis level'. When this disease ...pread throughout Britain in the 1950s ...he rabbit population was almost ...wiped out. It was only then, when the rabbits were removed, that farmers realised how much damage the rabbits had been doing to their crops.

A few 'super rabbits' were immune to myxomatosis. These rabbits were the founding fathers and mothers of a new breed of rabbits. These have even adopted a different lifestyle. They now live in smaller families to reduce the risk of infections. Now, with the rabbit population on the increase, farmers are worried that their crops will suffer a~ ~in. Experts have estimated that rabbits caused some £4 million worth of crop damage in 1989. Changes in farming practices have meant that the fields are now more open to attack by rabbits.

For more information turn to page 89.

The Doomsday List

Between 50 000 and 100 000 sites poisoned by toxic waste are registered with the Department of the Environment. The registration is causing massive problems for local authorities. Each site has to be examined to determine precisely what the risks are. Regulations are then drawn up to control the future use of such sites.

But do these sites have to be left as wasteland for ever? Near London's Heathrow airport, 140 hectares of land have been cleared to make room for the new Stockley Business Park. Over 4.6 million cubic metres of domestic and industrial waste, which had been dumped there since 1912, had to be removed.

The newest rubbish was placed at the bottom of the tip and covered with a thick layer of clay. The old waste was then placed on top and capped with another layer of clay. The whole site is surrounded by deep trenches which have also been filled with clay. These measures are designed to stop any toxic substances from leaking out and poisoning local water supplies.

Supermarkets Lead the Way in the Recycling Stakes

The major supermarket chains have started to provide recycling bins. Aluminium, glass and steel are amongst the items that can be recycled through your local store. This 'green image' is important to companies battling in the high street for customers. The rise of the 'green consumer' during the 1980s has not caught companies napping. They have done their research. They have taken active steps to change their image to match what they think the customers want.

As a part of this drive to be 'greener' the major chains are labelling their products as being 'environmentally friendly'. But they give very little information to help the environmentally conscious shopper choose a best 'green buy'. What is needed is a green scale indicating the amount of ecological damage a product can cause.

Turn to page 82 for details of natural recycling.

SOS should stand for Save our Seas

The North Sea has become the dustbin of Europe. It gets untreated sewage waste from Britain, and rivers bring the run-off from farm fertilisers. The great River Rhine brings lead and arsenic. We even put radioactive waste into it. The North Sea is suffering, and we are starting to see the signs of its distress. There have been strange epidemics amongst seals and sea birds, toxic algal blooms causing the death of millions of fish, and many beaches ...b...... ..... they are dangerously dirty.

Not everyone agrees that all this is due to our mis-treatment of the sea. Is algal bloom a direct result of over-fertilisation of the sea? Does pollution play a major role in the deaths of seals and sea birds? The environmental groups say that it does. But the eco-system of the sea is so complex it is almost impossible to link these events. But how sure do we need to be before we act to protect our seas?

◀ Read on for information on food chains, food webs and the effects that pollution has on them.

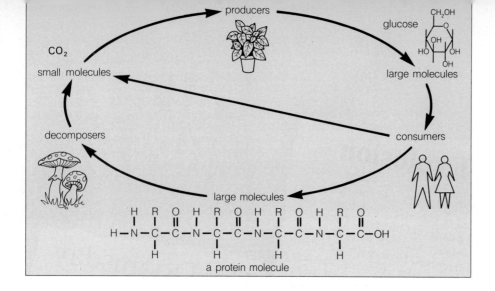

a protein molecule

Recycling materials

We are being urged to *recycle* valuable materials such as aluminium, steel, glass and even paper. This means using them again and again. We do this either because there are limited supplies of the basic raw materials in the world, or to save energy: recycling aluminium is much cheaper than making it from scratch. Nature also recycles materials, and for much the same reasons.

All of our food and most of the energy we use comes from plants and animals. Plants are called *producers*. Animals are known as *consumers*. Some animals get all their energy and nutrients from plants. These are the herbivores or primary consumers. Water fleas that eat plant algae in a pond are primary consumers. 'Primary' means 'first'. The water fleas might in turn be eaten by fish like sticklebacks. These are called secondary consumers. So the materials needed for life pass down the 'food chain'. But it doesn't stop there, with the secondary consumers. When plants or animals die their bodies are broken down by bacteria, fungi and other creatures. This releases materials for plants to use again. The organisms that do this are called *decomposers*.

Recycling carbon

Carbon is an element needed by all living creatures. You have probably come across carbon in the form of the charcoal used in barbecues. The 'lead' in pencils is really a form of carbon called graphite. But, most carbon is found in compounds, like the gas carbon dioxide used in fizzy drinks. Coal and oil are mixtures of more complicated compounds called hydrocarbons. Most of our 'energy food' is starch or sugars, and these are similar compounds called carbohydrates. In fact, life on Earth is carbon-based. No other element could do its job as well.

Photosynthesis and the carbon cycle

Plants take carbon dioxide from the air by photosynthesis. They use the energy from sunlight to turn it into sugars. There is more about this in Chapter 9, *The green world*. Animals need far more energy than plants in order to live. Plant-eating animals get their energy from the carbohydrates made by plants. Other animals eat these herbivores (primary consumers) and use the energy that the herbivores have stored as fat or meat.

The carbon compounds (carbohydrates, fats, proteins) stored in the plant-eaters' bodies are broken down by respiration. The result is that carbon dioxide is released into the air. This completes one part of the carbon cycle. The carbon cycle is shown in the 'Reference section' on page 223.

Is carbon dioxide harming the Earth?

The amount of carbon dioxide in the atmosphere is increasing. Carbon dioxide is the main cause of what is called the 'greenhouse effect'. We are now producing extra carbon dioxide from burning fossil fuels such as coal, petrol or natural gas. All these fuels were once part of plants, so the carbon they contain was *removed* from the air millions of years ago. There is more about this in Chapter 12, *Fuels and the environment*.

Recycling nitrogen

Nitrogen is another important element for life. All proteins contain it. Proteins are the compounds that the 'bodies' of living things are made of.

Like carbon, nitrogen is found in the air, but as an element not a compound. The air is four fifths nitrogen. But plants and animals can't use it directly. Plants must take it in as the nitrate ion. Animals can only take nitrogen in the form of 'ready-made' protein.

The nitrogen cycle is shown in the 'Reference section' on page 223.

How does nitrogen get into the soil?

Nitrogen-fixing bacteria can absorb nitrogen from the atmosphere and build up nitrogen compounds such as ammonia. Some of these bacteria live freely in the soil, but certain strains live in the roots of a particular group of plants called the leguminous plants. By growing these plants farmers and gardeners improve the amount of nitrate in the soil. Peas, beans and clover are all leguminous plants. The plant produces special lumps or nodules on the roots for the bacteria.

Lightning causes the nitrogen in the air to react with oxygen to form oxides. These nitrogen oxides dissolve in the rain and end up as nitrates in the soil. But neither of these sources produce much useful nitrate. Nitrates have to be recycled. Most of the nitrates in the soil come from decaying animal or plant tissue, or from animal droppings or urine. These waste products are broken down by bacteria in the soil and the nitrogen appears in ammonia (NH_3). Then, some bacteria in the soil known as nitrifying bacterial use the ammonia as food. In the same way as we convert glucose to carbon dioxide and water in respiration, the bacteria convert the ammonia into nitrates. They get energy by doing this.

How nitrogen is removed from the soil

Plants take in nitrates through their roots and combine them with carbon

▲
The nitrogen-fixing bacteria are held in the roots of plants like this runner bean.

compounds to form proteins.

Because nitrates dissolve easily they tend to be washed out of the soil by rain. This is known as *leaching*.

Also there is yet another group of bacteria which use nitrates as food. These unhelpful bacteria get their energy by breaking down the nitrates, so releasing nitrogen gas back into the air. These bacteria are known as *denitrifying bacteria*.

▲
The crops on the right have been grown in nitrate-deficient conditions.

Nitrogen, waste and pollution

Nitrogen is such an important element for the growth of plants that farmers and gardeners often add it to the soil in artificial fertilisers. Because a lot of the nitrate is lost through leaching, they often add too much fertiliser. This excess is then washed into streams, where it can cause a lot of pollution problems.

▼
Nitrate fertilisers have been concentrated in the Mediterranean Sea. This has made the sea weed grow very fast. It is then washed up all along the coast as a thick green mass.

Using microbes to recycle human waste – a sewage works

Human sewage waste contains a large amount of nitrogen compounds and organic matter which must be treated before it is put into rivers or the sea. Untreated or partly treated sewage is not only a health risk but adds a lot of extra nitrogen compounds to lakes and seas, leading to the disastrous effects seen in the previous photograph.

Plastic and other debris that cannot be broken down is removed by passing the sewage through large metal sieves. The sewage is then allowed to flow into settlement tanks in which the suspended matter settles out forming sewage sludge. The liquid above the sewage is then treated in one of two ways.

Trickle-bed treatment

In the trickle-bed treatment the sewage is sprayed over a circular tank containing large stones. This allows bacteria to grow feeding on the organic waste breaking it down. The bacteria are fed upon by single-celled organisms which then go on to provide food for small aquatic invertebrates such as worms and insect larvae.

▼
Filter-bed treatment of sewage.

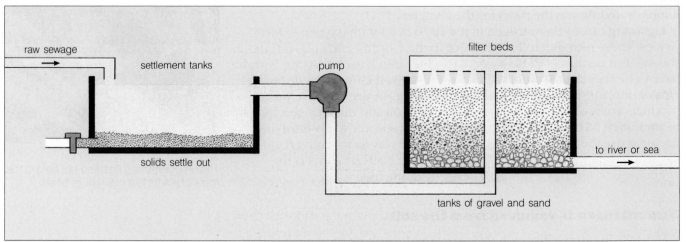

raw sewage

settlement tanks

pump

filter beds

solids settle out

to river or sea

tanks of gravel and sand

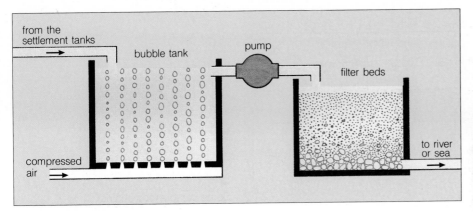

◀
Activated-sludge treatment of sewage.

▼
The air bubbles being forced through the sewage.

Activated sludge

In the activated-sludge technique, after passing through the settlement tanks, the sewage is passed along long channels with a small amount of sludge. Air is bubbled into the channels which helps the microbes to grow and digest the sewage.

Both systems add air to the sewage to help the breakdown of the organic waste. Without this extra supply of air the oxygen in the sewage is quickly used up and so most of the life in the sewage dies. This is what happens when untreated sewage is pumped into rivers with all the life in the river dying from a lack of oxygen.

▲
One of the first signs of raw sewage or other poisons being in a river is dead fish. There are no second chances when delicate ecosystems are upset.

Ecology

The word ecology comes from the Greek word for a house (*oiko*). The science of ecology studies all the living things that are living in the same 'house' – the world. We all depend on each other, like a family living in a house.

The house has many rooms, which we can call *ecosystems*. A key idea in any ecosystem is that of the *food chain*. A set of food chains is called a *food web*.

Another key idea in ecology is of what we call a *habitat*. This is a place where a 'web' of plants and animals live. It may be an ecosystem all by itself, but is usually part of a bigger one. A hedge may be a habitat, so might a field, a small wood, a garden pond, a compost heap, or even the underside of a large stone.

Food chains and food webs

As we saw earlier, living things must depend on each other. Animals depend on plants for their nutrients. In turn, plants depend on dead animals and the body wastes they produce – even the carbon dioxide they breathe out.

The nutrients and energy in grass are passed to a rabbit when the rabbit eats the grass. When a fox eats the rabbit, it gains energy and materials. This is a simple food chain. The next diagram shows a number of

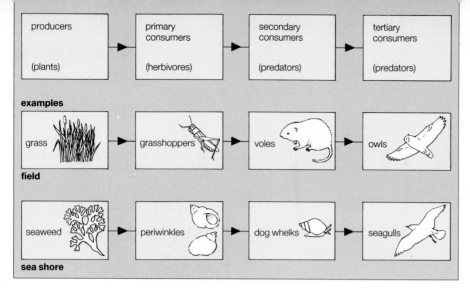

Some sample food chains.

different food chains. The direction of the arrow shows the way in which the materials are moving. The chains *all* begin with plants, which get their energy from sunlight.

The compost heap – an everyday habitat

One very common habitat is the compost heap that most gardeners set up to help get rid of garden rubbish. This is organic waste: grass cuttings, twigs, potato peelings, waste food and so on. Compost heaps are another good example of recycling in action. They also support a wide range of animals, which makes them ideal for an ecology study.

The material added to a compost heap is a source of food for the decomposers: fungi, bacteria, worms, woodlice and various insects. Most animals in the compost heap obtain their energy from the rotting vegetation. A simple food chain from such a compost heap might be:

However, mites also feed on bacteria and plant materials, and so do other animals in the soil such as nematode worms, earthworms and woodlice. So a more accurate picture would be:

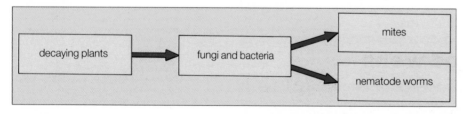

Nematode worms eat potworms, so the nematodes are attracted to the habitat. Various spiders join in to feed on the wide range of soil animals. Things start getting complicated. Although a food chain can be useful, a better idea of the feeding relationships can be obtained by drawing a food web.

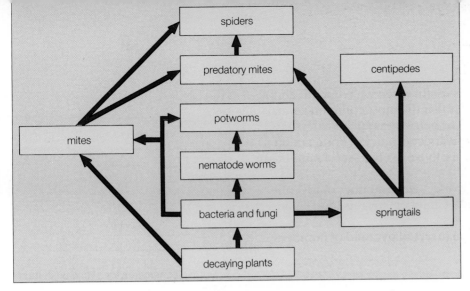

◄ Sample food web for a compost heap.

As well as the animals and microbes that *live* in the habitat, there are others that just visit for a snack – like birds, mice and snakes.

Each animal in a habitat has a particular feeding relationship with the other species. This relationship is called a *food niche*. A predatory mite and a spider may use the same kind of food but they occupy different niches. The mite feeds on small insects only. The spider feeds mainly on larger prey, using mites and springtails only as 'snacks' between main meals. In a particular habitat no two species can have exactly the same niche. A *species* is a set of animals of the same kind, that breed with each other.

Pyramids of number

When looking at the feeding relationships in a particular community, it is useful to know the number of animals and plants involved at each stage.

For example, a single rabbit needs to feed on a large number of grass plants, and it takes several rabbits to feed a fox. We can show this on a diagram. The number of individuals at each stage in a food chain can be shown by using different-sized boxes. The organisms in the higher boxes feed on the lower ones. The result is a kind of pyramid.

Plants always provide the energy and materials for animals and so they form the base of the pyramid. The rabbit is a primary consumer – it feeds on the plants directly. The fox is a secondary consumer.

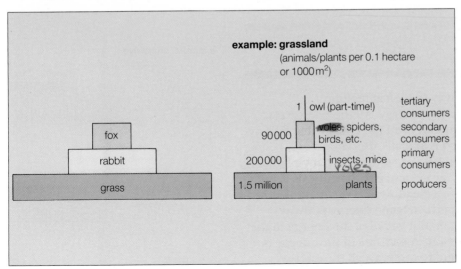

◄ A pyramid of numbers

The idea of the pyramid of numbers is useful when we come to sample an unknown area. It is a reasonable guess that the most common animals that we find are the primary consumers or herbivores (plant eaters). There will be a smaller number of secondary consumers. (For example, when you walk in the countryside you are more likely to see a rabbit than a fox.)

However, this idea does not always work. A large number of greenfly can live on one rose bush. So a pyramid of numbers for this food chain would be an upside down pyramid.

Other food chains that would show an inverted pyramid of numbers are:

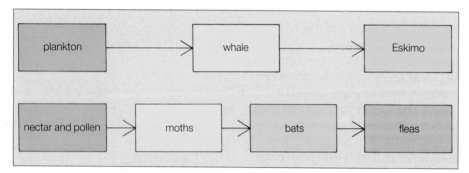

- Try to draw the pyramid for each food chain.

Building pyramids of biomass

Instead of *counting* the greenfly we could *weigh* all the greenfly on a rose bush, and the rose bush. Then we can compare the total mass of the greenfly with the mass of the rose bush. This gives us a better idea of how the greenfly depend on the rose bush. Such a pyramid is called a *pyramid of biomass*. Biomass is the total mass of all the organisms of one species in the area being studied. Ideally, it should be the *dry* mass (the mass with the water removed).

Energy pyramids

Energy is vital for life. Perhaps the best way to look at feeding relationships is to consider the movement of energy. All the energy to support life on Earth comes from the sun. But of all the energy that falls on the Earth, only one part in every hundred is actually used in photosynthesis. Most of the Earth's surface is sea, with hardly any plants. Also, plants cannot absorb all the light they get and photosynthesis is not perfect. Only 1% of all the light falling on a meadow is actually transferred to the grass. Energy transfers are never perfect. Some energy is always 'lost'. So, when rabbits eat the grass they do not get all of the energy in the grass. They do not eat the roots, for example. Also some of the energy is used up by the grass to produce seeds, and to grow. Of all the energy

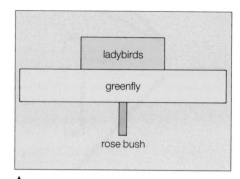

▲
A pyramid of numbers for a rose bush food chain.

◄
These food chains will give inverted pyramids of number.

▼
Pyramids of mass.

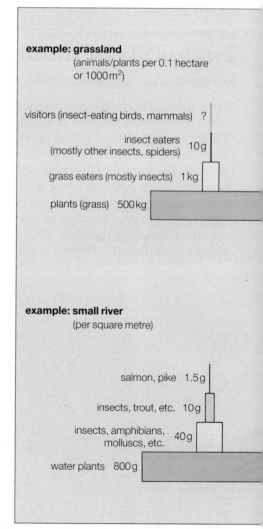

example: grassland
(animals/plants per 0.1 hectare or 1000 m²)

visitors (insect-eating birds, mammals) ?

insect eaters (mostly other insects, spiders) 10 g

grass eaters (mostly insects) 1 kg

plants (grass) 500 kg

example: small river
(per square metre)

salmon, pike 1.5 g

insects, trout, etc. 10 g

insects, amphibians, molluscs, etc. 40 g

water plants 800 g

taken in by the grass, less than one tenth is passed on to the rabbit. And only about one tenth passes from the rabbit to the fox.

Again, we can show this by a pyramid, a pyramid of energy.

The energy flow in a typical habitat is shown in the diagram below.

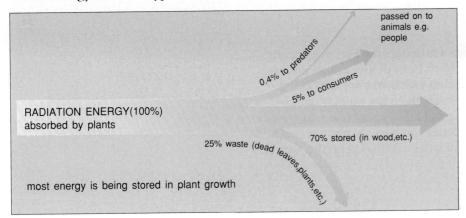

RADIATION ENERGY(100%)
absorbed by plants

0.4% to predators

passed on to animals e.g. people

5% to consumers

25% waste (dead leaves,plants,etc.)

70% stored (in wood,etc.)

most energy is being stored in plant growth

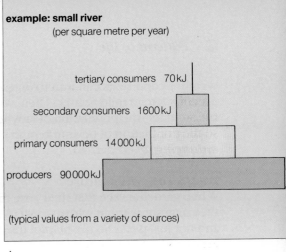

example: small river
(per square metre per year)

tertiary consumers 70 kJ

secondary consumers 1600 kJ

primary consumers 14 000 kJ

producers 90 000 kJ

(typical values from a variety of sources)

▲ A pyramid of energy.

What would you do with a field? A field can be farmed – used to grow plant food like wheat – or the farmer can keep animals such as cows or sheep on it. When we eat meat, we don't get anywhere nearly as much energy from it as the cow or sheep got from the grass. This is because animals can only get one tenth of the available energy from the grass. And if we then eat the meat we only get one tenth of *that* energy! This means that we only receive one hundredth of the energy originally in the grass. That is just 1%. So it is more efficient to eat the wheat directly. But of course, many people prefer steaks to plain bread.

◄ Energy flow in a young woodland.

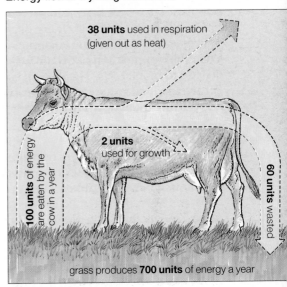

38 units used in respiration (given out as heat)

100 units of energy are eaten by the cow in a year

2 units used for growth

60 units wasted

grass produces **700 units** of energy a year

▲ The energy flow through a young cow.

Populations

Everyone wants to be a success and this is true of every animal and plant. How can we decide if a particular kind of animal or plant is successful? One guide is to look at a habitat, and see if the number of individuals in a species is increasing or getting less. This number is called the *population* of that species.

What affects population size?

The number of individuals in the habitat depends on several different factors. Some of these help the population to grow, others tend to reduce it. The more important factors are:

- the number of offspring,
- food supply,
- predators,
- suitable places to live,
- diseases,
- suitable climate or weather.

These are just some of the things that may affect population size. Can you think of any others?

Weather

Insect numbers are often affected by the weather. Have you noticed the number of insects that seem to be about after a mild winter? The right weather conditions can lead to plagues of locusts. We often find a lot of greenfly after a mild winter. Then, with all the greenfly to feed on during the summer, the population of ladybirds increases. They eat more greenfly so the population of pests is kept in check. This is a natural way of *balancing an ecosystem*.

Interfering with nature
When gardeners see that their rose trees are being attacked by greenfly, they may spray them with insecticides. Most insecticides kill all insects, and not just pests. So the helpful insects, like ladybirds, are also killed. Unfortunately, the greenfly are able to reproduce very quickly, and so their numbers are soon back to their original level. Ladybirds take longer to recover. Within a few weeks the gardener can have as many greenfly on the rose bushes as before. But the helpful ladybirds that keep the numbers in check are gone.

Disease
Disease is another factor that helps to keep numbers down. Usually, the population rises, diseases can spread more easily. So big populations are less healthy, and there are more deaths.

Plagues are an extreme example of the effect of disease on a population. The rabbit population of Britain was almost wiped out by the terrible disease myxomatosis. The disease is carried from rabbit to rabbit by fleas. Farmers helped to spread the disease by taking fleas from infected rabbits and putting them down the rabbit holes.

Predators and prey
Apart from natural disasters or plagues, like myxomatosis in the rabbits, animal populations stay more or less constant. The average number of wild animals such as rabbits, deer or mountain sheep tends to stay fairly constant. Most die from old age or are killed by predators. But the numbers can change very quickly in the short term. Suppose that the weather has been very good, and that there is plenty of plant food. The number of wild sheep would start to increase. This means that the wolves that feed on the sheep now have lots of food as well. This means that more wolf cubs tend to survive to become adult wolves. These eat more sheep, and breed more successfully. There are more wolves, so the sheep numbers drop. This makes life hard for the extra wolves – so the wolf population falls.

The graph below shows this effect with the numbers of hares and lynx in the Arctic. The data was obtained from the records of fur trappers, and shows the number of animal skins bought from the trappers by the Hudson Bay Company.

▼
The graph shows the number of animal skins bought from fur trappers by the Hudson Bay Company between 1845 and 1935. The lynx is a large wild cat that catches hares for its food. More hares mean more lynx, but more lynx mean fewer hares. . .

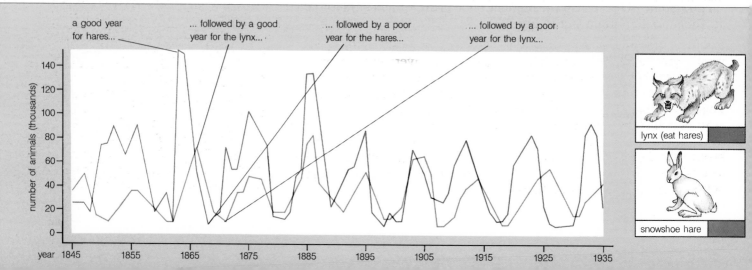

a good year for hares... ... followed by a good year for the lynx... ... followed by a poor year for the hares... .... followed by a poor year for the lynx...

number of animals (thousands)

lynx (eat hares)

snowshoe hare

year 1845   1855   1865   1875   1885   1895   1905   1915   1925   1935

Cruelty from kindness

An example of how humans affect animal populations is the fate of the deer population on the Kaibiba Plateau in Arizona, America. Up to 1906 the number of deer had been roughly constant. Then it was decided to protect the deer by killing all the predators in the area. So pumas, wolves and coyotes were systematically killed over the next 20 years.

This seemed a kind thing to do (for the deer). But without any predators to keep their numbers in check, the deer population rose from 4000 to 100 000 by 1924. There was only enough grass to feed about 30 000 animals, and so many deer began to starve. The weakened deer died from disease. The grass was so damaged by overgrazing it could no longer support even 30 000 animals, and by 1940, the deer population had dropped to 10 000 animals.

Human populations

Humans are very successful animals. Human populations have grown greatly over the past few years. Improvements in health care and food production mean that most of us live reasonably well. More children survive to become adults, and adults live longer. This growth in population can cause problems too. This was first considered by an economist, called Malthus, as long ago as 1798. He said that the population would always outrun the food supply. He predicted that there would be widespread famine, disease or war. He said that this would be the 'natural' way of keeping the human population steady.

The increase in the population of the world.

This has not happened as quickly as Malthus thought. He was not able to predict the massive increase in food production brought about by artificial fertilisers, new strains of plants and animals, and changes in agricultural practices.

However, we may be running out of essential materials such as oil, aluminium and other metals. Also, some people think that food production is no longer able to keep up with the population. Will Malthus's predictions be proved right in the end?

Like humans, all other living organisms produce more young than is needed to replace the adults. So for example, a single female fish such as a trout can produce anything up to 10 000 eggs. Obviously all the eggs cannot grow up to become adults. If they did, the rivers and seas would be solid with fish! The number of animals in a river stays fairly constant. So only two out of the 10 000 eggs survive long enough to become adults. This means that the young fish *compete* with each other.

Some fish survive because they are lucky – not getting eaten! But each fish is slightly different from the others, just as you are different from your brothers and sisters. These small differences might make all the difference to a fish fighting against its own brothers and sisters to survive. It might be better *adapted* to its surroundings.

Hundreds of young eels are produced – but how many will survive?

Adaptation

Animals are adapted to the environments where they live. The adaptations may be physical (camouflage, special teeth) or behavioural (living in groups). These adaptations have developed over millions of years. For example, different animals have adapted to life in running water in different ways.

- **The trout**. These fish are predators, and so have developed into strong swimmers. Their bodies are streamlined. This improves their ability to catch their prey.
- **Caddis fly larvae**. The larvae of the caddis fly hatch and live in water. They have soft bodies, and so build protective shelters of small stones around themselves. They can attach themselves to rocks.
- **Limpets**. The limpet is found in tidal zones and has a strong muscular 'foot' that it uses to hold on to rocks. The strongest tides wash over the limpet, unable to remove it from its foothold.

Out of the thousands of young trout produced, one fish could be slightly better camouflaged against predators; another might be slightly faster, or be able to react faster.

The differences are hereditary; they have come from one or other of the parents. How exactly this genetic difference happens is dealt with later. But if these small changes give the young trout a slight advantage it stands a better chance of surviving. It is better adapted to its surroundings and its lifestyle.

Activities

1 (a) Look in your garden or on some ground near your school. Turn over a stone, a piece of wood or something similar. Try and catch as many creatures as you can. Look at them carefully with a hand lens or microscope. There is some information on page 198 of the 'Reference section' that will help your collecting.
(b) Collect some animals from a bush or tree by shaking it over a white tray.
(c) Compare the animals from each of the two places. How is each animal suited to where it lives and feeds?

2 Take a walk near your home. Make a list of as many different habitats as you can. Name at least two life forms that live in each habitat. For example: cracks in pavements, a piece of rotting wood, a wall, a hedge, and so on.

3 Find an old bucket, or a large plastic container, old aquarium, or something similar. Put some grass in it and a very small amount of soil. Put it in a shed or in the garden or somewhere similar. Look at it every few days for several weeks. Find the names of any organisms that you see there. Try and work out the number of each type of organism. Write down what you find out. You might find a hand lens or a microscope useful. Try to work out what eats what. Which type of animals or plants did you find there first? Can you suggest why? What happens to these life forms over the weeks?

4 Try taking some moss and putting it in a jam jar. Soak the moss with water and break up the sample gently with mounted needles or cocktail sticks. Take a drop of the water and look at it under a microscope. What creatures can you find in the moss? If you leave the moss mixture wet you will find that the types of life that live in the jar change. Eventually, the organisms there will resemble the microscopic life that you find in ponds. If you then let the moss dry out, it will start to grow again and the types of animals living there alter again. Why do the types of animals change as the moss gets wetter and drier? How do pond animals reach these moss pots?

5 Have you ever wondered how many snails there are in a patch
of ground?
    You will need some paint – poster paint or cellulose modelling
paint – and a fine brush. Make sure that the paint is lead free.
    Copy out the form below in your book.

Number of snails caught and painted first time,	M	= ......
Total number of snails caught second time,	S	= ......
The number of marked snails caught second time,	R	= ......

The population of snails is given by the ratio shown below:

$$\frac{\text{number of snails caught, } M}{\text{total snail population, } P} = \frac{\text{number of snails recaptured, } R}{\text{number of snails caught next time, } S}$$

This equation can be written as:

total snail population $= \dfrac{M \times S}{R}$

The total snail population = ...

Collect as many snails as you can from a particular spot, e.g. a compost heap or a similar place where snails collect together. Count them and mark them with a small spot of paint.

Put the snails back where you found them. (Preferably where they are not likely to be eaten by birds).

Leave the snails overnight. On the following day, collect as many snails as possible. Count them again: write the number of snails caught on the sheet in the space marked *S*.

Find the number of these snails that are already marked with paint. Write this number on the sheet in space '*R*'

Work out the number of snails as shown, by using the equation.

So, if you marked 12 snails on the first day, and you found 16 snails on the second day, with 4 out of the 16 marked. The sum is as follows:

$M = 12, \quad S = 16, \quad R = 4.$

Then the total population of snails $= \dfrac{12 \times 16}{4}$,

the snail population = 48 snails.

Questions

1 In a study of a piece of waste ground, some students observed the following as the most common or interesting forms of life:
Plants: grass, dandelions, daisies, thistles.
Animals: worms, beetles, bluebottles, aphids, field mice, a hedgehog, rabbits, a fox, an owl, two robins, sparrows, two blackbirds.
(a) Name one organism in each case that is (i) a producer, (ii) a consumer, (iii) a predator.
(b) Draw a simple food chain including three organisms.
(c) Draw a food web that includes: grass, dandelions, worms, robins, rabbits, mice, owl, fox.

2 In a pond, mayfly larvae feed on plant algae. Trout feed on stonefly larvae that feed on the mayfly.
(a) Draw a food chain for these organisms.
(b) Sketch a pyramid of numbers.
(c) What would happen to the population of mayfly and trout if something was added to the water that killed stonefly?

3 Dad says to his son Jim, "You know, I've noticed that after a mild winter there always seem to be more greenfly on my roses."
(a) How might Jim explain this to his dad?
(b) Go on to explain how this population boom in greenfly might affect the number of ladybirds. Would this change in the ladybird population affect birds that feed on the ladybirds?

4 Look at Activity 5 on estimating the number of snails in your garden. Explain which colour paint would be best to use for marking the snails – a bright yellow or a dull green? Why should you spread the snails out at random on the compost heap when you put them back?

5 The results of an ecological survey of shrubbery woodland were:

Number of aphids	Number of blue tits	Number of leaves	Number of owls
20 000	10	36 000	1

(a) List the organisms under the headings: producer, primary consumer, secondary consumer and tertiary consumer.
(b) Translate the information to a 'pyramid of numbers diagram'.
(c) Make some reasonable guesses to convert the information into a sketch of a 'pyramid of biomass'. State what guesses or estimates you have made.
(d) It has been found that some pesticides, like DDT, are stored in the bodies of insects and are passed along the food chain to predators. Imagine that the aphids on a rose bush have been sprayed with pesticide. What will happen to the pesticide levels in the bodies of the animals as we move along the food chain?

6 A manufacturer claims that a new type of lawn weedkiller more effective than another, cheaper brand. As an expert (and very cheap) young ecologist you are asked to test his claim. You are given samples of the weedkillers and the loan of a large lawn, which is infested with daisies. You are told to use the whole lawn for the trial.
   Draw up a plan for making the test. Ensure that it is safe, fair, and accurate. Explain clearly how you would count the number of daisies involved (bearing in mind that there are too many for you to count *every* plant). How would you check that soil organisms were not harmed by either weedkiller?

7 Look up in the 'Reference section' the diagrams of food webs in a pond and in a wood.
(a) Find a food chain in each habitat and write it out, labelling the producers and the primary and secondary consumers.
(b) What might happen to the food web in the pond if someone spilled insecticide in it and killed off all the water beetles?
(c) What are decomposers? What role do they play in the food web of a wood?

Checklist

These are the facts and ideas you should have learned by studying this topic.

To succeed at Basic Level you should:

- be able to sort living things into groups, and work out where they might live
- know the difference between collecting living things scientifically, and just hunting or killing them
- know that all animals rely on plants for their food
- know the difference between plant-eating and meat-eating animals
- know that people produce waste, such as litter, sewage and household waste
- know that some waste decays naturally, but that this might take a long time

To succeed at Foundation Level you should:

- understand that where animals and plants live is decided by such things as warmth, water and shelter, and that these are different in different places, and also change with the seasons
- be able to recognise differences between plants and animals of the same kind (species) and between different kinds
- be able to use simple keys to sort living things into their main groups
- know about the main methods of collecting and counting living things so that you can choose the best method for a job
- be able to write a simple three-step food chain, given the data
- know about predators and their prey
- understand how and why things decay and how this is important for recycling materials
- be able to tell if something is 'biodegradable' or not

To succeed at Merit Level you should:

- understand what makes particular organisms well-suited to their habitats
- be able to use a dichotamous key to classify organisms
- know how to use the main collecting and counting methods used in field studies (pooters, nets, quadrats, traps)
- understand the factors involved in the size of populations; pyramids of number and biomass; predator–prey relationships
- know that a biological community needs a balance of materials, and that this involves recycling processes that can be affected by human activity
- understand the role of microbes and other organisms in the carbon and nitrogen cycles

To succeed at Special Level you should:

- be able to analyse data to show how organisms are adapted to extreme environments
- be able to make your own dichotamous key from given data
- understand the practical limitations and inaccuracies of methods used in ecological studies
- understand how materials and energy flow through an ecosystem and be able to analyse data about recycling rates
- be able to make predictions about changes in population size given data about environmental or predator changes
- understand the role of microbes in disposing of human wastes

CHAPTER SEVEN

ENERGY AND THE EARTH

The Earth is a very energetic place. The pictures show things that need a lot of energy changes to make them happen. They are spectacular, and can cause a lot of damage. But all the time, every day, the energy sources that make these things happen are changing the Earth in much gentler ways.

Many of these changes are too slow for us to notice. It is hard to watch plants growing, although we can see the effects over a week or two. But it would take many lifetimes to see mountains grow or waste away. All these changes need energy transfers. Where does this energy come from?

Energy from the Sun

The most obvious source of energy is the Sun. By now you should have learned that the Sun provides the energy for plants to grow. You should also know that animals could not exist on Earth unless there were plants. Plants are the only organisms that can make use of radiation energy from the Sun to make food.

But the waves in the sea and the winds and storms in the air also get their energy from the Sun. Our weather systems are powered by solar radiation, just as life is. Snow is brought to us by air movements that get their energy from the Sun.

Energy from rocks

Volcanoes and earthquakes are different. They get their energy from deep within the Earth. There, the energy sources are *radioactive elements*. Most rocks contain very small amounts of radioactive elements, such as thorium and uranium. But added together, they release enough energy to make the interior of the Earth red hot.

Not all mountains are volcanoes. The highest mountains on Earth are the Himalayas, and the nearest volcano is hundreds of miles away. But it was still the energy from these radioactive elements that built these mountains.

This chapter is about how this all works. It explains how the Sun's energy is shared out on Earth to power climate and weather systems. It explains how rocks are made, and how mountains are built and worn down. We can learn how what we now call Britain was once a tropical country covered with rain forests.

Weather is important

Weather does more than just spoil or improve a summer holiday. There are freak events like gales or blizzards of snow that can stop the country working for days at a time. But every year companies may lose millions of pounds by just not listening to weather forecasts of 'ordinary' weather.

- Motorway restaurants can lose £70 000 a day if the temperature rises by just 2 °C. People don't eat the hot meals that have already been cooked! The restaurant managers should listen to the weather forecasts.
- People buy different kinds of bread when the weather changes. Supermarkets are beginning to make their plans in accordance with the next day's weather.
- The weather affects the way people work. A well-designed school, factory or office should be adaptable to weather changes, so that the people working there are always comfortable. Does the weather affect *your* school?
- It costs over £10 000 to spread grit and salt on the roads of the county of Suffolk. It costs a lot more in larger counties. If the Highways Department misread the weather forecast this money would be wasted – if the expected ice didn't appear – or they could decide not to treat the roads and there might be many more accidents than usual next day.

Weather patterns

We can forecast the weather because it has patterns. But the forecasts are not always accurate because the patterns are very complicated. Very large computers are used to store the patterns, and forecasts are getting more accurate. But even so, getting it right for more than a day ahead is always tricky.

You can make your own weather forecasts. This is not hard to do for a few hours ahead. You can make good predictions by using *clouds*, and make even better ones with the help of a *barometer* to measure air pressure. To learn how to do this we need to understand the two main weather patterns that we get in Britain.

▲
Hurricane devastation.

Depressions

A *depression* is often called a *low*. It is a huge whirlpool of warm air up to five or six hundred kilometres across. It is swirling around like the eddies of water you can often see in rivers. The air has come from the tropics, as explained on page 101. Because it is warm, the air expands. This means that it is less dense than the air that surrounds it. So:

- the *pressure* of the air inside a low is less than normal; it is called a low because it is a low-pressure area;
- the air in the low may carry a lot of water vapour – warm air picks up water vapour quite easily from the sea;

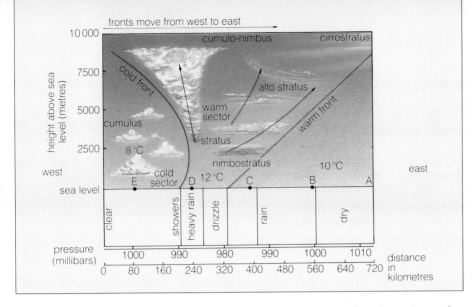

A diagram showing a section through a weather system with labels: fronts move from west to east, cumulo-nimbus, cirrostratus, cold front, warm sector, alto stratus, warm front, cumulus, 8°C, stratus, cold sector, nimbostratus, 10°C, 12°C. Points E, D, C, B, A at sea level. Weather conditions: clear, showers, heavy rain, drizzle, rain, dry. Height above sea level (metres): 10 000, 7500, 5000, 2500, sea level. Pressure (millibars): 1000, 990, 980, 990, 1000, 1010. Distance in kilometres: 0, 80, 160, 240, 320, 400, 480, 560, 640, 720. West on left, east on right.

◄ This shows a section through the weather system below, cut along the white line.

- the low is undercut by the colder denser air surrounding it, so it tends to float up like a bubble.

The picture shows what a low is like. The huge mass of air moves across from west to east at an average speed of 40 km per hour. As it comes along, the most obvious changes are the ones that you can see in the clouds. These are the main cloud types.

Imagine standing and watching a low approach. First of all, you would see a clear sky gradually being covered by a layer of thin, high cloud. High feathery clouds of ice crystals called *cirrus* clouds join together to become a layer of *cirro-stratus*. This thickens to *alto-stratus* and may hide the sun completely.

Soon, the wind grows stronger and rain clouds appear in a dark layer — *nimbo-stratus*. The air gets a lot warmer and feels damp or 'muggy'. It may start raining for a while. The clouds are higher and not so dark, but they still cover the sky — as *stratus*.

Next, the clouds may start breaking up. There may be heavy showers falling from large broken clumps of cloud — *cumulo-nimbus*. If you are lucky the showers get less and they are not so violent. If you aren't so lucky, the showers come with very strong winds behind them. These are called *squalls*. There may be hailstones and even lightning. If you are *very* unlucky the next depression will be following very close behind, and the showers will turn into the steady rain we get from the nimbo-stratus clouds.

▼ A low-pressure area crossing the UK.

▲ Altostratus clouds.

▲ Cumulo-nimbus clouds.

▲ Cumulus clouds. Note how these clouds often line up in great rows.

What makes the rain?

The warm air in a low is usually very damp. It contains a lot of water vapour, especially in the lower regions. At the edges of the low the warm air is cooled by mixing with colder air. This causes the water vapour to condense into drops. Small drops from clouds. The drops are too small to fall as rain, they are held up by the moving air, but if the drops collide they get bigger.

At low levels there is more water vapour and the clouds are thick. There are many more water drops, and they may be already quite large. As they collide and start to fall they can get bigger and bigger as they sweep up the smaller drops. The result is heavy rain.

All this is part of the *water cycle*. There is a diagram and an explanation of the water cycle in the 'Reference section'.

Winds and pressure differences

Barometers measure the *pressure* of the air. The cross section through a low showed that a low is funnel-shaped. Long before we might notice any clouds the leading edge of the low is far overhead. The air pressure begins to fall, and the barometer shows this. It gives the lowest reading in the middle of the depression. This is where there is the greatest thickness of warm air with a low density. Barometers are marked to give an idea of the weather we can expect at different pressures.

Air flows from high pressure to low pressure. But it doesn't move in a straight line. It is like water running out of a bath. As it flows it swirls. This is caused by the spinning of the Earth. The air moves into a low very gradually, moving anticlockwise. This means that when you stand with your back to the wind the low pressure is always on your left.

A typical low has a central pressure of about 980 millibars. Normal air pressure is about 1000 millibars. If the central pressure falls to less than about 970 millibars we get very strong winds, maybe gales or hurricanes. This happens often enough in Britain for us to worry about – but not as often as in the Caribbean. The 'great storm' of October 1987 was caused by a low with a central pressure of 950 millibars. This caused winds of over 140 km per hour.

Warm fronts and cold fronts

The boundary between cold and warm air is called a front. As the low reaches us we pass through the *warm front*. We are now inside the low, in its warm air. As it passes over and the outside colder air reaches us we move across the cold front. You can see these fronts on the satellite photograph on page 97.

A weather map shows the pressure patterns of the air. The lines on the map are *isobars*. They are drawn through places at the same air pressure. The closer these lines are together the stronger the winds. It means that there is a steep *pressure gradient*. It is just like the contour lines on a map showing how steep the ground is.

The warm fronts and cold fronts are shown. But there is also a line with the symbols for cold and warm fronts mixed. This is where the low is beginning to be lifted higher into the atmosphere. On the ground we would be in cold air, with the bubble of warmer air high above us.

▲
Although the British hurricane of October 1987 caused a lot of damage, places like the Caribbean regularly suffer from bigger hurricane winds.

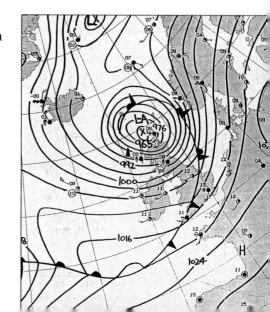

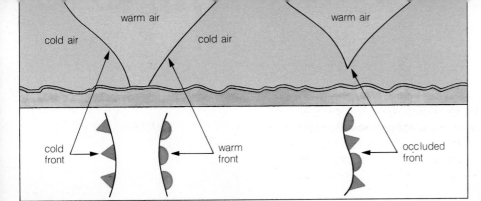

cold air warm air cold air warm air

cold front warm front occluded front

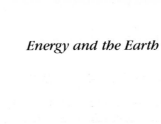

A low is often lifted up by the colder air surrounding it. This makes an *occluded front.*

High-pressure regions — anticyclones

The weather map above shows regions of high pressure, labelled H. These *highs*, or *anticyclones*, contain cold air. The air is dense and dry. This causes the high pressure. These areas have very few clouds. In winter they cause hard frosts. This is because radiation can escape into space from the ground. There is no cloud blanket to reflect or re-radiate it back.

In summer, anticyclones let the Sun's radiation through to warm up the land. The isobars are usually very far apart so the winds are light. This makes good sunny weather.

The energy trapped in a typical low is much more than in a hydrogen bomb. Luckily, it is spread over a large area so doesn't do any harm. Where does this energy come from? The next section explains this, and also tells how lows and highs are formed.

clear sky

At night, infra-red radiation is radiated from the ground. This causes mist and frost as the heat is lost to space.

cloud layer

On a cloudy night, the infra-red radiation is absorbed by the clouds. These warm up and radiate some of the energy back to Earth, and so the ground does not get so cold.

Why cloudless nights are colder than cloudy nights.

Energy from the Sun

We take the Sun for granted. But if you lived in Lapland you wouldn't even see Sun for one or two months of the winter. In June and July it would never set. In the tropics the Sun is nearly overhead for most of the year. These effects are caused by the fact that the Earth spins on a *tilted* axis, and also moves around the Sun. It takes 12 months to complete this orbit, which accounts for the times of the seasons.

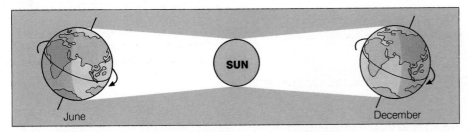

SUN

June December

Summer and Winter are caused by the tilt of the Earth's axis. The northern half of the Earth gets more sunlight in June than in December.

The drawing shows the position of the Earth at different times of the year as it orbits the Sun. When it is midsummer in Britain – and Lapland – the North Pole is tilted towards the Sun. For us the Sun appears high in the sky. As the Earth spins on its axis Lapland, in the Arctic, is always in sunlight.

In December the Earth is in a different place in its orbit. The North Pole still points in the same direction, but this means that now it is tilted away from the Sun. For us, the Sun appears low in the sky. Lapland doesn't get any sunlight at all.

This is one reason why there is so much ice and snow at the poles of the Earth. For many months of the year they get little or no energy from the Sun. But there is another reason. Imagine three equal shafts of sunlight reaching the Earth. The one that lands on the equator covers much less ground area than the ones that land near the poles.

This means that each square metre of the Arctic has a much smaller share of energy than a square metre in the tropics. Plants can't grow as well because each leaf gets less energy for photosynthesis. The soil is colder.

How energy gets into the atmosphere

The air is transparent. Most radiation from the Sun passes right through air and is absorbed by land and sea. If there are clouds, they normally reflect the energy straight back into space. The air is not warmed directly by solar radiation. It gets its energy by being in contact with warm land or warm sea. But air is free to move, and it is the movement of the air which carries energy received at the tropics to help keep northern countries warm.

The air movement is due to *convection*. The picture shows this happening in a beaker of water. When water is heated it expands. As a result it gets less dense and the warm water floats upwards. Colder water flows down to take its place. Convection can happen in air, or any fluid that is free to move.

Convection currents in the atmosphere

Convection currents in the Earth's atmosphere work in the same way as the hot water. Hot air rises from the tropical sea and lands at the equator. It cools and sinks to reach the ground at about the latitude of the British Isles. At the same time, polar air, which is heavy and cold, moves south from the Arctic. It is being replaced by slightly warmer air that rises over the warm seas and lands of the Atlantic, Europe, North America and the North Pacific Ocean. Similar convection currents flow in the southern half of the Earth.

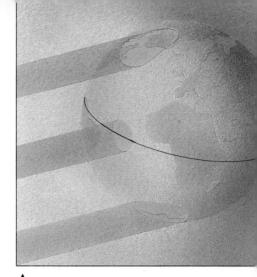

▲ The beams are all equal, but at the poles, the beam of light has to cover a greater area of ground and has had to travel through more atmosphere than at the Equator.

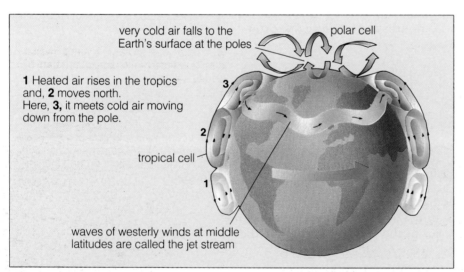

very cold air falls to the Earth's surface at the poles

polar cell

1 Heated air rises in the tropics and, **2** moves north. Here, **3,** it meets cold air moving down from the pole.

tropical cell

waves of westerly winds at middle latitudes are called the jet stream

◄ Huge currents of air are caused by convection in the atmosphere. This convection produces the major wind belts of the Earth. The jet stream is formed at the boundary between two sets of convection currents – the cold polar air and the warm tropical air.

In a simple way this explains the typical British weather. Sometimes we get cold dry air from the poles. At other times we get warm, damp air from the tropics. Sometimes it's fine, sometimes it's wet.

But it isn't quite as simple as this. There are two main complications. One is that the Earth is spinning. The other is that sea and land behave differently when they get energy from the Sun. The sea warms up more slowly than the land does.

The spinning Earth

This diagram (right) shows the general flow of high-level air from the tropics towards the poles. Underneath, cooled air flows back to the equator – this is not shown in the diagram. Also, the diagram doesn't take account of the fact that the Earth is spinning.

Whilst this air movement is taking place, the land is moving under it. The result is as shown in the second diagram (b). The air flow seems to us on Earth to be moving towards the north-east. Underneath, the air flows back along the same line. This makes the steady winds known to sailors as the Northeast Trade Winds. But this is a broad and simplified picture. Other convection currents appear at about 45° from the equator. On land, mountains get in the way. Also, the land gets hotter than the sea in summer and is colder in winter. This affects the global movement of air, so that the patterns are more complicated in practice.

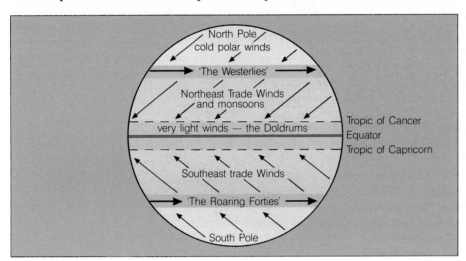

But the main fact is that these air movements carry energy from the tropics towards the poles. The energy is not only the kinetic energy of the high-level wind. In fact it is mostly the energy carried because the air is *hot*.

When hot air meets cold air

It wasn't until the 1940s that high-flying aircraft became common. During the Second World War there were lots of aircraft crossing the Atlantic between Britain and North America. Pilots found that they could fly much faster on the route from America to Britain than when they were going the other way. They had discovered the *jet stream*.

This has nothing to do with jet engines. The jet stream is a thin river of air that travels from west to east at a height of about 10 000 metres. It winds and twists like a river, and doesn't stay in the same place for long. It is usually above or close to Britain, however. The air in it travels at over 200 km per hour.

Cold polar air meets warm tropical air at about 50 °N – just about where the British Isles are. The temperature difference between these huge blocks of air is what powers the jet stream. Below the jet stream the air is dragged along from west to east more slowly. This causes the winds

(a) If the Earth didn't spin, then the tropical air would rise and then flow due north.

(b) Because of the spin of the Earth, the high air flow is deflected eastwards.

▲
The drawing shows the northern half of the Earth, although there is a similar pattern of air movements in the southern half as well.

◄
At ground level, the convection 'winds' look like this. They produce the main wind belts of the Earth.

▼
By using the jet stream, Richard Branson and Per Lindstrom crossed the Atlantic in a hot-air balloon.

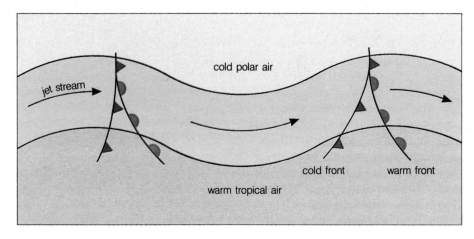

As the polar jet stream 'wobbles', huge bubbles of warm air break into the cold polar air. These are the lows that cause most of Britain's weather.

known as the 'westerlies'. This means that most of the time the wind in Britain comes from the west – it is the *prevailing wind.*

The diagram on page 100 shows the main *convection cells* of the Earth, and the *polar jet stream.* The jet steam is on top of the boundary between the cold and warm air. As the jet stream snakes up and down from north to south and back again, so does this boundary. Huge swirls of warm air break into the cold air. They may be three or four hundred kilometres across. They move in the westerly winds like eddies in a stream. Less often, similar eddies of cold air separate from the main polar block. This is shown below. These are the lows and highs that produce our typical weather, as described above.

Hot and cold fluids don't mix very easily. The swirling masses of warm air stay in one piece for several days. Most of the ones that reach Britain form in the North Atlantic. The air may get even warmer as it crosses the warm band of sea water called the Gulf Stream. Sea water evaporates into it. The air is now both *warm* and *damp.*

Frost and snow

In winter, cold polar air may spread over Britain. This air is 'dry', with only a small amount of water vapour in it. Thus it is free of clouds. The land is usually warmer than the air, certainly during the day as the sun shines on it. At night the ground loses energy, radiating it away into space as infrared radiation.

The ground cools very quickly. It can become much colder than the air. When water vapour in the air touches the ground, or cold buildings and vegetation, it immediately freezes. It has changed straight from water vapour into solid ice. It has produced *frost.*

A layer of cloud may stop frost from occurring. The cloud is made of drops of water, or even tiny ice particles. But the cloud can absorb the infrared radiation from the ground. It gets a little warmer. Clouds also *emit* infrared radiation. Half of this will go downwards, back into the ground. So, on cloudy nights the ground loses barely half of the energy it loses on clear nights. So frost is less likely: the cloud acts like a blanket.

Mist and dew

On clear summer nights the ground also cools. *Dew* forms. The water vapour isn't cold enough to freeze. In autumn, similar conditions might produce a *mist* or *fog.* The water vapour condenses out as drops of water in the air. This happens more easily when there is dust in the air.

Making an atmosphere fit to breathe

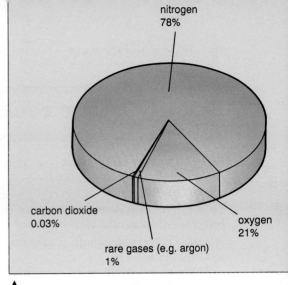

The gases in the Earth's atmosphere.

When the Earth was formed it had an atmosphere just like the atmosphere the planet Venus has today. It was mostly carbon dioxide. Carbon dioxide is a 'greenhouse gas'. This means that it traps radiation, as explained in Chapter 12, *Fuels and the environment*.

So the young Earth was very hot. But somehow, life began in the warm seas. To start with, it was very simple. It was probably like the algae that you can find in stagnant ponds. This life survived without oxygen.

One kind of algae evolved which used the carbon dioxide as a source of food. It used energy from the Sun's radiation to change the gas into the solid materials it needed to grow. There was a by-product: oxygen. This type of algae turned out to be a very successful form of life. Nowadays, most living organisms on Earth use this method of gaining food. They are the *green plants*.

The very earliest green plants lived in the sea. They needed some oxygen to live, and they got it from the small amount dissolved in sea water. As more and more of them developed it was easier for the first *animals* to appear. Animals couldn't make their own food, they had to live off the sea plants. Then, of course, they started living off each other. The big change happened when plants colonised the land.

At that time the land was a desert, completely empty of life. Green plants took it over quite quickly. This invasion took place about 450 million years ago. As a result, the 'waste product', oxygen, became more and more plentiful in the atmosphere.

Meanwhile, rain was washing carbon dioxide out of the air. It made a weak acid, carbonic acid. This reacted with the calcium compounds in rocks to form a solid material, calcium carbonate. This ended up as the huge deposits of chalk and limestone we find all over the world.

Two hundred million years after the first green plants moved on to the land, the atmosphere was rich in oxygen. It was now possible for animals to emerge from the seas and find enough oxygen to breathe. The Earth became very like what it is today.

Some of these changes are summarised in the Earth-history time chart, on page 245 in the 'Reference section'.

The atmosphere today

The atmosphere is now made up of several gases. We must remember that this is quite a delicate balance. If all the plants died, the air would gradually lose its oxygen. Burning rain forests, or covering land with buildings, cuts down the rate of oxygen production. It also increases the amount of carbon dioxide in the atmosphere. The effect of quite small changes on the whole Earth is hard to predict, but it is worrying scientists, and some politicians. There is more about this in Chapter 12.

Energy in the rocks

Chemists and geologists analyse what the Earth is made of. They have discovered that nearly every type of rock contains a very tiny amount of radioactive material. On average, about 5 atoms in every million are radioactive. This doesn't seem very much, but it adds up to about a hundred million billion tonnes (10^{17} tonnes). The Earth is a big place, after all. You could run quite a few nuclear power stations with this amount of fuel!

These atoms decay very, very slowly (see Chapter 12, page 182). As they do they give out energy which heats the interior of the Earth. This causes volcanoes and hot springs. But how can radioactivity cause earthquakes and build mountains? First, what exactly are earthquakes?

Earthquakes

Every hour of the day there is an earthquake somewhere on Earth. Most of them are too small to be noticed. They are only detected by special instruments called *seismographs*. The result is a trace on a sheet of paper. The trace is quite complicated. Earthquakes produce three different kinds of wave, which travel through rocks. Some can even get through to the other side of the Earth.

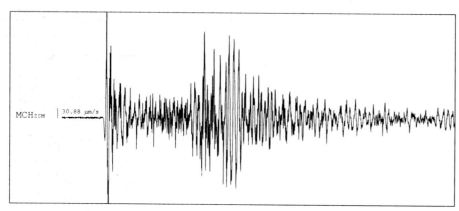

MCHzsm | 30.88 µm/s

◄ A recording from a seismograph. It is a record of an earthquake in N. Wales in 1984. The trace lasts 70 seconds.

▼ Earthquakes release huge amounts of energy. This picture shows what happened in Mexico City in 1985.

An earthquake is a set of shock waves. They start deep within the Earth, probably at a quite small place. This place is called the *focus* of the earthquake. Rocks deep inside the Earth have been stretched. They then move and probably break apart at the focus. A very large amount of energy is released.

The damage caused by an earthquake depends on the energy released and how far it spreads out before reaching the surface. Earthquakes are typically 5–20 km deep. The deeper they occur, the less damage they do as the energy spreads out more.

Most damage is done at what is called the *epicentre* of the earthquake. This is the point on the surface nearest the focus, where the earthquake started.

Most damage is done by a fairly slow sideways movement of the ground. Even so, a normal building can't move quickly enough to follow its foundations, so they tear away from the rest of the building. The taller the building, the more likely this is to happen. In earthquakes, most people are killed by buildings falling in on them.

The strength of an earthquake is usually measured by how much energy it releases, using the *Richter scale*.

Every whole-number step on the scale represents an increase in energy of 10 times. An earthquake of magnitude 4 is quite gentle. One of magnitude 7 can kill hundreds of people and destroy cities. But the effects depend on how deep the focus is. If the focus is near the surface much more damage is caused.

Earthquakes as Earth probes

This is what the inside of the Earth is like. How do we know this? The deepest mine is only a few kilometres deep. Scientists have worked out the structure of the Earth by using earthquake waves as probes.

A modern hospital can use sound waves to find out what the inside of a human body is like. Earthquakes make waves that are like sound waves – push-and-pull waves (longitudinal waves). But earthquakes also produce 'sideways' or *transverse* waves. These travel through rocks at different speeds. The speeds depend on the type of rock. Some waves arrive earlier than others.

This means that geologists can work out what kind of rocks there are between the earthquake and the seismic-recording station. Like all waves, these waves can be reflected at places where the medium changes. Careful analysis of the times of arrivals of waves at different places on Earth has produced the evidence for its layered structure.

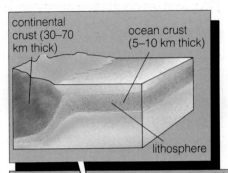

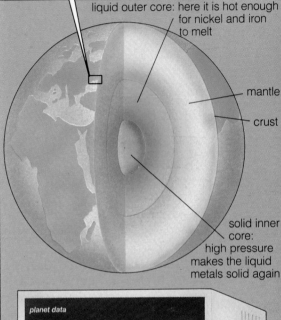

planet data	
crust thickness	50 km (variable)
diameter at the Equator	12 756 km
diameter at the poles	12 714 km
average density	5518 kg/m³
density of continental rock	2670 kg/m³
density of oceanic rock	2850 kg/m³
energy from radioactivity:	
continental rocks	130 J/s per m³
deeper rocks	35 J/s per m³

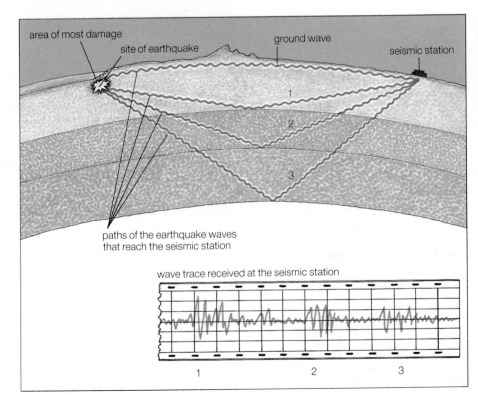

▲ The Earth is built in layers. The crust is very thin – about as thick as the line on the diagram compared to the rest of the Earth.

◄ The Earthquake waves can tell us what the centre of the Earth is like. Waves reflected from different layers arrive at the receiving stations at different times. Scientists can work out how thick the layers are, and even what kind of rock they are made of.

Push-pull waves, like sound waves, can travel through a liquid. But the other kind of wave (the sideways one) can't. Geologists found that there is a *shadow zone* for this kind of wave on the opposite side of the Earth from an earthquake. This shows that the centre of the Earth must be liquid. It is hot enough for iron and nickel to melt.

Volcanoes

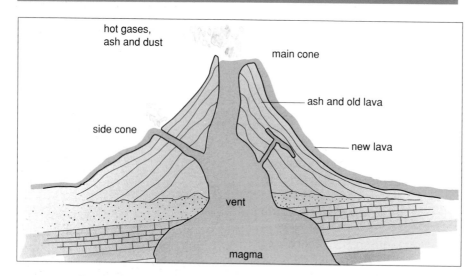

Volcanoes are found where the layer of solid rock in the Earth's crust is thinner than usual. They make a pathway for molten rock, called *magma*, to reach the surface, where it is called *lava*.

Some kinds of lava flow easily, and spread widely over the land. As the lava cools it produces a low cone-shape. In past times huge areas of countryside were covered by lava flows. We can see the remains of flows like this in Scotland, Wales and North America.

Other kinds of lava flow less easily and so produce steep cones. These are the kinds of volcano that we all recognise. A typical volcano like this is Mount Vesuvius, in Italy. Sometimes the molten rock doesn't break through to the surface. Instead it forms a huge mound of rock that cools slowly underground. Most of Cornwall is the weathered remains of a massive 'failed volcano' like this.

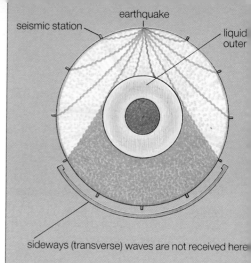

sideways (transverse) waves are not received here

▲ A shadow zone detected by seismic recording stations shows that there is a liquid region inside the Earth.

◄ The main parts of a cone volcano.

▼ A basalt lava flow – the Giant's Causeway in Northern Ireland.

◄ A typical cone-shaped volcano.

Igneous rocks

Rocks formed as a result of volcanic activity are called *igneous* rocks. These rocks contain many different types of *minerals*. One of the most common is *quartz*. It's chemical name is *silica* (silicon dioxide).

Where to find earthquakes and volcanoes

The map shows the sites of active volcanoes and major earthquakes. They seem to go together. This pattern has been known about for a long time. But it was less than thirty years ago that the true reasons for this were discovered. Britain doesn't have any volcanoes, but we do get small earthquakes several times a year.

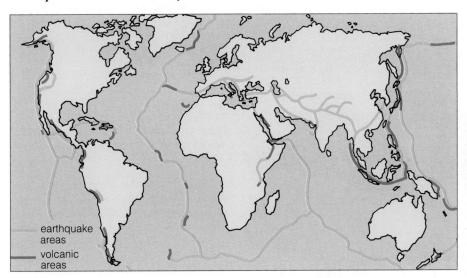

earthquake areas

volcanic areas

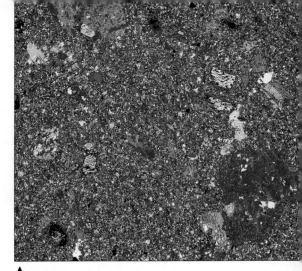

▲
The crystals in basalt rock are very small because the lava cools and sets very quickly.

▼
If the crystals have more time to grow, then they can become larger. This is granite.

The moving continents

It is very hard to believe that the solid ground on which we stand is actually sliding about the Earth. Britain was once on the equator! The idea that continents moved was first put forward seventy years ago, by a man called Alfred Wegener.

Why continents move

This is the story of the Earth according to present-day *theories*. Most of the theories were wrong 50 years ago, and in 50 years time there could be better ones. That's science! The evidence for the story is given below, but first follow the story.

When the Earth was formed it was very hot. Most of it was probably molten. The less dense materials floated to the top, and as they cooled they formed the continents. But the Earth was still half-molten. The continental material was like scum on the surface of simmering water. It formed into large lumps separate from each other. In between was denser material.

The dense material formed what we now see as the beds of the oceans. Deeper still came the lower crust, then the mantle and all the layers shown on page 105.

The Earth gradually cooled, and the outer parts became solid. But few things are really 'solid'. Ice can flow as glaciers, and if the forces are big enough, 'solid rock' can flow. This is when the radioactive elements came into play. They supplied enough energy to heat rocky material deep in the mantle. The rocks expanded and got less dense. Just as with water in a beaker, but millions of times slower, the rocks flowed in huge *convection currents*.

The diagram shows these, and their effects. They pulled sideways at the surface of the Earth. The surface was broken up into massive *plates*, like breaking ice in a river. Some plates

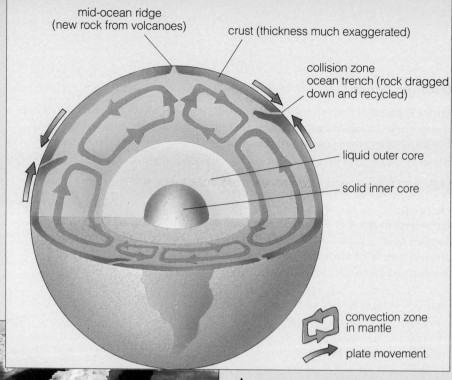

The huge convection currents within the Earth's mantle drive the continental plates across the surface of the Earth.

Page 244 in the 'Reference section' shows where the major continents were at different times in the past. Britain was a tropical country near the equator during the *Carboniferous* period. This was when our coal was formed from the dead remains of tropical rain forests.

The highest mountains on Earth, the Himalayas, have been formed by the Indian Plate colliding into Asia. This happened just 26 million years ago.

The map shows the main 'plates' of the Earth. Compare this with the 'volcano and earthquake' map on page 107.

You can think of tectonic plates as being like ice floes moving across the surface of water.

carry the continents, others carry the oceans. The plates grind against each other, causing earthquakes. Some collide head on. If two continental plates collide they form high mountains where they meet. If a continental plate collides with an ocean plate one dips under the other. This makes very deep holes in the ocean, and might also make high mountains.

Volcanoes occur where the hot current of semi-molten rock pushes up near the surface. This can happen in the middle of a continent. But, more importantly, it is happening in the middle of the oceans. The current pushes the ocean plates apart. It is this movement that causes the continents to drift.

The main tectonic plates of the Earth.

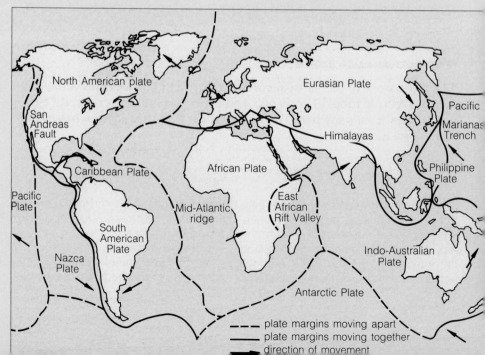

How do we know that the continents are moving?

The key evidence that made geologists believe that the continents were, and still are, moving came from research into the Earth's magnetism.

The Earth has a magnetic field. This is why compasses can tell you which way north is. But over the years the position of the *magnetic* North Pole changes. It is now in North Canada. Curious scientists tried to find out where the magnetic poles were a few thousand or even a few million years ago. This seems a useless bit of scientific research, but it has led to the theories that allow us to predict where earthquakes are likely to happen.

Scientists discovered that not only does the North Magnetic Pole wander about, it also changes from being a 'north pole' to being a 'south pole'. In other words, from time to time, the Earth's magnetic field changes direction. No one knows why.

This field swap has happened every few thousand years. Scientists found this out by measuring the 'fossil magnetism' left in rocks. All rocks contain some iron. Hot materials cannot be magnetised. But when volcanic rocks cool and become solid they are magnetised in the direction of the Earth's field at *that* time. It was found that such rocks had different field directions, depending on when they were made.

Then came the vital clue. Magnetic measurements were made of rocks under the North Atlantic. These rocks are still being made by a huge line of undersea volcanoes. We now know that this line – the Mid-Atlantic Ridge – is where a main convection current of hot rock reaches the surface.

▼
The formation of a mid-ocean ridge. This is happening in the middle of the Atlantic ocean.

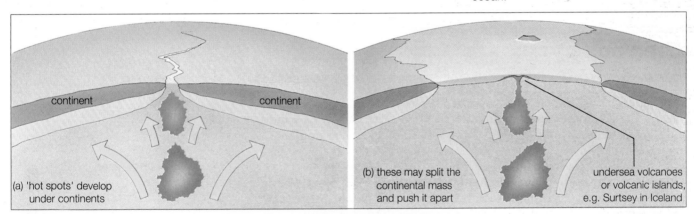

(a) 'hot spots' develop under continents

(b) these may split the continental mass and push it apart

undersea volcanoes or volcanic islands, e.g. Surtsey in Iceland

The rocks on either side of this ridge showed a strange pattern of magnetism. As we go away from the ridge the rock magnetism changes. This is because the rocks were laid down at different times in past few million years or so. *But the pattern of rock magnetism on either side is the same.*

▼
The magnetic patterns in rocks on the ocean floor show that some oceans are getting wider.

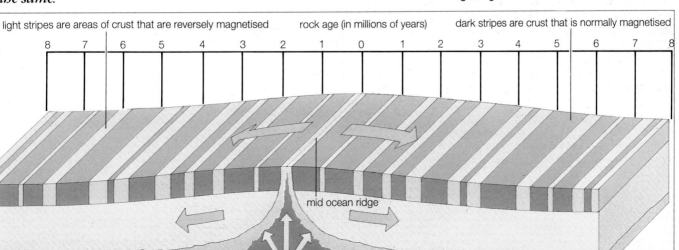

light stripes are areas of crust that are reversely magnetised   rock age (in millions of years)   dark stripes are crust that is normally magnetised

8   7   6   5   4   3   2   1   0   1   2   3   4   5   6   7   8

mid ocean ridge

What we have is like a huge tape recording – in stereo! It tells us that the rocks welling up in the middle of the Atlantic are moving sideways. As they do so, they are pushing the continents of Europe and Africa away from the Americas. The Atlantic Ocean is getting wider. It is doing so very slowly – at a rate of about 5 centimetres a year. This drift of the continents has been measured from space using satellites.

North and South America are pushing into the Pacific plate. This collision has produced the great mountain chain of the Rocky Mountains and the Andes. Here we find many volcanoes, and there are many earthquakes.

This movement has also produced deep oceans, as the American continental plates are dragged downwards, taking some ocean plate with them. The deepest parts of the sea are where continental plates are being dragged down by the returning convection currents. We find these at the edges of the Pacific Ocean.

But the patterns are quite complicated. For example the small plate carrying California is sliding sideways against the main plate that carries North America. In about 30 million years it will collide with Alaska. At present, it is tearing a huge rip in the Earth's crust, very close to the cities of Los Angeles and San Francisco. This is called the *San Andreas Fault*. Everyone who lives there is waiting for the 'great earthquake'. The last big one was in 1904. It destroyed most of San Francisco. The next one is overdue! All new buildings are designed to be 'earthquake proof', but even so there will be terrible damage. Scientists know exactly *where* the earthquake will occur – they don't know *when*.

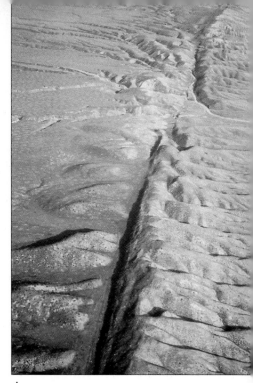

▲ The San Andreas fault. You can actually see the plates on either side of the picture. This massive fault is where California is moving slowly northwards along the edge of the American plate.

The rock cycle

The highest mountains and the hardest rocks are worn down by *weathering*. The particles from the rock are then carried away by wind and rivers. Eventually, they end up in the sea. They reach it as mud or sand.

All these processes take time. The layers of mud and sand grow thicker and thicker. The bottom layers have water squeezed out of them. They get hot. There are chemical changes. All this makes them harden into rocks. Because they were formed as sediments in water, they are called *sedimentary* rocks.

▼ Weathering and erosion: how rocks are worn down and carried away.

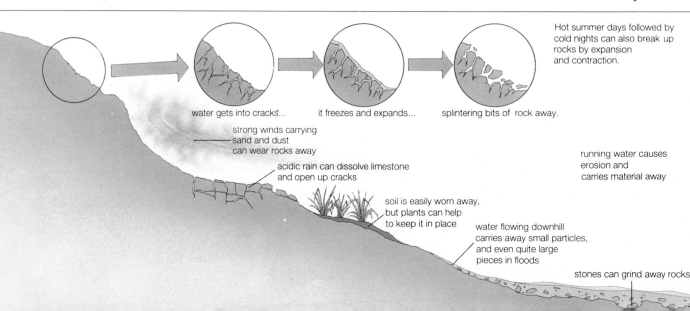

water gets into cracks...   it freezes and expands...   splintering bits of rock away.

Hot summer days followed by cold nights can also break up rocks by expansion and contraction.

strong winds carrying sand and dust can wear rocks away

acidic rain can dissolve limestone and open up cracks

running water causes erosion and carries material away

soil is easily worn away, but plants can help to keep it in place

water flowing downhill carries away small particles, and even quite large pieces in floods

stones can grind away rocks

Rocks like sandstones and mudstones were made like this. The clearest sign that a rock is sedimentary will be if it has fossils in it. These will usually be small shellfish that lived on the sea bottom at the time the sediments were laid down. Also, you might see that the rock is made of small grains, held together by a natural 'cement'.

One very common kind of sedimentary rock was made from living creatures. Sea water contains dissolved chemicals. One common one is calcium hydrogen carbonate. Animals take this chemical and turn it into their shells or bones. It is made into *calcium carbonate. Chalk* and *limestone* were made like this, and are almost pure calcium carbonate. They were often made in warm, shallow seas that were rich in life.

Sooner or later, the movement of the continents brings these sedimentary rocks to the surface. They are formed at the edges of the continents and so are most likely to be pushed up into mountains.

But they are also at risk of being pushed back under again! This makes them melt. They go back into the magma that may once again become lava from volcanoes. This means that over periods of millions of years the materials that make rocks are recycled. The drawing at the bottom of the page shows the main features of this *rock cycle*.

▲ A sandstone.

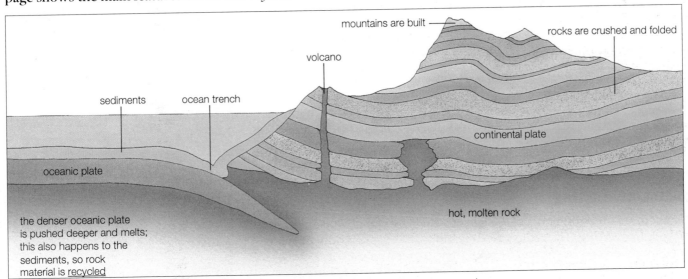

mountains are built — rocks are crushed and folded

volcano

sediments — ocean trench

continental plate

oceanic plate

hot, molten rock

the denser oceanic plate is pushed deeper and melts; this also happens to the sediments, so rock material is recycled

▲ What happens when plates collide. This is happening along the west coast of America. The process is called *subduction* ('drawing under').

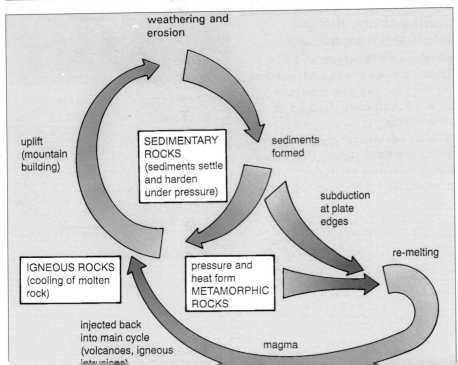

weathering and erosion

uplift (mountain building)

SEDIMENTARY ROCKS (sediments settle and harden under pressure)

sediments formed

subduction at plate edges

re-melting

IGNEOUS ROCKS (cooling of molten rock)

pressure and heat form METAMORPHIC ROCKS

injected back into main cycle (volcanoes, igneous intrusions)

magma

◄ The rock cycle: making, changing and destroying rocks.

Changed rocks

When the hot magma flows through the rocks in the Earth's crust it 'cooks' them. The high temperature and increased pressure changes the rocks chemically. They might partly melt and recrystallise. The result is a *metamorphic* rock.

For example, chalk or limestone changes into *marble*. Mudstone and shale might become *slate*. Sandstone turns into a hard white rock called *quartzite*. Igneous rocks are also changed when new magma or lava flows over them.

▲
Metamorphic rocks often have interesting patterns. Many of them, especially marble and slate, are very valuable and are used in decoration.

Earth history

You will learn more about how the Earth was formed in a later chapter in book 2. *Geology* – the study of what makes up the Earth – can't tell us much about this. But it can tell us how old the Earth is, and how it has changed over the billions of years since it was formed as part of the solar system.

How we can tell if one rock is older than another?

Look at the photograph of a cliff face. The rocks are sedimentary rocks. Unless they have all been turned upside down then the one on the bottom layer must be older than the ones above it. Until quite recently this is all we could say about the ages of rocks. It allowed geologists to help prove the *theory of evolution*. (This is dealt with in GCSE book 2.) Geologists could trace the changes in the fossils as time went on.

▼
The layers in the Grand Canyon. The canyon walls are a slice through time going back 2000 million years from the present day at the top.

Radioactive dating

For accurate measurements of the age of a rock we can now use *radioactive dating*. The radioactive elements in rocks not only provide the energy to make and change rocks, they can also be used as a clock.

Radioactive elements decay. This means that they change into other elements, firing off small atomic particles as they do so. (This is explained in Chapter 12) The radioactive element uranium decays through a whole chain of elements, finally ending as lead. This is not radioactive.

If we start with a gram of uranium it will take 4.5 billion years (4.5×10^9 years) for *half* of it to become lead. Thus if we get a rock and find that it contains an equal amount of lead and uranium we can date it to be 4.5 billion years old. A simple formula can be used to calculate the ages of rocks with different proportions of lead to uranium.

All this takes very careful measurement. After all, on average only two atoms in a 100 000 will be uranium! It also relies on the theory that when the rock was made the uranium wasn't somehow contaminated with lead to start with. This means that the dating is most likely to be correct if the rock is an igneous rock.

▶
The principle of radioactive dating.

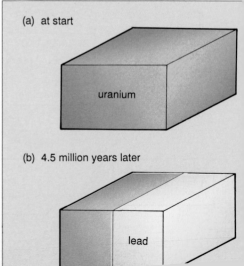

(a) at start

uranium

(b) 4.5 million years later

lead

Activities

1 Collect one or two weather maps. They are printed in newspapers.
(a) Copy the symbols they use to show:
cloud, rain, snow, sun, highs, showers, wind, isobars and lows.
(b) Can the symbols be improved? Design new versions.

2 The weather sometimes has a serious effect on everyday life. Try to remember the most serious weather situation in your area during the past year or two.
(a) Describe it, and its effects.
(b) Was this weather unexpected?
(c) Was there any preparation for it, to make its effects less serious?

3 Use your school or local library to find out as much as you can about a recent earthquake. Use the information to answer the following:
(a) How many people were affected by it?
(b) Was there any warning of the earthquake?
(c) Was it in a region where earthquakes are expected?
(d) Was it near the boundary of tectonic plates?
(e) Were the local buildings designed to withstand earthquakes?

4 Find out as much as you can about the geology of your area. Find the answers to questions such as:
(a) What are the main rocks on which your town or village is built?
(b) Did the area depend on any rock type for an industry?

Does it still depend on it? Describe and explain any changes.
(c) Is there any area of outstanding interest, geologically? Briefly describe it. Is there any tourist interest in this area?

5 Use reference books to describe and explain the following main landscape features:
(a) a geological fault;
(b) a river meander;
(c) a hanging valley;
(d) coastal erosion.

6 How accurate are weather forecasts? Collect the daily forecasts from newspapers, watch the evening television bulletins, or listen to the radio. How often are the forecasters right? Give them a mark out of 10! Do the forecasts warn you if things are 'uncertain' for some reason? Did the wrong forecasts – if any – really matter to anyone?

7 Use your local library to find out for your town or area:
(a) the average annual rainfall,
(b) the average number of sunny days per year,
(c) the average number of hours of sunshine in (i) December and (ii) June.

8 How useful are rocks? Look around your town or area and note where rocks are actually being used. Try to identify what rocks they are – at least classify them as *sedimentary*, *igneous* or *metamorphic*. For one example, find out why it is being used in preference to some other material. (Hint: try looking at shop fronts, buildings, roads and churches.)

Questions

1 Give three main differences between high-pressure areas and low-pressure areas.

2 What is the *water cycle*? Answer by writing a paragraph or two, or by drawing a well-labelled diagram.

3 What is the *jet stream*? How does it affect our weather?

4 'The sky over Britain is a battleground between polar air and tropical air.' Explain what this sentence means, and the role that these air types play in producing our weather.

5 Describe and explain one weather effect caused by or closely related to each of the following physical processes:
(a) convection;
(b) radiation;
(c) evaporation;
(d) condensation;
(e) absorption of radiation.

6 What are three main differences between *igneous* and *sedimentary* rocks? Name two rocks of each type.

7 How are *metamorphic* rocks formed? Give two examples of this kind of rock. Use diagrams in your answer.

8 How does the theory of plate tectonics explain the following:
(a) mountain building?
(b) that Iceland is a volcanic island?
(c) the presence of coal in the rocks of Great Britain?
(d) the distribution of volcanoes on the surface of the Earth?

9 Explain how the landscape of the Earth is caused or affected by each of the following physical processes (one example each):
(a) convection;
(b) melting;
(c) dissolving;
(d) crystallisation;
(e) freezing.

Checklist

These are the facts and ideas that you should have
learned by studying this topic.

To succeed at Basic Level you should:

- know that the weather changes, and that there are
  weather patterns
- be able to recognise the symbols used in weather
  forecasts
- know about the atmosphere
- know how rocks and buildings are worn by the weather,
  and how soil is made
- be able to describe an investigation about rocks or the
  soil

To succeed at Foundation Level you should:

- know about climate and its effect on agriculture
- be able to explain the water cycle
- be able to explain how landscapes are affected by rain,
  ice, winds, volcanoes and earthquakes
- know that the surface of the Earth is slowly moving
- know about some scientific discovery in Earth or
  weather studies, and the life of the scientist who made it

To succeed at Merit Level you should:

- understand how air movements are involved with
  weather changes and that these movements get their
  energy from the Sun
- be able to recognise the patterns of earthquakes,
  mountains, volcanoes and other large features on the
  Earth's surface and know something about why the
  patterns exist
- be able to explain how the main rock types are formed
  in the rock cycle (igneous, sedimentary and
  metamorphic)
- know that the Earth's surface is made of very large rocky
  plates that move very slowly, and how this is related to
  earthquakes and volcanoes
- know how the main theories in Earth science can
  explain what we see

To succeed at Special Level you should:

- be able to explain how atmospheric changes cause
  different weather phenomena, and know how solar
  energy affects them
- be able to describe what scientists believe is the
  structure of the Earth and explain the evidence for it
- know how the rock cycle is driven by both solar energy
  and the internal energy (from radioactivity) of the
  Earth, and be able to interpret evidence for the
  formation of different types of rocks and ores
- understand that the timescales for geological change are
  very long, and know about how such long times are
  measured
- understand the theory of plate tectonics and what it can
  explain, and how it's discovery revolutionised our
  understanding of geology

CHAPTER EIGHT

MOVEMENT AND FORCES
PLAYING AND WORKING

Downhill racing – it's speed that counts!

The Downhill is the oldest of the 'Alpine' skiing events, and still the most exciting. Speeds of 140 km per hour are reached, and the racer has to stay in complete control over the bumps, dips and curves of the course. The high speeds come from the tremendous drop in height. A typical course has a drop of a thousand metres in a race three and a half kilometres long.

▲ Martin Bell, Britain's fastest downhill skier.

▼ The body of a shot putter is developed so that she can put a massive effort into forcing the shot through the air.

most obvious. Like a motorcycle helmet, it has a hard, smooth outer shell to deflect objects, and a layer of padding to absorb any shock. The skis are fitted with quick-release toe and heel clips, which open in an accident. Skis used to be *tied* on! If they twisted in a crash, they would break the skier's leg or ankle.

There is no 'speed record' for downhill skiing, because the course changes at each location. Also, the International Rules say that the course must be designed so that it cannot be covered in less than about two minutes. So, as the skiers' top speeds get faster, courses have to be made longer, and more curves and gentler sections must be included. It's here that low air resistance, and low-friction coatings on the skis really count.

Getting going

You need to make something move in every sport. Often it's your own body. Sometimes it's a ball, a bicycle, a javelin or a car. They all need to be started, controlled and stopped. They must do this safely, and of course they try to be the fastest, go the farthest, or in some way be 'the best'. Making this happen is where the science comes in.

Friction is bad!

The racers spend as much time as they can in the 'egg position', crouched down to be as small and smooth as possible. The helmet is aerodynamically shaped, the one-piece suits are skin tight and even the boots are smoothed and shaped for low air resistance. Special bent ski poles are used to fit closely to the body.

Safety is vital

Modern racing speeds mean special safety equipment. The helmet is the

Starting

To start moving and to speed up you need a force. We can see that the sprinter's legs are pushing the rest of his body. The arrows show the direction of the force. It's diagonally upwards. This force does two jobs. It pushes the body along to accelerate, and it pushes up the body to counteract its weight. If he only pushed along, his weight would make him fall (look at the second diagram).

Of course, the more force the sprinter's legs can supply, the better acceleration he gets. That's why sprinters are very muscular. Distance runners aren't. They don't need the acceleration so much. Sprinting is all about acceleration, and that means *force!*

The forward force of the runner is made up of two forces...

... one pushing against the ground and the other upwards against his weight

▲
The forces involved as the runner sprints away from the blocks.

Force, mass and acceleration

Sprinters have big muscles, but they try to keep their mass as low as possible. Sprinters need a high 'force-to-mass' ratio. Weightlifters have much bigger muscles, which give much more force. But weightlifters can't sprint, they're too massive! Their muscles may give them more force than a sprinter's, but they've put on more extra fat than extra muscle. This means that they'd need even more force to get all that extra mass moving. These specially trained bodies have to take account of the laws of physics. The important law here is to do with force, mass and acceleration.

The mathematics of force, mass and acceleration

The laws of physics are usually very simple. But they act in a very complicated world. We start off by telling the simple story. The 'notes' show how the world makes things complicated!

The simple story
When a force acts on an object that is free to move it *accelerates* it. This means the object goes faster and faster, and it keeps on doing this as long as the force acts.

Note 1. Do you believe this? The accelerator of a car makes the engine provide a force to the wheels. But even when it is kept pressed down the car doesn't keep accelerating for ever. It soon reaches its maximum speed. It has *stopped* accelerating. The reason for this is that as soon as the car moves, another force is brought into play — *friction*. The faster the car goes, the bigger the force of friction. At its maximum speed, the friction force on the car is exactly equal to the engine force, and the car stops accelerating.

We measure acceleration in terms of how much the speed *increases*. A fairly good sprinter can run at a speed of 8 metres a second. It might take 2 seconds after the start of the race to reach this speed. The sprinter has increased speed by 8 m/s in 2 seconds; so they are accelerating at an average rate of 4 m/s every second. This is written as 4 metres per second per second, or 4 m/s^2.

Note 2. A force doesn't always change the speed of an object, even if the object is movable. It may just change the direction of movement at the same speed. This is what happens in circular motion (see page 234).

The bigger the force, the bigger the acceleration it produces.
Mathematically: a force is *proportional* to the acceleration it causes.
But a massive object is harder to accelerate than a less massive one. This is why sprinters try to keep unnecessary weight down. Another way of looking at it is to say that a massive object needs a bigger force to get the same acceleration.

Note 3. Mass is a measure of how much matter an object has. It is measured in kilograms: 2 kg of iron has twice as much material as 1 kg of iron. *Mass* is often confused with *weight*.

Mathematically: force needed is proportional to the mass being accelerated (for a constant acceleration).
We can put all this together in one mathematical equation:

force = mass × acceleration
or $F = ma$.

(F = force in newtons, m = mass in kilograms, and a = acceleration in metres per second per second.)

Suppose our sprinter has a mass of 80 kg. To get the acceleration of 4 m/s^2 as above would need a force, F, calculated by:

$F = m \times a$
   $= 80 \times 4$
   $= 320$ N.

Keeping going — the importance of friction

In pursuit cycling the aim is to keep going at the highest speed you can. After accelerating at the start, you try to stay at high speed all the time. Air

resistance and *friction* produce forces that try to slow the bike down. Energy from the cyclist is used to heat up moving parts of the bike that rub together. A lot of air has to be pushed aside. If the cyclist can't supply the extra energy, the bike will slow down. We can't see the lubrication and low-friction bearings, but we can see how to cut air resistance:

- streamlined helmet,
- head-down position,
- solid-disc wheels,
- ultra-smooth clothing,
- his legs are shaved smooth.

Why do solid wheels have low air resistance? Each spoke on a normal wheel sets up its own disturbance in the air. This takes energy away. The disc just has its two smooth surfaces. But solid wheels are *heavier* than spoked wheels. This means that the bike is more difficult to accelerate. But the mass of the bike doesn't matter if you mainly want to stay at the same speed. Mass is important only when you need to accelerate, or climb up hills. Friction is the great energy waster for things that move along the flat, at high speed. Think about the shape of high-speed trains and planes.

Cornering and moving in circles

Greyhounds often damage their legs by fast cornering. Normally a greyhound's legs only have to push it forwards and upwards, like the human sprinter. The diagram shows how in a corner the dogs have to lean over, and their legs push them sideways as well.

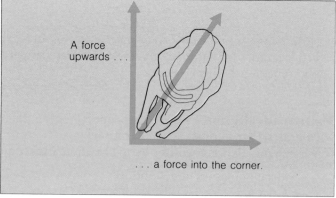

A force upwards . . .

. . . a force into the corner.

▲
Two different forces keep these dogs upright as they go around the corner. What are they?

To go round a corner, a force must push inwards

A hammer thrower must use force in the same way. The hammer is *pulled* towards the centre of the circle. In the photograph, the thrower is pulling hard on the handle. The force on the ball of the hammer is slightly upwards to counter gravity, but mostly inwards to make the hammer move in a circle.

Stopping

Just as force is needed to speed up, a force is needed to slow down. When the stunt man in this film reaches the ground he'll be moving fast, and will need a lot of stopping. A large force could stop him – but would hurt. A small force won't hurt, but it needs a long distance to stop him. That's why

the cushions are so deep. They supply a small force all the while the falling body squashes them. The important thing though isn't distance but *time*. The longer it takes the body to decelerate, the smaller the force needed.

When you slow down you are decelerating. Deceleration is the opposite of acceleration, but the same rules apply. The more massive an object is, the more force is needed to slow it down. A large bus needs a powerful engine – but it also needs very powerful brakes.

Force and time – the idea of impulse

A soft landing means that you stop over a longer time. This takes less force. A small force acting for a long time can produce the same effect as a large force acting for a smaller time. The combination of force and time is called *impulse*:

$$\text{impulse} = \text{force} \times \text{time}$$
$$= F \times t.$$

Suppose an object is travelling at speed v, and you want to stop it. Its deceleration is its change of speed per second. If it takes time t to stop, its deceleration is simply v/t. Deceleration is the opposite of acceleration, and we can use the same fomula that we used above (page 117).

Force = mass × deceleration,
or $F = m \times v/t$,
which gives, when we rearrange it,
$Ft = mv$.

Now for a given object moving at a given speed, mv is a constant.

> **Note 1.** The quantity mv is a very useful one in the physics of movement. It has a special name – *momentum*.

So Ft is always the same, and if time t is made large, the force F will be small. And vice versa.

Power and energy

In science, 'power' has a special meaning. It doesn't mean size or strength, it means how quickly energy is transferred. *Power is the amount of energy delivered in one second.*

A fast-moving car has a lot of kinetic energy (movement energy). This energy comes from burning the fuel in the car. The energy gets to the car via the engine, gears and wheels. As the energy is transferred quickly (high power) the car speeds up in a short time. If the energy transfer is slow (low power), the car takes longer to speed up.

Power is the quantity of energy transferred in one second. We can work out the power of an engine by measuring the energy. Power is measured in *watts*.

$$\text{Power} = \frac{\text{energy transferred (joules)}}{\text{time taken (seconds)}}$$

$$P = \frac{E}{t}.$$

A racing car can deliver 300 000 W. That's nearly a third of a million joules each second; enough to cook a Christmas turkey in 10 seconds!

A top sprinter can reach a speed of about 12 ms^{-1} in 8 seconds. At that moment, the body has about 7200 J of kinetic energy. To get this, the sprinter had to produce kinetic energy at the rate of 900 joules per second, or 900 W. This is enough to light 15 light bulbs!

$$\text{Power} = \frac{\text{energy transferred}}{\text{time taken}}$$

$$\text{Power} = \frac{7200 \text{ J}}{8 \text{ s}} = 900 \text{ W}.$$

To produce this sort of power, the sprinter needs powerful leg muscles – but also a good 'heart-and-lungs' system. Why?

Falling off a horse

Whether you're a world-class eventer or just a Saturday rider, being thrown off your horse can easily fracture your skull. Recently, the design of rider's helmets has improved enormously and so have the regulations that make sure they are worn properly in all types of events.

The shell is hard and strong. Its job is to throw off sharp penetrating objects, like branches or stones, and to spread the force of the blow from one point over the whole of the head. It's made of fibreglass, which is light and strong.

The padding used to be cork, about 6 mm thick. It's now special plastic foam, up to 24 mm thick. It softens the blow, but it mustn't be soft! The makers call it the 'energy-absorbing layer'. But what has energy to do with it?

A falling body picks up kinetic energy. When the body stops, that energy has to be transferred to something else. The thick padding gives a larger stopping distance and absorbs the energy from your head more slowly.

Most protective clothing works by spreading the load and increasing the stopping time.

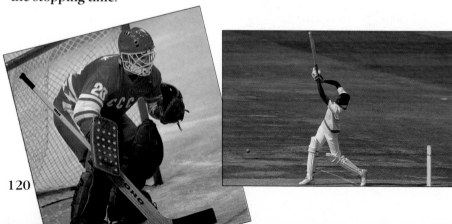

Nothing slows down without a force acting. This force causes the damage. Cars are designed to reduce this force. They do this by making the time it takes to stop as large as possible. Normally, the brakes do this. But when a car crashes, the force of the crash stops it. The people inside won't stop unless a force acts on them. Someone who is 'thrown clear' will get stopped by the ground or a tree. At 30 mph (13.4 m/s) this will usually kill you. You simply stop too quickly.

Cars can have safety designed in to give bigger stopping distances and so a longer time for you to come to a stop. 'Crumple zones', seatbelts and padding are all designed for this.

Speed, distance and time

Speed is a measure of how far (the distance) something moves in a certain time. In science we measure the distances in metres, and the time is always 1 second. So speed is measured in *metres per second.*

In everyday life, speed is measured in miles per hour or kilometres per hour. The table shows some typical speeds.

	Speed	
	m/s	km/h
Light (the fastest speed possible)	300 000 000	1 080 000 000
Earth in orbit around Sun	29 790	107 24
Speed needed for rocket to escape from Earth	11 200	40 320
Speed of typical Earth satellite	7 500	27 000
Military jet aircraft	833	3 000
Commercial jet airliner:		
Concorde	648	2 333
Boeing 747	268	964
Average speed of molecule in air	500	1 800
Sound	340	1 224
Fastest animal (peregrine: in its 'swoop' on to a prey)	97	350
High-speed train (French TGV)	92	315
High-speed train (BR)	44	160
Legal maximum, UK motorways (70 mph)	31	112
Fastest water animal (sailfish)	30	109
Fastest land animal (cheetah)	28	100
Legal maximum, UK towns (30 mph)	13.4	48
Fastest Tour de France cyclist (B. Hinault, over whole course)	10.5	37.8
100 m sprinter	10	36
Marathon runner	5.8	21
Average walking speed	1.7	6
Average speed of a snail	0.006	0.02

Average speed

If you are a good walker you should be able to keep up an average speed of 6 kilometres per hour, which is 1.7 metres per second. What does this mean? Do you walk at exactly 6 km/h, or 1.7 m/s, all the time?

No, probably not. Sometimes you go faster, sometimes slower. Sometimes you stop for a rest. But if you walked for 5 hours you should have covered a distance of 30 kilometres.

$$\text{Average speed} = \frac{\text{total distance covered}}{\text{time taken}}.$$

The graph illustrates this.

Unless you are fitted with a speedometer, you don't really know how fast you are walking. But you can work it out by measuring distance and time. You should have learned how to do this in earlier work. If you need practice try Activity 1 or Activity 6. There are also some questions at the end of the chapter to give you practice.

Accelerating

In theory, all things fall at the same rate due to the force of gravity. (See page 126.) How could we check this? The acceleration of an object is its change of speed in a standard time. In the metric system it is usually measured in terms of how much a speed measured in metres/second changes in a time of 1 second.

So we need to measure the speed at the start, then wait for a measured time and measure the speed again. Then we can calculate the acceleration:

$$\text{acceleration} = \frac{\text{speed at start} - \text{speed at end}}{\text{time taken for the speed to change}}.$$

This is easy enough to do for a car, say. You just look at the speedometer and use a stopwatch. In the school laboratory things could be a bit more complicated – not many things are fitted with speedometers.

One way is to use a ticker timer and some ticker tape. This is shown on page 207 in the 'Reference section'. Another way is to measure the speeds and the times electronically. Your school should have one or other kind of equipment to let you measure the acceleration of a falling object.

But an easy and very cheap way is to use some applied mathematics. All you need to do is to measure the time, t an object takes to fall a measured distance, h. You can then calculate the acceleration of free fall by using the formula:

$$h = 0.5gt^2.$$

Extension task 2 is about the mathematics of movement.

Pressure

These athletes don't seem to be under pressure. But each of them is supported by a very thin steel blade, which exerts a very large *pressure* on the ice. It is the effect of this pressure that makes ice skating like this possible.

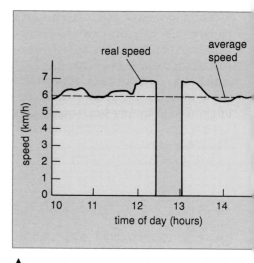

▲
The average speed of a walker.

▼
The area of the blades in contact with the ice is very small. This means that the skaters exert a great *pressure* on the ice.

Skating is almost frictionless. Ice dancers can glide for metres across the ice without any effort. But ice is not perfectly smooth. Its surface is quite rough.

Ice skating works because ice melts under high pressure. The skater actually moves along on a thin layer of *water*. The bumps in the ice are smoothed out, and the water acts as a lubricant, like a layer of oil in an engine. The water freezes again when the skater has moved away.

How much pressure does the skater exert? We work this out from the definition of pressure:

$$\text{pressure} = \frac{\text{force}}{\text{area}}.$$

An adult skater might have a mass of 70 kg. This is pulled down by the force of gravity at 10 newtons per kilogram, so the skater weighs 700 newtons. This is the force that is exerted on the ice through the skates. Modern 'hollow ground' skate blades will have an area in contact with the ice of 10 square centimetres (0.001 square metres).

So, we can calculate the pressure on the ice.

$$\text{Pressure} = \frac{700 \text{ N}}{0.001 \text{ m}^2} = 700\,000 \text{ N/m}^2.$$

This is seven-times the pressure exerted by the atmosphere.

By comparison, the same adult wearing ordinary shoes is standing on a 'shoe area' of about 200 square centimetres (0.02 m^2). This time the pressure exerted would be:

$$\text{Pressure} = \frac{700 \text{ N}}{0.02 \text{ m}^2} = 35\,000 \text{ N/m}^2.$$

This pressure is too small to make the ice melt. But it is still slippery enough to cause problems!

You might have wondered how glaciers can flow down mountains even though ice is solid. This property of ice under pressure explains why. The glacier is floating on a layer of melting ice.

Work and energy

Some play is very hard work! Professional sportsmen and women have to be very fit, and they have to do hard training. Playing tennis or football might not look like work, but as far as science is concerned it really is. (And the athletes would certainly agree!)

Work

Work has a special meaning in science and engineering.

People or engines do work when they produce a force and use it to move something. So the athletes in the picture really are working. You may remember from earlier studies that we measure work by simply measuring the force and also the distance over which it moves. Then we calculate the work done as follows:

work done = force applied × distance moved by the force

or $W = F \times d$

Work, *W*, is measured in joules, force, *F*, in newtons and distance, *d*, in metres. The distance has to be measured along the line of action of the force.

Energy

You need energy if you are going to do any work. In fact, we *measure* energy in terms of how much work it can do. This is why work and energy have the same unit – the joule.

The job of muscles and engines is to convert the energy locked up in chemicals into the moving forces that do work.

The sprinter's muscles use a process called *respiration* to transfer the energy locked up in food and oxygen into movement. A petrol engine uses a process called *combustion* to do the same kind of thing, using petrol and oxygen as the energy sources. These energy sources have what we call *potential* energy. The energy is there. It does exist but we can't see it. It isn't doing anything. But just think what happens when petrol burns!

The oxygen is important. A car would be useless on the airless surface of the moon, even with a full tank of petrol. Think about it!

The energy that lifted the can in the diagram above came from the body of whoever lifted it. Has the energy disappeared? You certainly can't see it. But think what would happen if the can fell off the shelf. it would fall faster and faster until it hit the floor. It would have gained kinetic energy. Where did this energy come from? Obviously, gravity has got something to do with it.

Gravity is a force that makes things fall towards the centre of the Earth. The work you do when you lift a can of beans on to a shelf is stored in the can as *gravitational potential energy*. You had to do work *against* the force of gravity when you lifted the can.

How much potential energy does a can of beans have?

Suppose the can has a mass of 1 kg. This is quite a lot of beans. If you ate them, you could get about 2.5 million joules of energy from them (2.5 MJ). This is about a quarter of the normal daily energy needs of an adult.

If the can fell a metre to the floor it would pick up just 10 joules of energy. To pick up 2.5 million joules it would have to fall a distance of 250 km, which is the average height of a satellite orbiting the Earth.

We can calculate the gravitational potential energy by using the work formula:

$$\text{work} = \text{force} \times \text{distance}.$$

It takes about 10 newtons to lift a 1 kg can of beans. This means that the work done in lifting the can through 1 metre is:

$$\text{work} = 10\,\text{N} \times 1\,\text{m},$$
$$= 10 \text{ joules}.$$

Doing this work has transferred 10 J of energy to the can as gravitational potential energy. It is this energy which is transferred into movement energy as the can falls.

These calculations should make you think. What do you do with all those 10 million joules of energy you get each day from your food? It would be enough to throw four large cans of beans into orbit every day! Perhaps human beings use a lot of energy just staying alive. You will learn more about all this in a biology topic in book 2.

The acceleration of free fall

All falling objects accelerate downwards at the same rate. The formula
shows this very well:

First, remember that force = mass × acceleration (page 117)

Rearrange this to give acceleration $g = \dfrac{\text{force}}{\text{mass}}$

But the force on mass m due to gravity = $m \times g$

So the acceleration of free fall $= \dfrac{m \times g}{m} = g$.

The value of g is the same for all masses – the mass m has cancelled out
in the equations.

Do all objects *really* fall at the same rate? If you drop a sheet of paper
and a pen, which reaches the ground first? You'd probably say that the pen
would. But this doesn't make the statement incorrect. There is another
force around that spoils the neat simple rule. This, as you might guess, is
friction caused by *air resistance*. This is why parachutes work so well!

Parachutes need air – they aren't any use on the Moon, for example. Ask
your teacher to show you an experiment in which a coin and a feather fall
through a glass tube – first in air and then in a vacuum.

Throwing things – projectiles

The picture shows the movement of a ball that has been thrown sideways.
It shows the ball every tenth of a second. You can see that the ball moves
at a steady speed *sideways*, but accelerates *downwards*. There is no force
acting sideways, so there is no reason for the ball to change its speed.

In the second drawing, we see the same effects. But this time the ball is
fired upwards and sideways. The movement of falling objects and
projectiles was first correctly analysed by an Italian scientist called
Galileo. He was born in 1564. He made many discoveries and is still
remembered as one of the most famous scientists who ever lived.

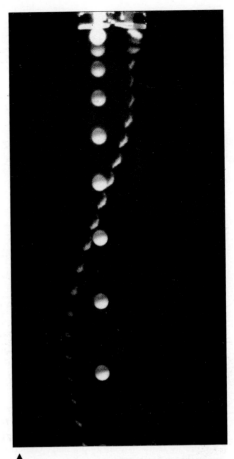

▲
Only air resistance makes the feather fall
more slowly than the ball. If you do the
experiment in a vacuum (below) they fall at
the same rate.

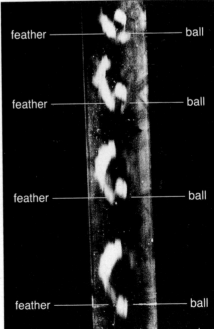

127

Activities

Conversion chart

Time in seconds	1.5	1.6	1.7	1.8	1.9	2.0	2.1	2.2	2.3	2.4	2.5	2.6	2.7	2.8	2.9	3.0
Speed in metres per second	16.7	15.6	14.7	13.8	13.2	12.5	11.9	11.4	10.9	10.4	10.0	9.6	9.3	8.9	8.6	8.3
Speed in miles per hour	37.4	34.9	32.9	31.0	29.5	28.0	26.6	25.5	24.4	23.3	22.4	21.5	21.0	19.9	19.2	18.5

1 Find a safe place where you can watch a straight section of road near where you live. Pick a street lamp or something else that is easy to see. Face in the same direction as the traffic. Take 50 ordinary paces along the side of the road. (This will be about 25 metres.) Time how long cars take to travel from the lamp post to you. (A digital stop watch is useful here!) A car travelling at 30 mph will take about 2 seconds. Time about 20 cars and record your results.

There are lots of ways that you can present your results. You could make a bar chart of how many cars there are for each time; 2.0 s, 2.1 s, 2.2 s, etc. use the times to work out the speeds, using the table below. Make a bar chart of your results. What do you think about the results you get?

2 Get a very blunt knife like a butter knife and some ice cubes still in the tray. Put the tray on a board and press the knife into an ice cube. (Keeping the cubes in the tray stops them slipping.) The knife will slowly sink into the ice. How can you prove that it's *not* because the knife is warm? Why does the knife go into the ice?

3 Design and make a box to keep an egg safe when you drop it from 3 m onto concrete! Remember that you need to transfer energy from the falling egg to the box. Thinking of the 'crumple zone' in a car might help. You can use a hard-boiled egg for any experiments.

4 Plan an experiment to measure the efficiency of a simple machine. You could use such things as a car jack or a pulley system (hoist). *Hints:* you will need to measure the effort force and the load moved (in the same units). You will need to measure some distances as well.

5 Connect two syringes together with plastic tubing as shown in the diagram. Push the smaller syringe in, and feel the force produced on the larger one.
(a) Explain what you observe.
(b) What has this experiment to do with brakes?
(c) Why would it be better to fill the tubes with water?
Remember that force = pressure × area.

6 Design experiments to find out one or more of the following. You may be able to carry one out.
(a) Use a map to find out how far you travel to get from home to school. Time your journey and work out your average speed.
(b) Time how long it takes you to run a measured distance (e.g. 100 metres, 800 metres, 1 kilometre). Work out your average speed.
(c) How fast do you swim?
(d) Measure the speed of the wind.

● Remember: $\text{speed} = \dfrac{\text{distance}}{\text{time}}$.

(e) Plan an experiment to measure the speed of a river.

Questions

1 The car is taking a tight curve. To get the car round the curve,

rather than straight on, the wheels have to push on the car.
(a) Copy the diagram and draw an arrow showing the *direction* of that force.

(b) At point *B*, the car hits a patch of smooth ice and loses all grip. Draw another car and arrow to show what direction the car will skid.

2 If you jump off a box in P.E., you land on your toes, with your knees bent. If you landed stiff-legged, you could be badly hurt. Explain why this is. Use the idea of 'energy = force × distance', or 'force × time = momentum'.

3 Which athlete uses the greatest *power*? A marathon runner, sprinter, high jumper or discus thrower. Which one do you think needs most energy? Give your reasons.

4 A bicycle rider used 12 kJ getting up to speed. Only 3.6 kJ of this is the energy the bike and rider have because of their movement. The rest has been wasted, mostly through friction.
(a) What is the efficiency of the bike?
(b) If the rider took 60 s to reach that speed, what was her power output?

5 At the end of a fair-ground slide, you are moving very fast, and have a lot of energy.
(a) What name do we give to this type of energy?
(b) Where did this energy come from?
(c) Explain how this energy has been transferred to you.

6 This bike is not very efficient. Suggest two ways of making the bike and rider more efficient. Explain why your suggestions would work.

Checklist

These are the facts and ideas that you should have learned by studying this topic.

To succeed at Basic Level you should:

- know what forces do to things
- be able to recognise energy sources and how they can make things work (like electric motors, rubber bands, petrol and diesel engines, etc.)
- know that we can make work easier by using machines (like spanners, levers, etc.)

To succeed at Foundation Level you should:

- know what instruments you need to measure force, distance and time
- be able to describe the effects of friction
- know why things fall
- understand how forces affect movement
- understand the idea of 'balanced forces'
- know enough about forces and their effect on moving objects to understand the problems of road safety, e.g. braking, collisions, safety belts, skidding, reaction time
- understand the importance of energy in movement
- understand that machines help to do work by transferring energy, but that some of this energy is always wasted

To succeed at Merit Level you should:

- be able to calculate speeds
- understand the difference between speed and velocity, and know what acceleration is
- be able to draw and use graphs of movement (distance–time, speed–time)
- be able to explain everyday effects involving force, pressure, friction, mass, velocity and acceleration
- know about kinetic energy and potential energy, and relate these to changes in speed and/or position
- be able to explain why machines are so useful, and understand the ideas of work and efficiency
- understand the idea of a turning force (moment of a force)

To succeed at Special Level you should:

- understand the difference between mass and weight, and between kinetic and potential energy
- understand the idea of momentum
- be able to make calculations based upon:
  - force, mass and acceleration ($F = ma$)
  - momentum (mv)
  - kinetic energy ($\frac{1}{2}\,mv^2$)
  - potential energy (mgh)
  - work, force and distance ($W = fd$)
  - power, energy and time ($P = E/t$)
  - efficiency $= \dfrac{\text{useful energy output}}{\text{total energy supplied}} \times 100\%$
  - average speeds, distances covered and accelerations, given the formulae and the data

CHAPTER NINE

THE GREEN WORLD

the present day
atmospheric pressure: 1 bar

argon
0.1%

nitrogen
1.9%

oxygen
trace

nitrogen 78%

oxygen
21%

carbon
dioxide
0.03%

argon
1.0%

carbon dioxide 98%

4 billion years ago
atmospheric pressure: 60 bars

The beginning

Without plants, you could not exist. You would never have come into being. The land would be as empty and bare as the surface of the Moon — no animals or humans, no grass, no flowers or trees. This is what the Earth was like when life on Earth began.

▲
A radar picture of the surface of Venus. This planet is supposed to be the one most like Earth, but just look at the surface. Why is it so different from Earth?

Three and a half million years ago, the air on Earth was mostly carbon dioxide with a little bit of nitrogen. The only living creatures to be found were in the oceans and seas. These were simple microbes, made of only one cell. Some were like the bacteria that are everywhere on Earth today. But others were quite revolutionary in their lifestyles. The very first life on Earth was plant life. Floating in the waters of the planet, these single-celled green microbes could use sunlight to make sugars and then use the sugar as a source of energy. As a waste product, they released oxygen into the atmosphere. These microbes were very successful organisms. As time passed, they became larger and spread widely through the seas.

Life developed very slowly, and it was over three thousand million years later before this microbial life colonised the land as simple plants. They enriched the atmosphere with a waste product — oxygen. Billions of years of rain washed the carbon dioxide out of the air. Soon, those active organisms that were greedy for oxygen could follow. *Animals* could now live on the land. Life as we know it had really begun.

◀
Cocoa bushes growing underneath coconut palms.

A foxglove. The heart drug, Digitoxin, is still made from this plant.

Who needs plants?

Everybody does! Plants are the basis of all life on this planet. Without plants, we could not survive. Think of the food and drink that you have consumed today. It will have come from plants, either directly or indirectly: cereals from wheat, corn or rice; milk from cows that have grazed on grass; orange juice, tea and coffee; sugar from sugar beet or cane; eggs from hens fed on corn. The list is endless.

As well as eating, you also need to breathe. All animals take in oxygen from respiration — to release the energy they need to stay alive. Green plants release oxygen into the air as a by-product of their own feeding process. Without this oxygen, large animals like ourselves could never have evolved in the first place. We depend on oxygen every moment of our lives.

Plants also release water vapour into the atmosphere by a process called *transpiration*. A large forest will release millions of tonnes of water into the air every year. This water will later fall as rain, soaking into the soil, allowing crops to grow.

Plants are important in our lives in other ways. Look at the pictures on this page, can you think of other examples?

The way plants feed: photosynthesis

Plants are much more self sufficient than animals. They can make their own food by using sunlight and simple raw materials from their surroundings.

Plants like living chemical factories, producing food in the form of sugars and starch. This is why green plants are often called producers. All animal life on Earth relies on this ability of plants to manufacture food. You cannot really get more important than that!

But why are green plants green in the first place? You can probably find the answer by looking carefully at the cross section of the leaf in the diagram.

▼
A cross section through a typical leaf.

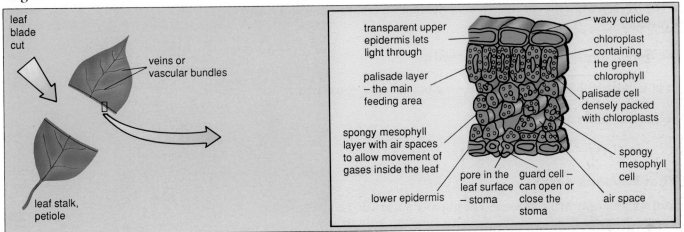

leaf blade cut

veins or vascular bundles

leaf stalk, petiole

transparent upper epidermis lets light through

palisade layer – the main feeding area

spongy mesophyll layer with air spaces to allow movement of gases inside the leaf

lower epidermis

pore in the leaf surface – stoma

guard cell – can open or close the stoma

waxy cuticle

chloroplast containing the green chlorophyll

palisade cell densely packed with chloroplasts

spongy mesophyll cell

air space

Most food production in plants takes place inside the cells of the *leaf*. Many of these cells contain small bodies called *chloroplasts*. Inside these tiny structures lies the key to the feeding process – a green chemical called *chlorophyll*. This is what gives plants their green colour. But more importantly, the large and complicated chlorophyll molecules allow the plant to absorb light energy from the Sun to make food.

The name of this essential process performed by plants is *photosynthesis*. 'Photo' because light is involved, and 'synthesis' meaning to make or assemble something.

What type of food is made by photosynthesis?

First, the plant makes a type of sugar called glucose. Glucose has the chemical formula $C_6H_{12}O_6$. In other words, it contains three elements: carbon, hydrogen and oxygen. A plant will therefore require raw materials containing these three elements if it is to manufacture glucose.

Carbon and oxygen come from carbon dioxide in the air. Carbon dioxide has the formula CO_2. Plant leaves have small holes called *stomata* in their surface to let carbon dioxide gas enter and reach the chloroplasts. Oxygen also leaves the plant this way.

Hydrogen comes from water. Water has the formula H_2O. The plant obtains water from the soil through its roots. Water enters the plant's *roots* by *osmosis*. This is the process by which water molecules move from an area of low solute concentration to an area of high solute concentration. The water molecules try to *dilute* the solute. You should

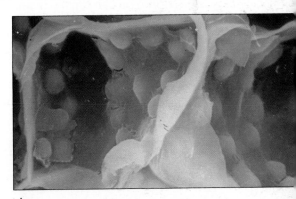

▲
You are looking at a plant cell that has been cut open. The lumps inside are the chloroplasts.

have learned about this last year. The water is carried up the stem and into the leaves through the veins or vascular bundles of the plant.

You can find out more about stomata in leaves and the transport system in plants (the *vascular system*) by looking in the 'Reference section'.

What happens in photosynthesis?

Photosynthesis consists of a very complicated series of chemical reactions. But the main stages or steps of the process are fairly easy to understand.

- Chlorophyll absorbs sunlight energy and uses it to split water into hydrogen and oxygen.
- The hydrogen is combined with carbon dioxide to form sugar (glucose).
- The oxygen from the splitting of water escapes from the plant as a waste product.

The complete process can be summarised as:

$$\text{carbon dioxide} + \text{water} \xrightarrow{\text{light energy}} \text{glucose sugar} + \text{oxygen}.$$

Or as a chemical equation:

$$6CO_2 + 6H_2O \xrightarrow{\text{light energy}} C_6H_{12}O_6 + 6O_2.$$

What happens next?

Plants do not only make glucose. The glucose sugar can be changed into other substances needed by the plant for survival, growth and reproduction. You can see the main substances that the plant produces in the diagram.

Note that plants do not store glucose. The glucose is changed into other sugars (*carbohydrates*) such as sucrose or starch. Starch is a large molecule (a polymer) made of many glucose sugar units joined together in a long chain. Carbohydrates are stored in parts of the plant such as the leaves, seeds and roots. The glucose may also be converted into oils for storage in seeds.

▼
How plants use glucose.

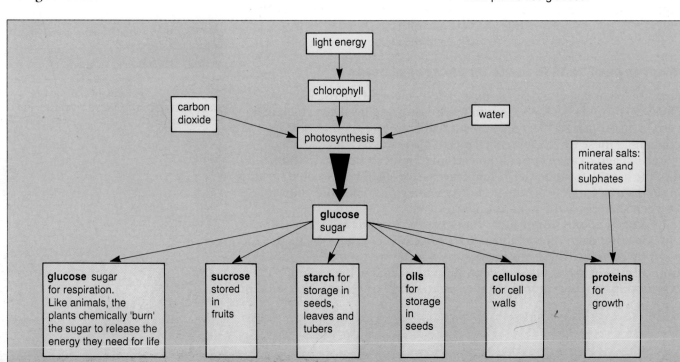

Plants in water

All land plants are thought to have evolved from simple green algae that once lived in the early oceans and seas of the Earth. These green algae were probably quite similar to the microscopic algae that exist today.

Seas, rivers and lakes still contain many different types of plant. Water plants tend to be smaller than land plants – they do not need to have strong stems or trunks because the water supports their weight. Green plants still need the energy from sunlight to feed. This means that they cannot survive in deep water because the sunlight does not penetrate that far. The carbon dioxide needed for photosynthesis is absorbed directly from the water. The plants also get vital mineral salts from the water, washed out from the land by rivers and rain.

Animals that live in water are just as dependent on plants as those that live on the land. There must be plenty of oxygen dissolved in the water that plants can use for respiration. This vital oxygen is released by the green water plants as a waste product from photosynthesis. The growing plants also provide shelter and food for fish and other forms of aquatic life.

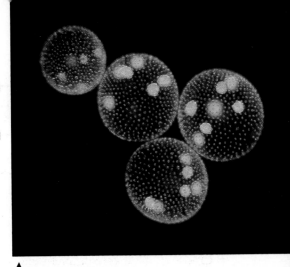

▲
A single-celled alga. The first plants were probably quite like this.

Respiration and photosynthesis

All living things *respire*. They take in oxygen and use it to chemically 'burn' food to release the energy they need for life. Carbon dioxide is given off as the waste product of respiration.

Green plants *feed* by photosynthesis. They take in carbon dioxide and give out oxygen in the light. In the daytime, when light is present, green plants will be feeding through photosynthesis *and* respiring.

The plant in the light takes in more carbon dioxide from photosynthesis than it gives out from respiration. It releases more oxygen from photosynthesis than it takes in for respiration.

In the dark, the plant cannot feed by photosynthesis because there is no light available to drive the reactions of photosynthesis. So, photosynthesis stops at night and the plant will only be respiring.

The relationship between photosynthesis and respiration can be seen in the diagram. This shows underwater plants. The processes are the same for *all* plants.

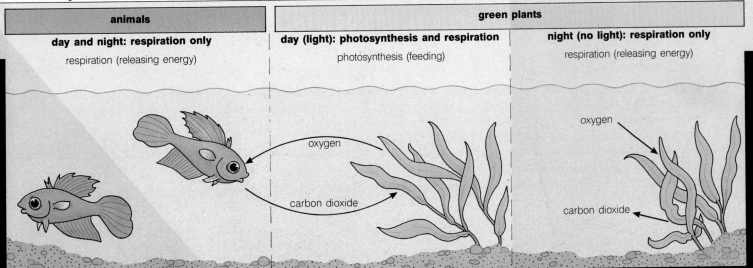

animals	green plants	
day and night: respiration only	**day (light): photosynthesis and respiration**	**night (no light): respiration only**
respiration (releasing energy)	photosynthesis (feeding)	respiration (releasing energy)

Flowers, fruits and seeds

The first small flowers of spring tell us that winter has passed. The beauty and fragrance of flowers is enjoyed by people everywhere. We use them to decorate ceremonies and celebrations all over the world. But why do plants go to so much trouble and effort to produce such amazing flowers?

The *flowering* is part of the survival of the plant. The flower's job is to produce fruits containing seeds. From the seeds, a new generation of plants will grow.

▼
Fruits. These all contain seeds. The seeds of the strawberry are on the *outside* of the plant.

Inside a flower

The drawing shows the male and female structures in a typical flower. You may already have taken a flower apart to find the parts that are used for reproduction.

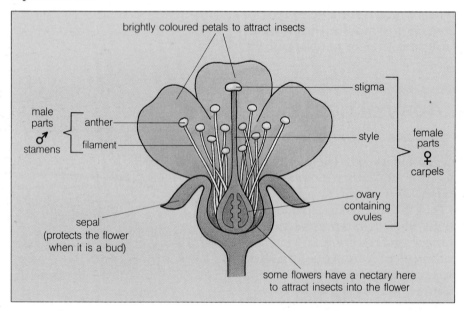

brightly coloured petals to attract insects

stigma

male parts ♂ stamens
— anther
— filament

style

female parts ♀ carpels

ovary containing ovules

sepal (protects the flower when it is a bud)

some flowers have a nectary here to attract insects into the flower

Sexual reproduction in plants — getting together

In any form of sexual reproduction, the male and female sex cells must join together for a new living organism to be produced. How does the flowering plant manage this?

The first stage is *pollination*. This is the transfer of pollen grains containing the male sex cells from the male part of the flower to the female part.

Pollination can be achieved in several different ways.

- Self-pollination. Here, the pollen grains are transferred from the anther to the stigma of the *same* flower.
- Cross-pollination. The pollen grains are transferred from the anther of one flower to the stigma of another flower of the same species.

Plants often go to great lengths to prevent self pollination. Their male and female parts are positioned so that the pollen can only be placed on to the stigma of another plant.

By making sure that *two* parent plants contribute to making the new plant, *variation* is introduced. Why do you think this is useful?

How does it happen?

Some flowers are pollinated by insects. Bees, butterflies and beetles are all used to carry the pollen from one flower to another. All insect-pollinated flowers:
- have brightly coloured petals to attract the insects;
- often have a nectary containing sweet, sugary nectar. The scent of this nectar also helps to attract insects.
- have the male and female parts of the flower *inside* where the insects will brush against them;
- produce large pollen grains, often with hooks or hairs so that they stick to the body of an insect.
- produce quite small amounts of pollen as this is a fairly reliable method of pollination. Compare this with the numbers of eggs that the fish or frog has to produce and the number of eggs that a mammal produces.

Insects are attracted to the plants by the bright petals, and by the scent of nectar. They land on the flower and become dusted with pollen. When the bee flies to another flower, some of this pollen will be brushed from the body of the bee on to the stigma of the second flower.

Wind-pollinated flowers

These use the wind rather than insects to transfer the pollen from flower to flower. All wind-pollinated flowers:

- have small dull petals with no bright colours;
- have no nectary or scent;
- have the male and female parts hanging outside the flower, exposed to the wind;
- produce tiny pollen grains that are smooth or 'winged' to catch the wind;
- produce huge amounts of pollen because most of the pollen is lost.

The anthers hang outside the flower and the pollen they produce is then blown away by any wind. Some of this pollen may then be caught by the 'feathery' stigmas hanging outside another flower.

Pollination is only the first stage in the reproduction of the flowering plant. The female sex cells lie deep inside the ovary of the flower. They must be fertilised by the male sex cells, which have landed on the stigma at the top of the flower – deposited there by wind or insects.

Each of the pollen grains starts to form a tube – the *pollen tube*. This grows from the stigma, down through the style, and into the ovary. It then enters one of the ovules through a tiny hole called the *micropyle*. The male sex cell can then pass down the tube and into the ovule. Each ovule must receive its own pollen tube and male sex cell. The male and female sex cells then fuse together inside the ovule. This second stage of reproduction is called *fertilisation*.

Making fruits and seeds

Now the female parts of the plant start to work. The ovules are stored in the ovary. This now swells and enlarges rapidly. It develops into a *fruit*. This may be a pod, like a pea or a bean; a fleshy fruit like an apple or a

▼
The hooks on these pollen grains ensure that they become attached to insects and are carried away.

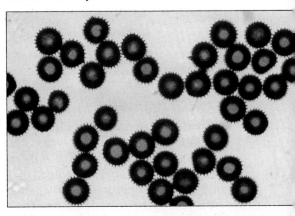

▲
As the bee crawls over the anthers, it becomes covered in pollen, which it collects on one of its back legs.

▲
The anthers on this grass are hanging well outside the plant so that the wind can catch the pollen and carry it away.

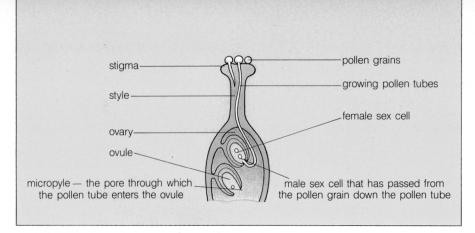

stigma

style

ovary

ovule

micropyle — the pore through which the pollen tube enters the ovule

pollen grains

growing pollen tubes

female sex cell

male sex cell that has passed from the pollen grain down the pollen tube

◄
A single pollen tube grows from each grain down into the ovary of the flower. The pollen grain flows down this tube to fertilise the female sex cell.

plum, or a capsule like those made by poppies and snapdragons. It can also take some other form, depending on the type of plant.

Inside the ovary, the ovules develop into the individual *seeds*. Eventually, when the fruit is ripe, these seeds will be scattered and spread, unless people or animals get to them first!

People and animals have been making use of the stored food in fruits and seeds for millions of years. Today, it may be the sweet, white flesh of an apple, or the stored starch in the rice grains, or wheat grains that are ground into flour to make bread. Fruit and seeds are just about the most basic and important food sources on Earth.

Fruit and seed dispersal

If all the seeds of a plant fell to the ground in the same place, the seedlings growing from them would soon become overcrowded. These new plants would have to compete for light, water and mineral salts from the soil. Most plants try to spread or scatter their seeds to new places over as wide an area as possible. This is *seed dispersal*. The fruits of many plants are designed to help this.

Different fruits use different methods of dispersal. You can see examples of these in the photographs. There are three main ways:

- explosive dispersal;
- wind dispersal;
- animal dispersal.

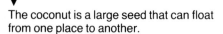
▼
The coconut is a large seed that can float from one place to another.

▲
This is a type of mushroom. A drop of water falling on to it has sent millions of spores exploding into the air.

▲
As the wind shakes the catkins, pollen grains are dispersed.

▲
Plants that rely on animals to disperse their seeds often have brightly coloured fruits to attract the animals to eat them. The seeds will pass through the bird and fall with its droppings.

Once the seeds are scattered and find a suitable place to grow, the life-cycle of the plant can start all over again. The illustration shows the complete life-cycle of the pea plant.

136

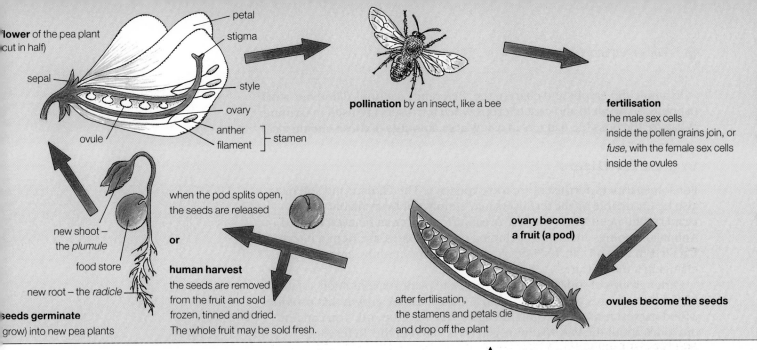

flower of the pea plant (cut in half)

petal
stigma
style
ovary
anther ⎤ stamen
filament ⎦
ovule
sepal

pollination by an insect, like a bee

fertilisation
the male sex cells
inside the pollen grains join, or
fuse, with the female sex cells
inside the ovules

when the pod splits open,
the seeds are released

or

human harvest
the seeds are removed
from the fruit and sold
frozen, tinned and dried.
The whole fruit may be sold fresh.

new shoot –
the *plumule*

food store

new root – the *radicle*

seeds germinate
(grow) into new pea plants

after fertilisation,
the stamens and petals die
and drop off the plant

**ovary becomes
a fruit (a pod)**

ovules become the seeds

▲
The life cycle of a pea plant.

Asexual reproduction

Sexual reproduction means that a new plant is formed from two parent plants. The new plant inherits features from both parents. If there is a combination of 'good' features, the plant can be very successful.

But some plants do not reproduce sexually. They can produce offspring through *asexual reproduction*. This can be an advantage if, for example, it might be difficult to get pollen from one plant to another – where the plants grow far apart or where there are no ways to pollinate the plants.

Taking a plant cutting is a form of asexual reproduction.

Farming methods have become so well organised that vast surpluses of food are produced in some parts of the world. However, there are food shortages in other parts. The surpluses are often referred to as 'mountains' and 'lakes' because they are so large. But many farmers still struggle against drought or poor soil and, like the earliest farmers, may have to face famine and death if their efforts are not able to produce enough food for themselves and their animals.

▼
One disadvantage for people settling in one place is that if the crops fail, you have a famine. This happened in Ireland in the 1840s when the potato crop failed.

Making plants grow better

Every man, woman and child in Great Britain is fed from the output from about 0.6 hectare of land (1.5 acres) per person. Farmers are constantly trying to increase the *yield* of their crop plants. This is the amount of food that can be grown in a certain area of land. One way of doing this is to use *artificial fertilisers*. There is more about this in the *Managing the Earth* chapter in book 2.

Plants need small amounts of chemicals called minerals to grow properly. These minerals are not food for the plant. They are more like the vitamins that we need in our own diets to stay healthy. Fertilisers supply extra amounts of these minerals.

137

Examine the graphs and chart in the 'Reference section'. (Find out what happens to the yield and cost of crops when fertilisers are used in farming. What are the possible dangers in using large amounts of these chemicals?)

Organic fertilisers

For some farmers, fertilisers are too expensive. The climate and soil may also be unsuitable or the fertilisers may simply not be available to the farmers who need them. Natural, organic, fertiliser can be used instead. Animal droppings and urine, including human wastes, are rich in nitrates. Bacteria in the soil can 'fix' nitrogen by taking it out of the air and changing it into nitrates.

Other groups of soil bacteria convert dead plant remains such as fallen leaves into nitrates. Some crops such as beans, can be grown that provide a food harvest *and* actually put nitrogen back into the soil. You can find out more about the way that nitrogen is recycled in the 'Reference section' (page 223).

Soils rich in decayed plant materials (*humus*) and minerals are fertile and tend to be better at retaining moisture from rainfall. They are also much less liable to erosion.

We must all be aware of how natural and artificial fertilisers can be used sensibly and that simple things like water conservation could be the key for more people all over the world to be able to grow enough food.

Horticulture – growing under glass

Many plants, from cucumbers to geraniums, are now grown commercially in large greenhouses. The horticulturalist must control the conditions inside the greenhouse so that the growing plants are provided with everything they need for photosynthesis and for vigorous, healthy growth.

The greenhouse

Greenhouses made of clear glass or plastic are designed to provide the best possible environment for plant growth. They are positioned so that the plants get the maximum amount of sunlight to use in photosynthesis. They also trap some of the sun's heat. Like all chemical reactions, photosynthesis proceeds more rapidly when it is warmer.

Water, containing the correct amounts of mineral salts, is piped directly to the plants.

The plants also require carbon dioxide for the feeding process. Normal air contains only about 0.04% carbon dioxide. This is why many glasshouses have methane burners – as well as increasing the temperature, the burners enrich the air inside the greenhouse with carbon dioxide. A small increase in the amount of the gas present can have a dramatic effect on the growth of the plants. Of course, the increased yield achieved must be large enough to justify the cost of installing the burners and the fuel needed to run them.

▲
Lettuces in this market garden are growing in a controlled environment. The temperature, composition of the air and the minerals in the water are all computer controlled.

New plants from old

Greengrocer stalls and supermarket shelves are stocked with a huge variety of plant foods. Hardly any of these foods come from totally 'natural' plants that you might find growing in the wild. They are the results of hundreds of years of careful plant breeding to obtain exactly the sort of crops that humans need.

Selective breeding, or artificial selection

Growers choose or *select* those plants with the qualities they require. allowing only these plants to breed and make seeds. By careful cross-breeding of the offspring of such plants, the good qualities of two different types can be combined together to produce a new and more useful variety.

Selective breeding of plants must be carried out over many generations if it is to succeed in producing improved crop plants. This is an extremely time-consuming and expensive business. Exciting new developments in *plant-cloning* techniques may change all this in the very near future.

What sort of plants do we want?

Plant scientists all over the world are trying to breed plants with the following advantages:

● healthier root systems;
● bigger and better-tasting fruits and seeds;
● higher yield with less added fertiliser;
● more resistance to disease;
● more hardiness (able to withstand cold or dry conditions).

Doing all this through cross-breeding takes many years. But new processes that use *genetic engineering* to change the very molecules that plants are made of will speed this up a great deal.

▲
Obviously, they are all tomatoes, but what a difference!

Plant cloning – step by step

▼
Clones of a plant being grown in tissue culture.

Take a plant. Make sure it is a 'good' example of its kind – free from disease and growing well.

Cut out a small piece of the plant containing a few growing and dividing cells. (Sometimes just a single cell will do.) Give the cells the conditions they need to grow and reproduce in a test tube. In a short time, many new cells will be produced. Separate them, and allow each one to grow into a complete new plant.

You would then have hundreds, even thousands, of identical copies, or *clones*, of your original plant. They will all be as healthy and vigorous as their common 'parent'. Plant them out, sit back, and look forward to a bumper harvest!

Cloning sounds a quick and convenient way of producing good plant stocks. In practice it is not so easy. Just making sure the plant cells are kept sterile (completely clean) is extremely difficult and costly. And what happens if a bacterial or fungal disease has attacked the 'parent' plant? The clones are all the same. They will all become infected and the entire crop could be wiped out in days.

But cloning could be one weapon against starvation in future years. At present rates, the world human population is doubling every twenty-five years. There could be six thousand million people on Earth by the year 2000. They will all be hungry for food. Without applying the most modern science to breeding and growing crops, it will be impossible to feed everyone in the World.

Activities

1 Look very carefully at the place where you live. Go into every room and look around the outside of the building itself. Also look at the area that the building stands in. Make a list of all the ways that plants have been used to create and improve your home. Organise your list into a chart giving different headings for the different ways in which plants are useful in your life. You should use your own headings for the chart, but these are a few that might start you off: 'Plants used for food'; 'Plants used for building'; 'Plants used for decoration', etc.

2 Make your own apparatus to carefully observe how seeds grow, or germinate, from seeds. You could make sketches or even take photographs to show the different stages of seed germination. Use different kinds of seeds. Design your investigation to answer as many of the following questions as possible.
(a) Do all seeds germinate in the same way?
(b) Does it matter if the seed is planted 'upside down'?
(c) Do seeds germinate more quickly if they are soaked in water overnight?
(d) Does temperature change the rate at which seeds germinate?

3 Make a list of the different fertilisers that you can buy from a garden centre. Summarise the following information in a table.

• What are the exact components of fertilisers?
• How do they work?
• What plants are they used for?
• Do they contain any other types of chemical?
• What is the cost of using them according to the instructions?
• When are they to be used?

Design a pamphlet or poster to show the benefits or dangers of using fertilisers.

4 Find out what *phototropism* and *etiolation* mean. Use bean, mustard or cress seedlings to investigate these effects.

Questions

1 A plant is like a factory: it takes in raw materials and uses energy to make a product. Copy the flow chart and label it with what goes in and what comes out.

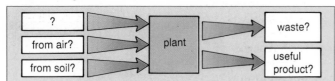

2 Using your knowledge of photosynthesis, predict how well a plant would feed and grow if it was placed under the following conditions.
(a) The plant is placed in a dimly lit room.
(b) The plant is growing in a sandy soil that could retain very little rain water.
(c) The plant is placed in a sealed jar containing air from which all of the carbon dioxide has been removed.
(d) The plant is placed inside an unheated greenhouse during a very cold winter.

3 An experiment was done on a water plant to find out how much oxygen it produced in different conditions. The results are shown in the chart.
(a) Draw a graph of oxygen produced against light value.
(b) Explain each section of your graph fully.

Oxygen produced (cm³ per hour)	Light value (lux)
0	0
2.0	2000
4.0	4000
6.0	6000
8.0	9000
8.5	10000
8.5	12000

4 (a) Explain fully why plants need (i) chlorophyll, (ii) pores, or stomata, and (iii) veins or vascular bundles.
(b) (i) How does the shape of a leaf help the plant to feed by photosynthesis? (ii) Why is the top layer of cells in a leaf (the upper epidermis) transparent? See the diagram on page 220.
(c) (i) From where does a water plant like pond weed get the carbon dioxide that it needs for photosynthesis? (ii) How does photosynthesis help the fish and other animals living in the pond?

5 Plan an investigation that you could do to find out if plants grow better if there is more carbon dioxide in the air. Your experiment must be a fair test.

6 Say what plants have to do with the following:
(a) how much oxygen there is in the atmosphere;
(b) the greenhouse effect.

Checklist

These are the facts and ideas that you should have learned by studying this unit.

To succeed at Basic Level you should:

- be able to label the main parts of a plant
- know what plants need to keep alive (water, light, carbon dioxide, small amounts of minerals from the soil)
- know that we give extra minerals to farm plants (fertilisers) but that this might cause pollution
- know about the life cycle of a flowering plant

To succeed at Foundation Level you should:

- be able to name the major organs of a flowering plant, and say what they do (leaves, stem, roots, flower)
- know that plants use sunlight to make their own food, and that this happens in the green parts of the plant
- know that plants take up nitrates and phosphates from the soil
- be able to argue about the good and bad effects of using fertilisers in agriculture
- be able to describe the way in which a flowering plant reproduces (pollination, fertilisation, seeds and fruits, seed dispersal)
- know how to take a cutting of a plant

To succeed at Merit Level you should:

- know how vascular tissues (xylem and phloem) are arranged
- know what the stomata in leaves do
- understand transpiration and the role of osmosis in it
- know that photosynthesis needs light energy, water and carbon dioxide, and that it produces sugars and starches, with oxygen as a byproduct

To succeed at Merit Level you should:

- know that the products of photosynthesis can be combined with minerals from the soil to make other materials that the plant needs
- know that plants play a large role in the recycling of natural materials, and that human activity can affect this (e.g. the recycling of carbon dioxide is affected by the destruction of forests)
- know that sexual reproduction produces variety in plants
- know that taking cuttings is a form of asexual reproduction so that the offspring is a 'clone', and that runners are a natural cloning process

To succeed at Special Level you should:

- know the arrangement of cells in a leaf and understand the reasons for it
- know how the main organ systems of a plant are able to maintain its internal environment (temperature, gases in the leaf, turgor)
- understand what happens in osmosis, and how minerals are taken into the root
- be able to analyse and understand experimental data about how environmental factors and material supply affect the life processes of a plant
- know the details of the carbon cycle, and the ways it is affected by human action
- know how plants prevent self pollination and the differences between insect and wind pollination
- be able to describe and evaluate a range of cloning methods for plants and their uses in agriculture

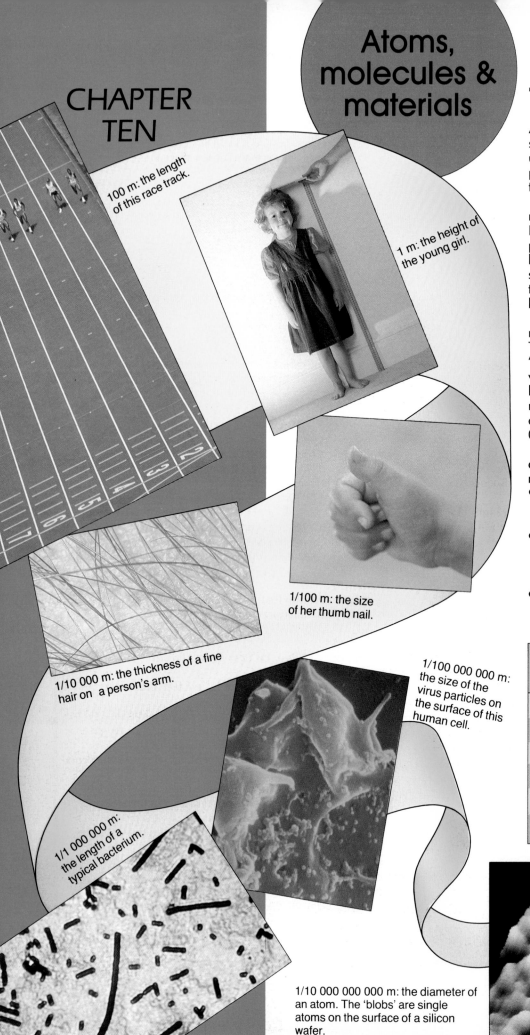

CHAPTER TEN

Atoms, molecules & materials

100 m: the length of this race track.

1 m: the height of the young girl.

1/100 m: the size of her thumb nail.

1/10 000 m: the thickness of a fine hair on a person's arm.

1/100 000 000 m: the size of the virus particles on the surface of this human cell.

1/1 000 000 m: the length of a typical bacterium.

The size of atoms

Atoms are the smallest particles of any substance. The pictures may help you to understand how tiny an atom is. Each picture shows something one hundred times smaller than the picture above it.

High-powered light microscopes can magnify bacteria so they may be seen. Electron microscopes allow us to see pictures of viruses. Atoms, the building blocks that make up everything, are too small even for the most powerful electron microscope. But they can be seen by using special microscopes.

The size or diameter of an atom is measured in fractions of a nanometre. The table gives the sizes of some atoms. 'Nano' comes from an ancient Greek word, it means nine. The decimal point has to move nine places when 1 nanometre is written as the decimal of a metre: 1.0 nanometre (nm) = 0.000 000 001 metre.

You can get a feel for the size of an atom by comparing the following statements.

- One million atoms laid side by side would make a row about the same length as the thickness of a hair.
- One million 15-year-old children laid head to toe would stretch from Land's End in Cornwall to John O'Groats in the north of Scotland.
- One thousand million hydrogen atoms laid side by side will be 7 cm long.

Size of atoms in nanometres (symbol nm)	
Carbon	0.15
Copper	0.27
Hydrogen	0.07
Iron	0.23
Oxygen	0.13
Potassium	0.41

1/10 000 000 000 m: the diameter of an atom. The 'blobs' are single atoms on the surface of a silicon wafer.

States of matter and the kinetic theory

There are three states of matter: gases, liquids and solids. Details of their properties are summarised in the table.

Solids	*Liquids*	*Gases*
• have a fixed shape • do not change shape unless hit or squeezed • have a fixed volume • will support the weight of something • have both a melting point and a boiling point that are above room temperature, 20 °C	• have no shape • flow along pipes • pour from one container into another • have a flat, horizontal surface on top • have a fixed volume • cannot be squeezed into a smaller volume • mix with some other liquids but not with all liquids • have a melting point below room temperature	• have no shape • fill any container they are put in • flow along pipes • always mix together • have no fixed volume • can be squeezed into a smaller volume • have both a melting point and a boiling point below room temperature, 20 °C

The properties of solids, liquids and gases can be explained by using the idea that everything is made from tiny particles. These particles are either:

* *atoms*,
* small groups of atoms, called *molecules*, or,
* charged atoms or groups of atoms, called *ions*.

Whether the particles are atoms, molecules or ions depends on the particular structure and bonding in the substance. There is more about ions and bonding in Chapter Five, *Chemical patterns*.

The *kinetic theory* explains the properties of substances in terms of the movement of these tiny particles. It is called a theory because it cannot be proved. No one can actually see the atoms, molecules or ions; they are far too small. However, the explanation that the kinetic theory gives fits the facts as we know them. It provides a simple understanding of what is happening when, for example, solids melt and liquids boil. It is called the kinetic theory because the word kinetic comes from a Greek word which means moving.

Why are solids solid?

Solids are made from particles that are closely packed together in a regular arrangement. The particles do not move around but stay in the same position. At room temperature they shake slightly or vibrate. As the solid is heated so the particles shake more and more until the structure collapses and the solid melts. The particles have too much movement energy (kinetic energy) for the bonds to hold them.

▼
Solids have particles that are close packed and regular.

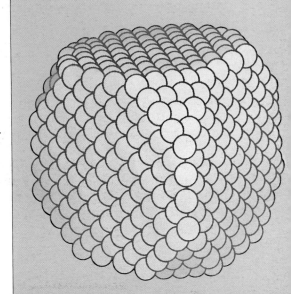

The particles in a solid are held together by chemical bonds. The stronger the bonding between the particles the more energy is needed to melt the structure. This makes the melting point high, over 1000 °C in strongly bonded solids such as ionic compounds.

Some solids can be squeezed into different shapes. This usually means making the particles slide over each other. Metals are a good example of this; they can be drawn into wires, beaten into sheets and bent into amazing shapes.

Other solids, like ionic crystals, shatter into tiny fragments if they are hit. In these solids the bonds that hold the particles together are attractions between positive ions and negative ions. If the positive particle is moved, instead of it being next to a negative ion it is next to another positive ion. These two ions repel each other and force the particles apart.

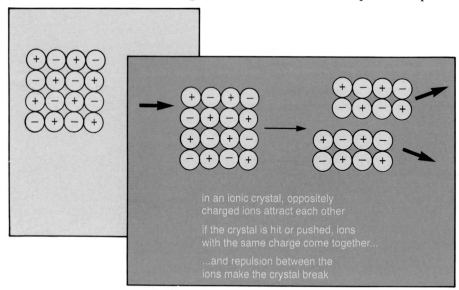

in an ionic crystal, oppositely charged ions attract each other

if the crystal is hit or pushed, ions with the same charge come together...

...and repulsion between the ions make the crystal break

◄
This salt crystal (far left) has split along a line between the ions. A general ionic structure is shown below.

Why are liquids liquid?

The particles in liquids are as close together as they are in solids. But they are not arranged neatly, in an orderly way. The particles are free to move and roll over each other. This means that a liquid can flow. Liquids take the shape of the container that they are kept in.

There is some attraction, or *intermolecular forces*, between particles in a liquid but these are nowhere as strong as in a solid. Some liquids have particles that are more strongly bonded together than other liquids. The stronger the bonding is between the particles, the higher the boiling point.

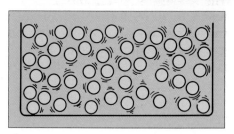

▲
How the particles are arranged in a liquid. The particles are close together and moving about.

Boiling point

When you heat a liquid you give the particles more energy, called *internal energy*. As the temperature increases so the particles roll about more rapidly. Now gaps between the particles open up because they are moving around more. This creates some empty space. Faster molecules break away and can move into these spaces. At the boiling point they form bubbles of gas. These rise to the surface – the liquid is boiling.

Even below the boiling point some molecules are moving fast enough to break away from the others. But they can only escape at the surface of the liquid. This is what is happening when liquids *evaporate*.

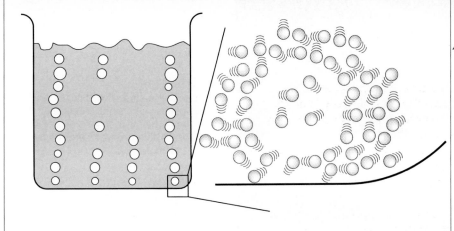

◄
Boiling. Bubbles of vapour are formed by
the faster molecules deep inside the liquid.

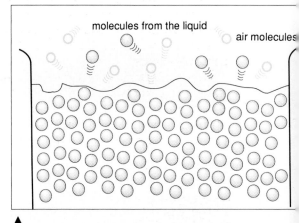

▲
Evaporating. Faster molecules break away
at the surface and escape into the air.

Why are gases gases?

The particles in a gas are widely spaced apart. The particles are also
moving very fast; whizzing around all over the place at the speed of a rifle
bullet. They are in rapid, random motion. The gaps between the particles
are very large compared to the size of a gas particle. Most of the gas is, in
fact, empty space. This explains why a litre of water becomes 1700 litres
of steam when it boils. All this extra volume is actually empty space,
through which the molecules of steam hurtle about at speeds of over 300
metres per second.

   The gas particles are continually colliding with each other and
bouncing off the walls of any container they are in. There are no forces
between the particles because they are only in contact with each other for
a tiny moment as they bounce off each other.

   If you increase the temperature of the gas, the particles go even faster.
This makes the particles hit the walls of the container even harder. This is
why the pressure of a gas increases when the temperature goes up.

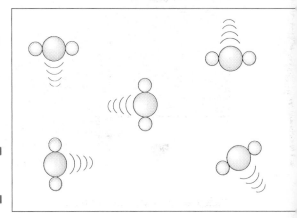

▲
Steam is a gas. The water molecules are
far apart and move very fast.

The gas laws

The volume of a fixed amount of gas can be altered by changing either the
temperature or the pressure on the gas. If the temperature is increased,
the gas particles go faster and spread out more. This makes the volume of
gas increase. The gas expands. If the pressure on the gas is increased the
gas particles are squeezed closer together and the volume decreases. The
gas laws were put forward in the 18th century.

Boyle's Law

For a fixed mass of gas at constant temperature the volume is inversely
proportional to the pressure.

$$V \propto \frac{1}{P}$$

Charles' Law

For a fixed mass of gas at constant pressure the volume is proportional to
the absolute temperature of the gas.

$$V \propto T$$

We can, of course, show both of these laws as graphs.

►
The gas laws as graphs. The bigger the
pressure, the smaller the volume. The
second graph shows that gases become
liquids at very low temperatures.

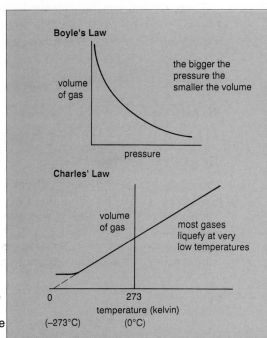

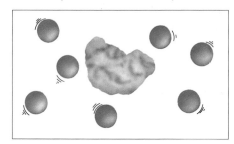

A smoke cell to study Brownian motion. The smoke is in the small chamber at the front. Under the microscope you can see the particles being buffeted around by invisible air molecules.

Smoke is made of solid particles. They stay in the air because of Brownian motion. Fast–moving gas particles continually bombard the smoke particles.

Evidence for the kinetic theory

You cannot see molecules with an ordinary light microscope. Not even the special very high-powered electron microscopes can show atoms or molecules moving. But you can see the effects caused by invisible moving molecules in what is called *Brownian motion*.

This was first noticed by a Scots botanist, Robert Brown, in 1827. He was looking at pollen in water, using a very powerful microscope. Small grains from the pollen were *moving* about in the water. To him, it looked as if they were swimming about, like small creatures that you can find in pond water. But he decided that they were not swimmers – the only explanation was they were being pushed about by something even smaller than themselves.

Later experiments used tiny drops of oil and smoke particles that were obviously not alive. The particles that pushed them about could only be the water molecules, dashing about at high speed and knocking into the oil droplets. All this was very likely, but it was not until 1905 that a physicist actually did the mathematics needed to explain the Brownian motion fully. This was the first definite proof of the existence of water molecules moving according to the rules of the kinetic theory. The physicist was a young man called Albert Einstein.

Diffusion

Brownian motion gives good evidence to support the kinetic theory. The way smells spread out through a room is another piece of evidence. It does not take long for the scent from a strong perfume to be noticed. The reason for this is that perfume molecules are being knocked all over the place by the gas molecules in the room. Eventually they reach your nose and you smell the perfume. This process is known as *diffusion*. You can see the effects of diffusion nearly every day.

A close look at useful materials

Detergent *diffusing* into the water around it.

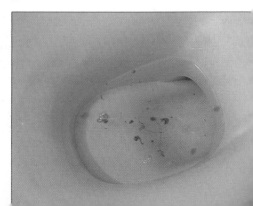

Classifying materials

There are a number of ways different substances or materials may be grouped together. For example, a material can be classed as solid, liquid or gas, depending on its physical appearance at room temperature. It is easy to tell which is which when you can see them. There is a classification key in the Activities Pack that shows how to do this when all you have is some data in a table.

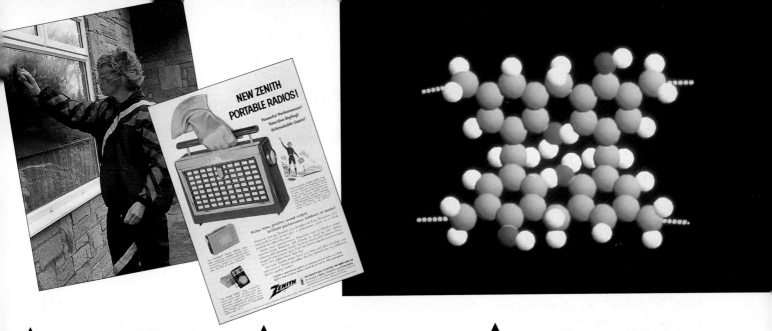

▲ The plastic, Nylon can be made into a fabric by drawing its molecules into long fibres.

▲ One of the first ever plastics was Bakelite. Plastics were immediately successful as strong and light materials.

▲ This is a bakelite *monomer*. Millions of these in cross-linked chains make up the plastic.

Fibres

Most animal and vegetable materials are made of *fibres*. The molecules which make up living material are mostly either tiny water molecules or enormously long chains of molecules. These very long molecules are known as *polymers*. Fibres are formed when bundles of polymers twist together to form long strands. A large number of plastics can be made into fibres, because plastics are made of polymers. Many plastics will easily form fibres if they are warmed and drawn into strands.

In some plastics, however, the polymers are cross-linked to form giant three-dimensional structures. These huge structures are very strong and do not alter when heated.

Glass

Glass is a rather special material. It is, in fact, a supercooled liquid rather than a true solid. This is the reason it softens as it is heated and hardens when it cools. It is also the reason that it can be formed into almost any shape.

What makes materials different?

The properties of a material depend on:

● the forces between the particles which make it;
● the way that the particles are arranged or grouped.

The combination of the way the particles are arranged and the strength of the forces holding them together decides the strength of the internal structure of the material. Some examples of different types of structures are shown in the tables. Many materials have different properties in one direction than in another. Wood is stronger along 'the grain' than across it, for example. Newspaper tears in straight lines in one direction, but rips very roughly in the other. The strength in different directions depends on the way the particles are joined or bonded together.

Forces between particles

Solids and liquids hold together because of forces between the particles they are made of. In a solid, the forces are stronger than in liquids. Liquids can flow. You can walk *through* water – but not *on* it!

Liquids are much the same, although 'thick' oil does not flow as easily as water. This is because there are stronger forces between the oil molecules than between the water molecules.

There are much bigger differences in the properties of solids. Think of the differences between steel and stone, or between cotton and glass. Solids have more complicated structures than liquids.

Forces between atoms

Properties of materials start with the forces between the particles. If the particles are atoms, then we often get what are called *giant structures*. Diamond is a good example of a material with a giant structure. It is made of carbon atoms, linked to each other very strongly by forces acting in all three dimensions. Each atom is bound to six other atoms. Diamond is one of the strongest and hardest materials known. This is due to its interlocking structure.

Graphite is also made of carbon. But it is a very weak and soft material. It is softer than paper – which is why pencils work! The 'lead' in a pencil is made of graphite. This time, the carbon atoms are joined together in a different structure. There are strong forces in two directions but very weak forces at right angles to these two. This means that crystals of graphite slide away from each other very easily, so leaving a mark on the paper.

Comparing graphite and diamond

Graphite	Diamond
black	colourless, clear
conducts electricity	non-conductor
soft, leaves marks on paper	hardest mineral known
used in grease as a lubricant	used in drills and saws to cut rock

The very useful material called silica (silicon dioxide) is also very hard and strong. It has a similar structure to a diamond, but the forces are between atoms of silicon and atoms of oxygen. It makes crystals which we find in many rocks as the mineral quartz. We use silica – in the form of sand – to make concrete and mortar. Silica does not dissolve in water and is usually the toughest part of a rock. This was why there is so much sand at the seaside.

The bonds in diamond, graphite and silica are *covalent bonds* (see Chapter Five, *Chemical patterns*). Some materials are held together by *ionic bonds*. These are also giant structures, and produce crystals. Table salt (sodium chloride) is held together by ionic bonds. Ionic bonds make

▼
For such a small change in structure, we get a huge change in value.

▼
The molecular structures of graphite and diamond.

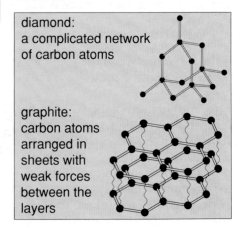

diamond:
a complicated network of carbon atoms

graphite:
carbon atoms arranged in sheets with weak forces between the layers

the material brittle. But they can be very strong. Limestone is a good building material. It is mostly calcium carbonate, which has ionic bonds.

Both ionic and covalent bonds are caused by the attraction between the negative and positive particles in atoms (protons and electrons). The atoms in metals are also held together by electric forces. These forces come from electrons that can slip away easily from metal atoms. They float around inside the metal, behaving almost like a gas of electrons, holding all the atoms together. The free electrons make metals good conductors, both thermally and electrically.

Metals also have a giant structure. Some metals are stronger than others because they have stronger forces between their atoms. But the everyday properties of metals are decided not so much by these inter-atomic forces as by the forces between groups of atoms. This is explained below.

Forces between molecules

Forces between molecules are usually much weaker than the forces between atoms. Substances like wax, iodine, carbon dioxide (dry ice) and water (ice) are held together by molecular forces. These materials are weak and melt at low temperatures. These materials have weak molecular structures.

Molecular solids

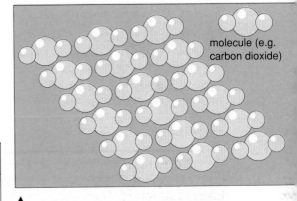

molecule (e.g. carbon dioxide)

▲
In a simple molecular structure, there are strong bonds between the atoms in the molecules but weak forces between the molecules themselves.

Simple structure		Giant structure	
substance	melting point (°C)	substance	melting point (°C)
oxygen	−219	wilframite	1557
carbon dioxide	−56	silica (quartz)	1610
iodine	114	diamond	3550

▼
The surface of a piece of steel. You can see the crystals that make up the metal.

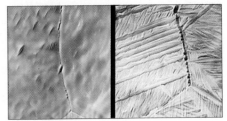

Grains and fibres — forces between groups of atoms

The strength and stiffness of metals are decided in practice by the fact that they are made up of interlocking metal crystals. The photograph shows the inside of a 'tin' can. What you can see are crystals in the thin layer of tin which covers the steel from which the can is made.

Steel is made up of crystals of iron. These crystals are very small. The breaking strength of a metal is decided by how much force is needed to drag these crystals apart. This force is a lot less than the force needed to separate the layers of atoms inside a crystal. Steel is mostly iron, but steel is stronger than iron because the iron crystals in steel are anchored together by small crystals of carbon. This also makes the steel more elastic (flexible).

Single crystals of iron can be grown as thin 'whiskers' a few centimetres long. These are very strong indeed. If they could grow them long enough a steel beam could be replaced by a single crystal a hundredth of its width. Single crystals of carbon are easier to make. They are very light as well as very strong. They are used – as carbon fibres – to reinforce plastics and even steel.

▶
Carbon fibres make very strong materials.

More about fibres

A single fibre is strong because of the bonds between its atoms. Most fibres are made of complex chemicals, for example:

- artificial fibres like nylon, acrylic and terylene;
- plant fibres like wood, cotton and hemp;
- animal fibres like silk, wool, muscle and tendon.

But to be effective there have to be bonds along the fibres joining one fibre to the next. This allows the fibres to join together to make long strands. This means that it is hard to slide the fibres lengthways against each other. Quite short fibres of cotton, wool and silk have to be spun together to make long threads. These can then be woven into cloth.

Strands of threads are strong when pulled lengthways. But they are much weaker when pulled sideways. The fibres can easily come apart, even when they are twisted together. You can see this if you experiment with a piece of string, or a cotton thread.

Wood is made of long fibres that are made of long cellulose molecules. We see these fibres making the strands we call the grain of the wood. The bonds between the strands are weaker than the bonds along them. This makes it easier to split wood along the grain with an axe, compared with cutting across the grain.

Learning from nature – designing new materials

The first modern 'designer materials' were the plastics. Chemists learned how to turn plastics into fibres, to make ropes and cloths. By cross-linking the molecules they could be turned into substitutes for wood and even metals. Plastics are light, strong and cheap. Look around your home. How many things are now made of plastics that used to be made of wood or metal?

Thousands of years ago people were already making artificial materials. They used 'artificial rocks' for building. Hard bricks were made out of soft clay and made crack-resistant by mixing in straw. Limestone was turned into quicklime and used to make forms of cement, mortar and concrete.

Many modern materials are *composites*. This means that they combine two or more substances in the same material. A typical example is glass-reinforced plastic (GRP). Concrete is another, much older, composite material. Both of these materials use a tough material embedded in a weaker or more flexible *matrix*. The tough material (e.g. the glass) gives strength, and helps to stop cracks growing.

Ceramics are materials like porcelain and china – pottery made from clay heated in a kiln. They tend to be brittle – cups do not bounce when you drop them! But modern ceramics have been developed that are strong enough to make aircraft engines. They do not crack easily, and can withstand much higher temperatures than metals can.

▼
A cross section through a concrete beam.

The making of a material: cement

Cement is made in two slightly different ways depending on the raw materials used. The 'dry' method uses limestone and shale. These are quite hard rocks. The 'wet' method uses chalk and clay, both of which are soft and hold a lot of water.

What are the raw materials like?

The materials that are used to make cement show that the way the particles are arranged leads to very different materials.

- *Clay* is made of tiny particles of aluminium silicate, together with a lot of water.
- *Shale* is also tiny particles of aluminium silicate, but they have been squeezed together with no water present.
- *Chalk* is calcium carbonate. It is a soft rock that soaks up water.
- *Limestone* is also calcium carbonate. It is a hard rock that does not hold a lot of water.
- *Gypsum* is calcium sulphate. It is added to cement to slow down the setting reaction.

The process

Mixtures of the crushed raw materials are fed into a rotary kiln. At the other end of the rotary kiln powdered coal and air are blown in and burn

▼
It takes 25 tonnes of coal to make 100 tonnes of cement. The coal is first ground up to make a fine powder. This powder burns with a very hot flame when it is blown into the kiln. In 1987 and 1988 1.4 million tonnes of cement were made per year.

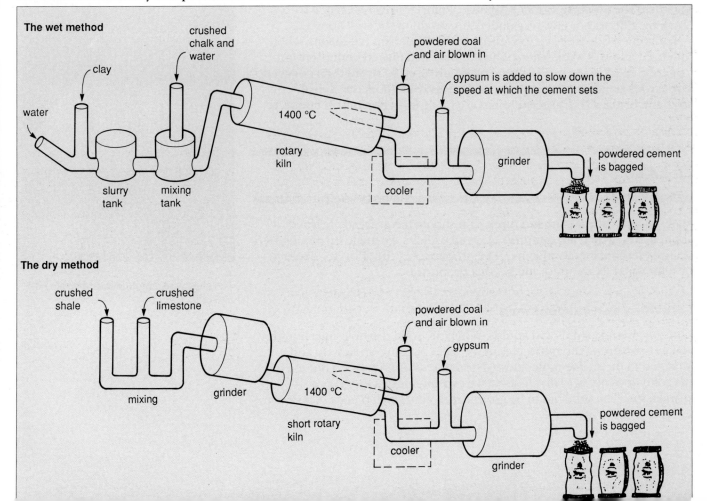

together. The temperature reaches 1400°C. Only at this temperature do the raw materials react. The word equations for the reactions which take place are:

$$coal + air \longrightarrow carbon\ dioxide + energy$$
$$carbon + energy \longrightarrow carbon\ dioxide$$
$$C + O_2 \longrightarrow CO_2$$
$$shale\ or\ clay + limestone\ or\ chalk \longrightarrow cement + carbon\ dioxide$$
$$aluminium\ silicate + calcium\ carbonate \longrightarrow calcium\ silicate + calcium\ aluminate$$

When water is added to cement, fine, needle-shaped crystals grow out from each particle. These crystals start to fill all the space around the cement particle and join up any pieces of stone or sand in the mixture. The millions of crystals form a lattice that links the whole structure

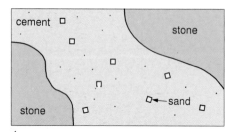

▲
Cement sand and stone are mixed together. Water is added to the mix and fills the gaps.

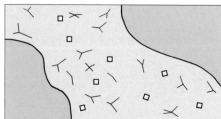

▲
The cement particles use the water to grow crystals that link the sand and stones together.

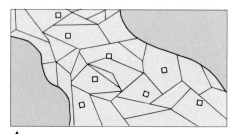

▲
Millions of links make mortar and concrete strong and hard.

together and gives mortar and concrete its strength.

Mortar is a mix of sand, water and cement. It is used to hold bricks together. The most important property of mortar is its resistance to crushing. It must not give way under the weight of the wall above it.

Concrete has stones in it as well as sand. Like mortar it is strong when squeezed, but it is weak when pulled or bent and placed under tension. Concrete reinforcing rods, or wire mesh, are used to strengthen concrete. These rods are strong when pulled so they give the concrete tensile strength. Bridges and large buildings are made from *reinforced* concrete.

Mixtures

Many useful materials are mixtures. You should have already learned about alloys, which are mixtures of metals. Alloys are made by mixing two or more molten metals together. The properties of the alloy are decided by which metals are used, and in what proportions.

Solutions and suspensions

You can also mix solids and liquids. When the solid dissolves in a liquid it makes a *solution*. The molecules of the solid become broken up and attached to the *solute* molecules. (The solute is often water.) But even if the solid does not actually dissolve we can get it into a liquid as a *suspension*. The solid has to be ground into very small pieces. A mixture

▲
The steel wires through the concrete add strength.

of flour and water is a *suspension*. If the solid bits are small enough they may be held up by the Brownian motion of the liquid molecules. But usually they sink to the bottom. You will have come across medicine bottles or paint cans with 'shake well before use' written on them. This is often because the material inside is a suspension.

Emulsions and gels

Liquids can dissolve in each other. Alcohol, for example, dissolves in water. But oil and water 'don't mix' like this. To get oil or fat into water you have to make it into very small drops. Small drops of fat or oil suspended in water make an *emulsion*.

Milk is an emulsion. It is mostly water, but has tiny drops of oil and fat (the cream) suspended in it. Just as a suspension will sooner or later separate out, so will an emulsion. To slow this effect down, a chemical called an *emulsifier* is used. This forms a layer on the outside of each drop of oil to stop it joining together with other drops. Milk contains a natural emulsifier.

Mayonnaise and other salad creams are emulsions. They consist of tiny drops of salad oil in vinegar. In fresh mayonnaise the emulsifier is egg yolk. Many face creams and ointments are emulsions. There may be far more oil than water so they are really emulsions of water-in-oil.

A *gel* is a liquid suspended in a solid. In a traditional jelly, water is trapped between thin strands of a protein called gelatin. You can make a gel by heating flour in water. The starch grains in the flour burst open when it is cooked. The long molecules of starch then surround the water molecules and trap them in a criss-crossing network. This is very useful in cookery. Gravy and sauces are gels, in which flour is used to 'thicken' the liquid.

Because 'dry' gels trap water vapour in the air they can be used in packaging to keep expensive instruments dry. The water vapour is picked up by the gel rather than settling on the things being packed.

▼ Many cosmetics are emulsions of a scented oil in water.

Bubbles — hard and soft

A mixture of a gas and a liquid is called a foam or a mist. If there is more gas than liquid we have a foam. Foams are very useful. They are used in industry to separate metal particles from crushed ore. They are also a handy way of keeping a gas in place. Fire extinguishers often use this idea. A foam of carbon dioxide in soapy water is heavy enough to stay on the fire. The carbon dioxide gas on its own would soon disperse into the air.

A foam has a strong structure. The bubbles push against each other and form a strong honeycomb shape. Expanded polystyrene is a common example of a *foam plastic*.

► The structure of the foam holds the gas over the fire and starves it of oxygen.

Activities

1 There are a number of ways to test for hardness. One way is to hit the material under test with something very hard, and then measure the dent formed. Another way is to use a series of comparative tests to find which substances will scratch your material, only harder materials will make a mark.

The Brinel Test for Metals
Brinel's test was first used in 1900. A hardened steel ball is pressed into the metal under test with a fixed force. Then the depth of the dent is measured.

Brinel hardness numbers for metals (the larger the number the harder the metal is)		
	aluminium	20
	copper	45
	gold	33
	platinum	38
	silver	25
	tin	5
	tungsten	225

Mohs' scale of hardness for minerals and rocks
This was invented in 1812 by Mohs. He placed ten minerals in order of hardness. Diamond is the hardest – it scratches everything. Talc is the softest.

Mohs' scale of hardness The hardest materials are at the top, they will mark everything below them.	Mohs' original minerals	Everyday objects of similar hardness
	10 diamond	
	9 corundum	carborundum stone
	8 topaz	
	7 quartz	hardened steel file
	6 feldspar	
	5 apatite	window glass
	4 fluorite	
	3 calcite	drawing pin, 2p piece
	2 gypsum	finger nail
	1 talc	

(a) Empty out your school bag and try to arrange the bits and pieces into an order of hardness. You may use your own comparative tests or some type of Brinel test to help you decide the order.
(b) Design a piece of apparatus to test different types of plastic to find out how easily they dent. You should try to find a way of measuring the depth of the dent. (Remember to use a constant force for a fair test.)

2 This is something you can do at home. Take a dessert spoonful of custard powder (or cornflour) and put it in a cup. Add just a little water, stirring it into the powder a drop at a time until the powder is only just runny. It should look and behave like a thick liquid, and it can be poured.

Now try pushing it about with a spoon or small spatula. If you have got it right, you should see some interesting events which make it hard to say whether what you have got is a solid or liquid. (If you have got it wrong, you have probably put too much water in.)

Draw or describe how this material behaves. Imagine you had to cross a lake of this stuff: what would be the best way of getting across?

3 (a) Newspapers are printed on paper, which is made out of wood fibres. These are pulped in water, laid out flat and then dried.

Take a large sheet of (old!) newspaper and try to tear it to make a neat straight-line tear, without folding the paper first. Try doing it by holding the sheet in both hands and tearing it:
(i) across from side to side (i.e. from one long side to the opposite side);
(ii) from top to bottom.

Draw and describe what happens. Then explain it in terms of the structure of the paper.
(b) Parcels or packages are often held together with thin plastic straps. If you can get a piece of this plastic, investigate it to find out where it is strong and where it is weak. (It behaves a bit like the newspaper – only the differences are even more obvious.) What can you suggest about its structure, based on your tests?

4 This can keep you busy for hours.
(a) Get some cooking oil (or olive oil) and vinegar. Put them in a bottle and close the top. Shake it until the liquid turns cloudy. Time how long it takes for the oil to separate. Does it depend on (i) how long you shake it for? (ii) The proportion of oil to vinegar?
(b) The next bit must be done paying great attention to cleanliness. Beat an egg yolk in a separate dish. Add a few drops of vinegar. Mix them carefully with a fork. Then add the oil, a drop at a time. Keep mixing. Then add the oil in a slow stream, while whisking gently. If it gets too thick add some more vinegar. You are making *mayonnaise*. Describe what happens at each stage. If you are working in a kitchen area, try tasting what you have made. (You should not eat anything that you have made in a laboratory.)

5 Look at food packets in the kitchen and find the names and 'E-numbers' of as many emulsifiers as you can. For one or two, explain why they are needed for a particular product.

6 (a) Put a large spoonful of flour into a small saucepan. Add half a cup of water, slowly, mixing the flour into the water as you do so. Make sure that you do not get any lumps.
(b) Now heat the mixture very gently. Keep stirring with a spoon – especially when the mixture starts to thicken. Let it come to the boil for a few seconds.
(c) Let the result cool. You now have a gel. Devise some simple tests so that you can write a report about its (i) flexibility, (ii) elasticity, (iii) strength and (iv) rigidity.

7 Investigate the bubbles in a bubble bath and produce a report describing their appearance and their behaviour under the action of forces. You could do this while doing the washing up instead.

Questions

1 How many times bigger is an atom of potassium than an atom of hydrogen?

2 The table below shows different kinds of substances. Copy out the table and complete it by writing down the letter(s) of the substance(s) that fit the description:
(a) elements only;
(b) compounds only;
(c) elements made only from molecules;
(d) ionic compounds;
(e) compounds made only from molecules.
Give only the letters of the boxes for your answers.

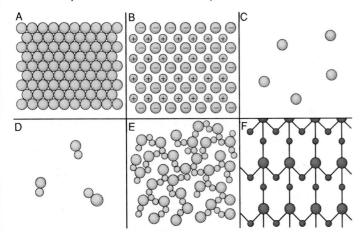

3 (a) When a cube of sugar dissolves, the corners break off and dissolve first. Draw a diagram to show why corners are more easy to dissolve. (It may help to look at a dice or some other cube.)
(b) Which part will dissolve next, the edges, the centre of the faces or inside the cube? Explain your answer.

Description	Letter
(i) a liquid	
(ii) a gas	
(iii) substance(s) made of one element only	
(iv) compounds	
(v) ionic compound(s)	
(vi) a giant structure	
(vii) a compound with a solid molecular structure	

4 If you have a small heap of sand on a tray and you shake it gently, it eventually spreads to form a film of sand one layer thick. It cannot spread any more without leaving holes on the tray.
   Use this idea to explain why when a small piece of butter melts on the surface of a bowl of hot water, the layer formed stops spreading after a certain size.

5 Explain the differences between:
(a) an alloy and a pure metal;
(b) an element and a compound;
(c) a solution and a suspension.
Use diagrams to help you give clear answers.

6 The table below gives data about some pure chemicals. Use it to answer the questions below.

(a) (i) Which of the above substances are metals?
(ii) Give one piece of evidence from the table which you used to help you decide the answer to part (i).
(b) (i) Which of the above substances conduct electricity *only* when they are dissolved in water?
(ii) What kind of structure do these substances have?
(c) (i) Arrange the substances in the table into two groups:
A — low melting point; B — high melting point.
(ii) Which group, A or B, is likely to contain the stronger materials?

	Melting point (°C)	Boiling point (°C)	Conducts electricity:	
			as a solid?	when dissolved in water?
copper chloride	498	993	no	yes
iodine	114	183	no	—
calcium	850	1492	yes	—
magnesium chloride	714	1818	no	yes
vanadium	1917	3377	yes	—
naphthalene	80	218	no	—
potassium iodide	685	1324	no	yes

7 The bar chart shows the amount of cement sold by manufacturers over eight years.
(a) Place the years in order, starting with the busiest year for cement manufacturers.
(b) Explain how the amount of cement sold is a good way to measure how busy the building and construction industry is.
(c) Cement is used to make paving slabs. List five more things that cement is used for.

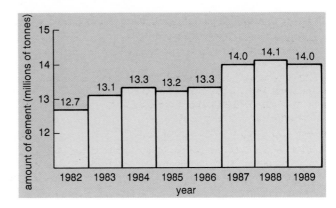

155

Checklist

These are the facts and ideas that you should have learned by studying this topic.

To succeed at Basic Level you should:

- know that some materials can be melted by heating and made solid again by cooling them (like ice and water), but that other materials will change into a new substance
- know that some materials can dissolve in water but that others will not
- know that everything is made up of very small particles
- be able to describe everyday materials and what happens to them when they are squashed or stretched
- be able to group materials according to their properties (like hardness, flexibility, transparency), or by what they are made of (like metals and plastics)

To succeed at Foundation Level you should:

- understand what it means to say that things have changed their state, or dissolved, and be able to explain this by using the idea of particles
- know that all materials, including gases, can be weighed, but that only solids and liquids have a definite volume
- be able to group materials as gases, liquids and solids by observation or by using given data
- know that everything is made up from very small particles called atoms
- know the difference between a mixture and a compound
- be able to compare materials using the properties strength, hardness, flexibility, and solubility and use these ideas to explain how the materials are used in everyday life
- know that metals have high melting points (usually), conduct electricity and are shiny

To succeed at Merit Level you should:

- know that the volume of a gas depends on its pressure and temperature
- be able to use the kinetic theory to explain solids, liquids and gases, their changes of state, evaporation, diffusion and dissolving
- be able to interpret data and observations to distinguish between elements, mixtures and compounds, and describe the differences
- understand the meaning of the following terms and use them to help group the main classes of materials (metals, ceramics, glass, plastics, fibres): strength, hardness, elasticity, solubility, density, melting point, electrical and thermal conductivity
- be able to describe how the properties of minerals and rocks make them useful as raw materials
- be able to interpret models and diagrams of molecules, and use simple word equations to describe chemical reactions

To succeed at Special Level you should:

- understand the gas laws and be able to use them
- be able to apply the kinetic theory to explain a range of effects
- be able to select and use data about materials to make judgements about their manufacture and use (with reference to economic, health and safety, social and environmental issues)
- be able to relate the bulk properties of the basic materials to their internal structure (metals, glass, ceramics, plastics, fibres, water, ionic and other 'giant structures')
- be able to use symbolic equations to describe reactions

CHAPTER ELEVEN

STRUCTURES

An interview with a designer

(Ken Rawlinson, Phoenix Mountaineering Ltd)

on the roof (in January) and get somebody to throw a bucket of cold water over you every half hour.

What I'm trying to say is that the first thing to think about in a mountain tent is that you have to *carry* it up there. So it has to be really light. When you get it there you have to put it up, often in the dark, in a mist or a howling gale, on snow or on rock, and wearing thick gloves. So it has to be really easy to put up. Then it's supposed to stay there!

After all that, it had better do its job — keeping out the wind and the rain — without getting blown away or squashed in a snowfall. We have to choose material that's windproof and watertight, and the structure has to be really strong.

Now there's no such thing as a perfect tent — we are changing our design all the time. When we started nine years ago there were just three of us. As mountain climbers we knew the problems and we thought we knew how to solve them. Well, we haven't done too badly; we employ a hundred people. The directors of the firm are still climbers — and we also do the designing. And the testing — I was on Everest in 1986.

For our Extreme Tent we use a geodesic dome-plus-funnel design, with five poles. The poles are made of a flexible alloy, 10 mm thick. They have to be light and strong, but still able to bend enough to make a semicircle for the dome. We chose a dome because it is very stable and good in high winds and snow. The tent can hold three people and weighs 6 kilograms. It is held down by pegs which guy directly onto the poles, so the guy ropes don't put much strain on the fabric. It's made in two parts. The outer bit is the flysheet. You can put this up first and then put the proper tent up inside it. Handy when it's raining! You also get a repair kit — like splints for a broken pole: you can't go back to the shop when you're half-way up Everest or in the middle of a jungle in Thailand.

If you want to make a living out of designing tents — or anything else — you have to produce something that people want at a price they can afford. Of course, if their comfort depends on it — let alone their lives — they'll pay a good price! And we'd be foolish to skimp on quality if that's what's at stake. I must admit that climbing mountains is my hobby, my life, almost! It's nice to turn your hobby into a living, and it's also nice to design and make something *you* want to use and get other people to pay for using it as well.

Of course, if you've never climbed up a twenty-thousand foot mountain with a full rucksack — tent, sleeping bag, stove, food, ropes, spare gear — you won't know what I'm talking about. You'll just have to use your imagination, or try climbing up and down the stairs two thousand times with the kitchen sink on your back. Then you could sleep out

What makes a good structure?

To answer this, we have to know what the structure is for. A well-designed tent is very different from a well-designed aircraft or car because they have to do very different things. But there are some rules that apply to every good design.

- It has to suit its purpose.
- It must make the best use of available materials.
- People must *like* it.
- It must not be too difficult for people to make, or too expensive for customers to buy.

All this is easier said than done. But every designer has to know something about the science of structures — about why things keep their shape and do not fall apart.

Inside every large animal there is a skeleton. The rest of the animal is built on this structure.

Tunnels have to be built to take heavy loads and stand up to high pressures from the land (and sea) above them.

This microscopic animal is only 0.001 mm across, and yet its structure is amazingly complicated and beautiful.

This is the molecule that carries the oxygen in our blood. Its structure is designed so that it can pick up and release the oxygen molecules easily when it has to do so.

There are at least two large structures here. The scaffolding is obvious, holding up the other one – the statue – while it is being repaired.

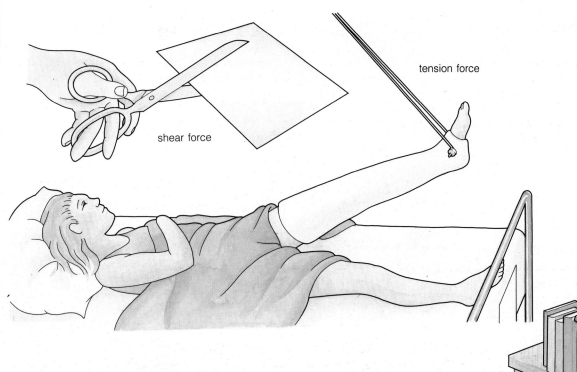

shear force

tension force

bending force

compression force

Forces in structures

The forces in a structure are named after the effects they produce.

- *Compression* forces tend to squash an object, making it shorter
- *Tension* forces pull on an object, making it longer
- *Torsion* forces twist an object
- *Shear* forces tend to tear an object.

The drawings show examples of these kinds of force acting on everyday structures. Structures are not always complicated, like a bridge or a TV tower. A piece of string or paper is a structure. So is a shoe.

Materials have different *properties*. For example, some materials are hard, others are soft. Some are strong, others are weak. A good designer chooses the material with the best mix of properties for the job.

The main questions that we can ask about a material are, is it:

- stiff, or easy to bend?
- hard or soft?
- strong or weak?
- elastic or inelastic?
- brittle or plastic?
- smooth, rough or fibrous?

We also need to know how *dense* the material is. Sometimes we want a structure to be heavy, other structures need to be light. You can identify these in photographs and drawings in this chapter.

If the structure is likely to get hot, we need to choose a material that does not melt or burn at the temperatures it is used at. These ideas are illustrated in the diagram on the next page.

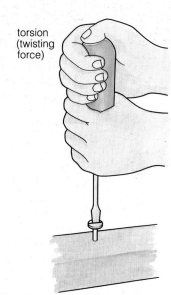

torsion (twisting force)

159

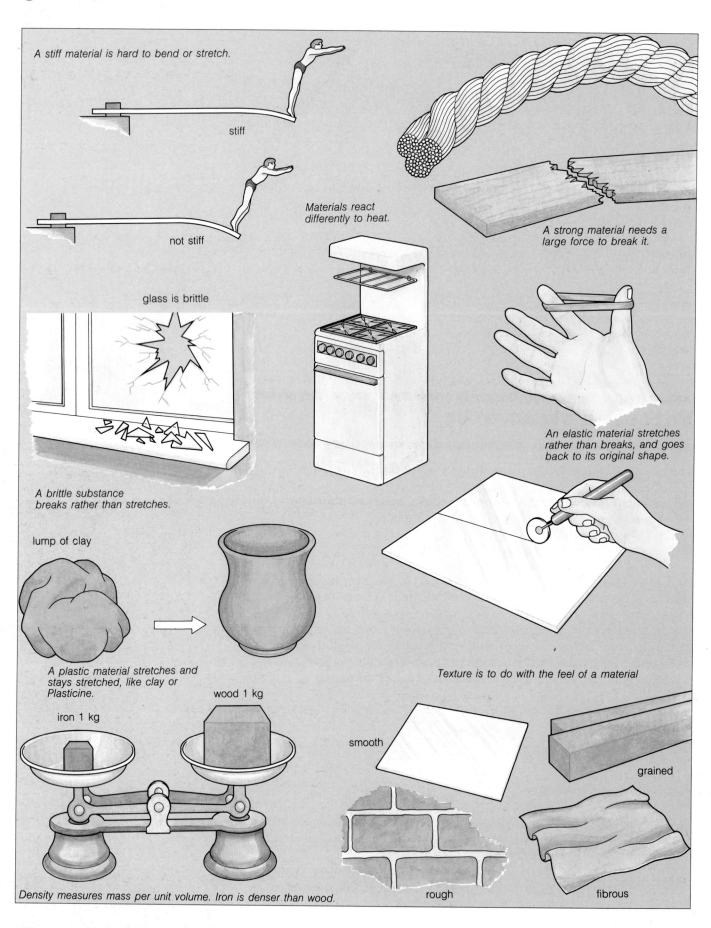

A stiff material is hard to bend or stretch.

stiff

not stiff

Materials react differently to heat.

A strong material needs a large force to break it.

glass is brittle

An elastic material stretches rather than breaks, and goes back to its original shape.

A brittle substance breaks rather than stretches.

lump of clay

A plastic material stretches and stays stretched, like clay or Plasticine.

Texture is to do with the feel of a material

wood 1 kg

iron 1 kg

smooth

grained

Density measures mass per unit volume. Iron is denser than wood.

rough

fibrous

Structure and weight

The biggest load that many structures have to bear is their own weight. Very old buildings made of stone usually have very thick pillars. The Stone Age tomb and the Greek temple show this. They only carry the load of their own weight.

Later buildings, like the great cathedrals of the Middle Ages, were better designed. They used arches and buttresses to help support the weight of the building. They could be built much taller. But the load was still their own weight. People who used the buildings stayed on the ground floor.

Modern materials can combine lightness and strength. The first iron bridge the world ever saw still exists, at Ironbridge in Shropshire. It was built in 1779. Although iron is denser than stone it is very much stronger. Compare the amount of material needed for an iron arch with that in a stone arch.

There is a very important difference between most metals and stone. Both steel and granite are strong materials. But steel is strong in tension as well as in compression. Granite is strong in compression, but much weaker in tension. Steel can be used in cables, granite cannot! Cables and ropes are used in structures to carry tension forces. Suspension bridges are designed to use this property of steel.

▲ A 10 000 year-old neolithic site in Wales. This is a gravestone.

▼ The Parthenon in Athens, a very famous Greek temple built in the 5th century B.C.

Top, Britain's first iron bridge at Ironbridge in Shropshire. The stone bridge is the same size as the iron bridge, but it has to be much more massive. This is because of the properties of iron and stone.

▲ Salisbury cathedral. Developments in understanding of structures mean that the very thin columns can support the weight of the huge ceiling and roof.

▶ The steel cables support the weight of the bridge and everything that crosses it. You can see a single cable running from one end of the bridge to the other. Notice how thick the cable is.

Fitting shapes together

Some structures are mostly empty space! Sometimes this is because they have to carry things. Trains, boats and buildings are obvious examples.

But other structures are full of holes because they need to be light. The electricity pylon needs to be as light as possible, and to use as little steel as possible. The skeleton of a bird is very light because the bones are hollow. The cheek bones in your face are hollow so that your head weighs as little as possible. These structures are strong but light. They have a good *strength-to-weight ratio*.

Hollow objects are still strong objects

One way to make a structure light and strong is make it from hollow parts. A tube of steel is as strong in compression and tension as a solid piece of steel of the same size, but it is much lighter and cheaper.

Natural objects make good use of this fact. This picture shows how bones are really hollow. The filling of animal bones is not there to give strength, but to do other jobs (like make blood). Birds' bones are hollow. Many plants have hollow stems so that they can grow tall very quickly. Hollow stems need be built from less material than more 'solid' plants such as trees. Bamboo has a hollow stem. It is very strong and grows very quickly.

We use the principle of hollow structures in many everyday objects, such as tent poles, bicycles, scaffolding and foam plastics (see page 153).

▼
A cross section through the shoot of a maize plant.

Triangles are strong shapes

One snag with a hollow tube is that it is not good at coping with bending or twisting forces. Beams are better, as explained below. But structures can be designed to use light, hollow parts as long as they are in compression or tension. One way of doing this is to make the supporting parts triangular.

A support for a shop sign could be made of hollow tubes. The forces in a triangular-shaped object are channelled so that they are *along* the sides of the triangle. You will see many examples of objects made of triangular sub-units. A bicycle is a very good example. So are electricity pylons and cranes.

If the force on the bar of the triangle is pulling the bar in tension, the bar is called a *tie*. If the force is compressing it then the bar is called a *strut*. A tie can be replaced by a cord or cable. But this may only work in a simple structure. Depending on the loading of a complicated one, a tie might become a strut. It is hard to work this out in advance.

A roof frame is a good example of a triangular structure. The weight of the roof compresses the sides, so they are struts. The base of the triangle is being stretched sideways, so is a tie.

Supporting a roof has always been a problem for architects. Very large buildings used to need huge *buttresses* on the outer walls to stop them moving *sideways* under the weight of the roof. We no longer need to do this. Modern materials, like steel, are good in tension, so they can be used as a tie *inside* the building. This holds the walls together. If stone is used it has to be used in compression, so is outside the building.

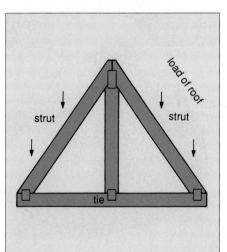

▲
A roof showing ties and struts.

▲
Massive stone buttresses compress the building.

▲
The steel ties are under tension – pulling the parts of the building together.

Where the weight is

A laboratory stool may have many good design features – struts to give it strength, strong joints, tubular metal legs to give strength with lightness – but most of them have one serious design fault: they are easy to knock over. This is to do with where the weight of the stool *appears to act*: the centre of mass. This place is decided by how the mass of the object is

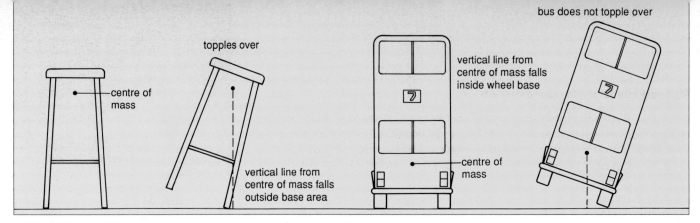

bus does not topple over

topples over

centre of mass

vertical line from centre of mass falls outside base area

vertical line from centre of mass falls inside wheel base

centre of mass

arranged. If most mass is at the top, the centre of mass will be high, and this means that the object will be easier to knock over. The diagrams illustrate this.

Strong shapes

Triangles are not the only strong shapes. Circles can also be very strong. Modern aircraft and train carriages are based on a tube shape. Parts of circles or spheres, such as arches and domes, are often used in buildings. All these shapes can channel the force along the material so that it is either in compression or tension. Most materials and objects are stronger for these forces, compared with twisting, bending or shear forces. Domes have been used for thousands of years, from Eskimo igloos and skin tents held up by bent poles, to the huge structures that cover sports arenas.

Square shapes are less strong. They lack strength at the corners, so they twist very easily. Things are improved if a rod is fixed across each corner. But, of course, this turns the square into a set of triangles.

Beams

Beams are some of the oldest human structures. The very earliest bridges and buildings used planks of wood, tree trunks or long stones.

The forces on a simple beam are shown in the diagram. It shows that a bending force actually both stretches and compresses a material. It is compressed at the top and stretched at the bottom.

When a beam fails it usually starts breaking at the bottom where it is being stretched. All materials are likely to have faults which produce cracks in them. Tension forces widen the cracks and eventually they get big enough for the structure to fail. This will happen very suddenly.

Materials like stone and concrete are more likely to have cracks and so are not good for making beams. Wood is fibrous and is less likely to crack across the grain. This is why so many buildings have wooden beams. Metal (steel) beams can be stronger, and in a metal cracks can often be self-closing.

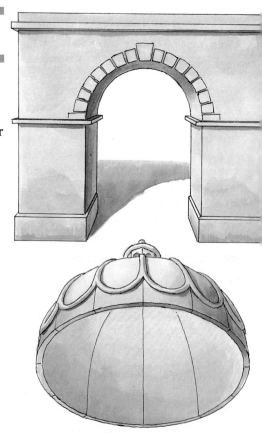

▲
Arches and domes all use the great strength of circles.

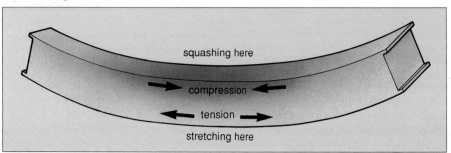

squashing here

compression

tension

stretching here

Pressure

A structure is only as strong as its foundations. A tall, heavy building or bridge has to be supported. Usually, ordinary soil is not strong enough for this. The builder may have to dig down to the base rock. If this is a strong rock then the building can be built directly on that.

New York sits on an area of solid rock. This is why it has been a suitable place to build skyscrapers that need deep and very strong foundations.

London is built on a bed of soft clay. It was thought that very tall buildings could never be built in London. But, by building a concrete raft or platform, the 'load' of the building can be spread over a large area. Very tall buildings can now be built on 'unsuitable' ground. The important physical idea is that of *pressure*. The weight of the building presses on the ground, putting the ground under *stress*. Pressure is defined in exactly the same way as stress. It is the *applied force per unit area*.

The force exerted by most structures is due to their weight. So to work out the pressure exerted by a structure on its supports you need to know how much it weighs and the area of contact:

$$\text{pressure} = \frac{\text{force}}{\text{area}}, \qquad \text{or, } P = \frac{F}{A}.$$

The standard unit is *newtons per square metre* (N/m^2). You will find that this is also called the *pascal* (Pa) in some books.

The stress applied by the building on its supports is measured in the same units and calculated by using the same formula. Stress is an important idea for designers and engineers. The middle of a pillar is *under stress*, even though it does not make much sense to talk of *pressure* inside a pillar. (There is more about pressure on page 122.)

▲
New York's skyscrapers are built on a bed of solid rock. London is built on soft clay and so tall buildings have to be built on huge concrete 'rafts' to spread the weight over a large area.

Pressure under water: hydrostatics

Pressure can be caused by the weight of a liquid or gas. Atmospheric pressure is caused by the weight of the atmosphere. Water is much denser than air, so underwater structures like submarines and diver's suits need to be strong. Below a certain depth the human body has problems. It is hard to breathe, and for blood to be pumped. Bones and flesh may even be crushed.

The size of the pressure depends on the weight of the fluid and the depth. The weight of the fluid depends on its density. Combining these ideas, we get:

hydrostatic pressure = depth × density × strength of the gravity field

or, $$P = hdg.$$

Both liquid and gas pressures can be increased by pumps. The pressure in a car tyre is usually two to three times as much as the normal pressure of the air outside.

▼
This diving helmet is designed to be used at great depths, where the water pressure is very high. The helmet is almost spherical.

Materials for making structures

For thousands of years people have made tools, clothing, ships and buildings with natural materials. They have used wood, stone, bone, animal fur and skins, mud, straw and leaves. Many of these materials have to be *treated*. This usually means making a simple chemical change. The aim is to make the material harder or softer, stiffer or more flexible, or more resistant to rotting.

Synthetic materials

'Synthetic' describes materials made from other materials. One very ancient synthetic material is brick; concrete is another. These were invented thousands of years ago. But in the last century many more synthetic materials have been produced. It is very hard to find a modern room which does not contain a lot of them.

Elastic and plastic behaviour

Metals and other materials are tested by applying forces to them and measuring how much they change. A typical set of results for metal wires is shown in these graphs. Steel is very stiff, so it takes a large force to make it stretch. Copper is less stiff, and stretches more for the same force. Both materials stretch in a regular pattern: *the bigger the force, the greater the stretch*. If you unloaded them they would both return to their original lengths. They are behaving as *elastic* materials.

Many materials behave like this. They are said to obey the *Hooke Law*: when a force is applied, the change produced is proportional to the applied force.

But what happens if we keep on loading them? Eventually, both wires break. But before it breaks, the copper wire suddenly starts getting longer and longer for the same force. It is acting like a thin piece of Plasticine. It is behaving as a *plastic*. A plastic material will stretch and stretch without any increase in force. When the force is removed it stays stretched.

Why plastics are not plastic

What we call 'plastics' are not plastic at all. They are 'ex-plastic'. They were plastic as they were being made. After they are moulded into shape a chemical change takes place so that they become stiff. This is why many plastics are so useful. They can be made into any shape very easily, then they keep that shape for a long time afterwards. It is harder to do this with metals. They have either to be cut in machines or stamped or moulded when they are very hot.

Glass

Glass can be a very strong material. The main problem is that it is *brittle*. When a metal is hit it will become elastic for a moment and change its shape permanently – think of dents in crashed cars. A glass car would shatter, just like a car windscreen.

A brittle material is one in which cracks can grow very, very quickly. If we want to make use of the strength and lightness of glass we can do so by putting a 'crack-stopper' in it. This can be done by putting metal wires in the glass, or a layer of clear plastic.

▼
Wires being tested with loads, and behaving as elastic and plastic materials.

copper

load (kg)

steel

extension (mm)

plastic 'cree

load (kg)

extension (mm)

THIS IS AN EX-PLASTIC!

But one of the best ways of using glass is to make it into thin fibres. These are very strong and can be put into a plastic – glass reinforced plastic. The plastic is usually quite weak. But it is flexible and can take gentle forces without any problems. A sudden force will produce cracks, but the glass fibres stop them travelling through the plastic and getting wider. The glass also gives the finished material strength. There is more about this in Chapter Ten.

One way to stop cracks growing in concrete is to lay steel wires in it as it is made. This produces *reinforced concrete*. If the wires are kept under tension as the concrete sets the concrete is even less likely to crack.

The fibres in wood stop cracks from growing very quickly. This goes to show how many modern materials are based on the structures of natural ones.

Activities

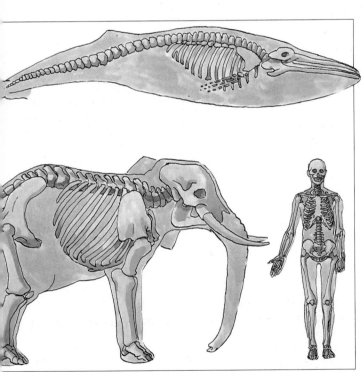

1 The diagrams show the skeletons of three kinds of animal. Look at them and then, in groups, come to an agreement on the answers to the questions.
(a) Whales washed up on a beach often die, even if they are put back into water quite soon. What is it about their *structure* that explains this fact?
(b) Compare the ribs of a human being with those of an elephant. Why do the elephant's ribs go all the way back to the pelvis? Why do human ribs stop a long way from the pelvis?
(c) Is the backbone designed for *compression* or for *tension* forces? Why do humans get so much back trouble?

2 Design and make some toys that work on the principles of *stability*. For example:

- a model tight-rope walker,
- toys that bounce back up when they are knocked over,
- ornamental 'mobiles'.

Explain the principles on which the toys are meant to work.

3 Plan an experiment to find out which of several types of glue is best at sticking (a) wood or (b) plastic. Your plan should make sure that the test is 'fair', and should include the measurements which need to be taken. Give as much practical detail as you can, including any safety precautions that need to be taken.

4 In the autumn of 1987 the south of England was hit by the strongest gales for over 250 years. Fifteen million trees were blown down. Apart from the sheer strength of the winds, two key factors were that the ground was quite wet and that the trees still carried their full load of leaves.

Design and carry out an investigation into these factors as they might affect 'model' trees.

If you are interested you could go further and investigate the effect of forces on tree trunks of different lengths and thicknesses.

Collect photographs of different tree shapes – is there any pattern between trees that shed their leaves in winter (deciduous) and those that do not (evergreen)?

(*Hints*: roots can be modelled by using string with the strands teased out; simplify the leaves by making them into one big leaf; tree trunks can be modelled by thin dowelling – of different widths and lengths.)

5 Investigate or do a survey on one or more of the following:
(a) Why some drinks are sold in glass bottles, others in plastic ones.
(b) What materials are used to package large quantities (of bottles, cereal packs, biscuits, etc.).
(c) How packs and cases for large quantities of items are designed, and the problems that designers have to allow for.
(d) How the fact that packs have to be transported long distances affects their design.
(e) How the nature of the product affects the design of the packaging.

Questions

1 Which of the following would be easiest to knock over accidentally? Why?

2 Suggest *structural* reasons for each of the following facts:
(a) Poles for lightweight tents are made of *metal*, and are *hollow*.
(b) The threads used in making clothes are usually made of many small strands *twisted together* rather than a few larger strands, and the strands are often slightly *hairy*.
(c) Leg and arm bones are filled with a kind of honeycomb (i.e. mostly full of holes).
(d) Cardboard packing material is made as shown in the diagram.

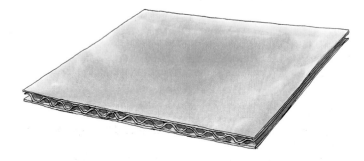

3 Draw diagrams showing structures or objects withstanding,
(a) bending forces,
(b) twisting (torsion) forces,
(c) shear forces.

4 Use the table of *Useful materials and their properties* in the 'Reference section' to help you to answer the following questions.
(a) Why is copper often used on the bottom of expensive saucepans?
(b) Why are car bodies made of steel?
(c) Why are the knobs and cases of TV sets made of plastic?
(d) Why are the suspension cables of bridges made of steel, but the pillars made of concrete?
(e) Why are socks often made of a wool and nylon mix?

5 When you walk in deep snow your feet sink into it. If you wear skis or snowshoes they don't. Explain why.

6 Use the formula $P = \dfrac{F}{A}$ $\left(\text{pressure} = \dfrac{\text{force}}{\text{area}}\right)$

to calculate the following. (The answer should be in N/cm^2 or N/m^2.)
(a) The pressure under the wheels of a tractor that weighs 12 000 newtons, if the area of tyres in contact with the ground is $1.2\,m^2$.
(b) The pressure under the foot of a man weighing 800 newtons when he stands on one leg. The area of his shoe sole and heel is $240\,cm^2$.
(c) The man of part (b) now sits on a chair. The area of the chair legs in contact with the floor is only $16\,cm^2$. What pressure does *each* chair leg exert on the floor?

These are the facts and ideas that you should have learned by studying this topic.

To succeed at Basic Level you should:

- be able to describe materials and what happens to them when forces act on them
- be able to group materials according to their properties (like hardness, flexibility, transparency), or by what they are made of (like metals and plastics)
- know that 'stable' structures are hard to knock over
- know how to measure force (in newtons)

To succeed at Foundation Level you should:

- be able to recognise when tension, compression, bending and twisting forces are acting on something
- be able to compare materials using the properties of strength, hardness and flexibility, and relate these to their everyday uses
- know that structures are more stable if they have a large base area and a low centre of mass
- know that the effect of a force on an object may depend on the area of contact
- know that weight is a force and is measured in newtons
- understand the idea of 'balanced forces'
- know that some shapes are stronger than others (you should know about triangles, arches and circles compared with squares)
- be able to describe how you tested a structure

To succeed at Merit Level you should:

- be able to recognise the following forces and know what effect they will have on materials: tension, compression, bending, twisting and shear forces
- understand the meanings of the following properties of materials and relate them to their everyday use: strength, hardness, elasticity and density
- be able to distinguish between the main types of materials: metals, ceramics, glass, plastics and fibres
- understand how base area and the distribution of mass in a structure affects its stability, using the idea of the turning effect (moment) of a force
- understand what pressure is
- be able to evaluate a design by balancing the factors involved in making and using it

To succeed at Special Level you should:

- understand that bending involves both tension and compression forces
- be able to select and use quantitative data to evaluate the use of various materials for a structure
- understand the idea of centre of mass and be able to apply it to a structure
- be able to use the idea of pressure and the formula $P = F/A$
- be able to relate forces to their effects when testing a structure or artefact

CHAPTER TWELVE

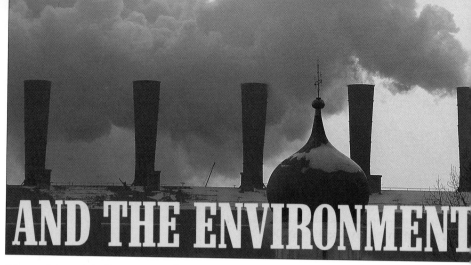

FUELS AND THE ENVIRONMENT

Fuels and people

People need fuel. We cook food, we wash and bathe in hot water; we need to keep our buildings warm and well lit. But we also need energy to move people and goods about. It takes a lot of energy in factories to make the things we use.

To get the energy from fuels we have to burn them. The everyday fuels that we use are coal, oil and gas (methane). These are *fossil fuels*, and we get most of our energy from them. They are called 'fossil' because they were formed, millions of years ago, from dead plants and animals.

Much of the fossil fuels we use are burnt in *power stations*. The energy is then carried to where it is needed as electricity generated in the power stations. This needs a huge network of wires and transformers called the National Grid System.

Energy supplied electrically is 'clean' and very easy to use. Not many factories will bother with their own supplies of coal or oil to make their machines work. But they will probably use oil or gas to *heat* the factories, and these fuels are still the most popular and cheapest ways of heating our homes. Most of us rely on electricity to make things work at home. We wouldn't be too keen on petrol-driven vacuum cleaners!

All this relies on a good supply of fuel — and a good system for moving it around the world. Oil is carried across the seas in large tankers, and across the country in pipes or special tanker lorries. Coal usually goes by rail. 'Natural' gas is pumped from under the ground and is carried to homes and factories through large pipes. In some places, different kinds of fuel gas (pentane and butane) are carried in high-pressure containers that keep the fuel liquified until it is used.

One of the pictures on these pages is different from the others. It shows some people preparing wood for burning. Most of the world's energy comes from fossil fuels, but most of the *people* in the world use wood as their main energy source. They use it for cooking and for heating all over the world.

Wood is a *renewable* energy source — in theory. It grows on trees! But if people use wood faster than trees can grow, sooner or later we will run out of wood.

The world's energy is not shared out very equally. This chart shows how much energy people in different parts of the world actually use.

There are problems about the world's use of energy. How long will the fossil fuels last? What would the world be like if everybody had a fair share of its energy sources? What about the pollution caused by burning so much fuel? What happens to the plants and animals in the sea if an oil tanker is wrecked? Are we paying a fair price for the energy we use? This chapter will deal with these questions. It might not give you the answers, but it will give you the information and ideas that you need to start answering the questions for yourself.

Energy used by each person in a year (x 10^{11} J)

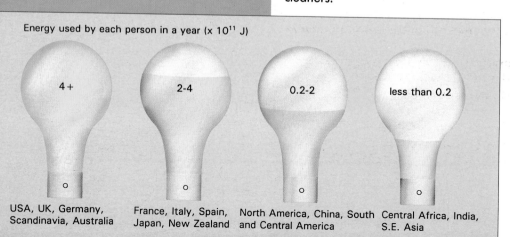

4 +	2-4	0.2-2	less than 0.2
USA, UK, Germany, Scandinavia, Australia	France, Italy, Spain, Japan, New Zealand	North America, China, South and Central America	Central Africa, India, S.E. Asia

Fuels

The fuels we use are mostly compounds of carbon and hydrogen. We call them *hydrocarbons*. For example, ordinary 'gas' is a fossil fuel that is almost pure *methane* (CH_4). *Propane* is a fuel used in portable gas heaters. It has a more complicated chemical formula than methane: C_2H_6. *Coal* is not a pure substance, but contains a great deal of carbon, mixed with other solid hydrocarbons.

When fuels burn they release energy which heats up the waste gases and can be used to heat the surroundings. Burning is the chemical reaction *combustion*. In this reaction the hydrocarbons combine with oxygen.

For example, for carbon:

$$\text{carbon} + \text{oxygen} \longrightarrow \text{carbon dioxide}$$
$$C + O_2 \longrightarrow CO_2,$$

and for methane:

$$\text{methane} + \text{oxygen} \longrightarrow \text{carbon dioxide} + \text{water}$$
$$CH_4 + 2O_2 \longrightarrow CO_2 + 2H_2O.$$

Energy is released, so these are *exothermic* reactions.

Pure carbon is commonly known as *charcoal*. This fuel is used in cooking and does not produce a flame. Charcoal is made by heating wood in an airless space. This process drives off unwanted chemicals.

Carbon monoxide

Burning a fuel in a limited air supply is dangerous. The carbon does not burn completely, and produces the gas *carbon monoxide*. This gas is a deadly poison. It combines with the red chemical in blood (haemoglobin) and the blood stops being able to carry oxygen. Most gas fires and all car engines produce carbon monoxide. Every year many people die through using gas water heaters that are wrongly set up. Gas heaters are always dangerous when they are used in rooms with poor ventilation. Not enough oxygen can get to the flame.

Fossil fuels

Fossil fuels are the remains of plants and animals that lived and died millions of years ago. How these fuels were made is explained in Chapter Two, *Raw materials*.

Fuels from oil

The oil found under the Earth's surface is a mixture. It contains many different liquid chemicals, with other chemicals dissolved in them. Some of these dissolved chemicals are gases. It comes out of the ground as *crude oil*.

Crude oil is not much use in its natural state. It has to be processed in an oil refinery. This process separates and purifies ('refines') the different kinds of oil present. It uses the fact that the different oils boil off at different temperatures.

The first to boil off are *spirits*. These have a low boiling point. They are used mostly for fuels such as aviation fuel, petrol and paraffin. Then come the *light oils* which are used for both fuels and lubrication (fuel oil, diesel

▼
Fuels from crude oil.

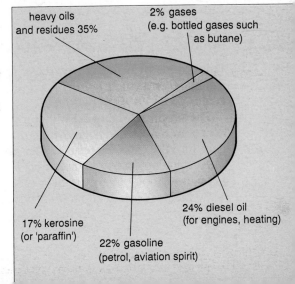

heavy oils and residues 35%

2% gases (e.g. bottled gases such as butane)

24% diesel oil (for engines, heating)

17% kerosine (or 'paraffin')

22% gasoline (petrol, aviation spirit)

fuel). After this come *heavy oils*, which are treated chemically to make all kinds of new substances such as plastics.

The chart shows the main fuels obtained from crude oil. Refining crude oil is the basis of the huge *petrochemical industry*.

Which is the best fuel?

There is no answer to this question! It all depends on what you want the fuel to do. A fuel that works well in a house heating system may not be good for running an engine.

Just think of home heating. You have the choice of coal, various types of gas, coke, fuel oil and even wood. They all have advantages and disadvantages. Fuel has to be suited to its purpose.

Not all these questions have 'scientific' answers. But many of them can give measurable answers. The most important of these, for most fuel users, are *cost* compared with *energy output*.

▲
Burning oil wells in Kuwait. This shows what is put into the atmosphere when we burn fossil fuels.

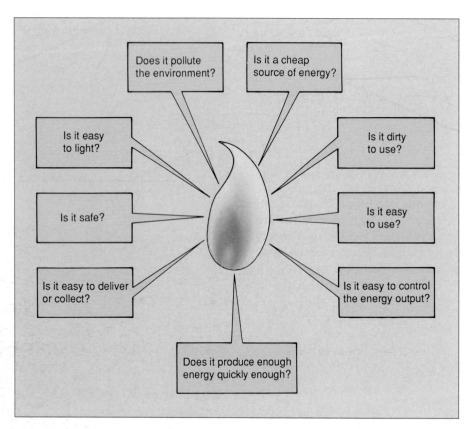

Does it pollute the environment?

Is it a cheap source of energy?

Is it easy to light?

Is it dirty to use?

Is it safe?

Is it easy to use?

Is it easy to deliver or collect?

Is it easy to control the energy output?

Does it produce enough energy quickly enough?

◀
What makes a good fuel?

▼
A simple fuel calorimeter.

Measuring the energy output of a fuel

This is done by using a *calorimeter* of some kind. Then, results for all fuels can be given as their *calorific values*. For example, the calorific value of coal is about 28 MJ per kilogram.

The simplest kind of calorimeter uses a measured amount of the fuel to heat water. A good design tries to make sure that all the energy released goes into the calorimeter and does not escape into the air. This is difficult!

To calculate how much energy is produced by the fuel you need to know how much energy it takes to heat water. This is well known to be 4180 joules for each kilogram of water heated through 1 °C. This number

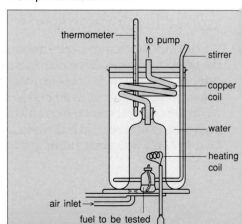

thermometer — to pump
stirrer
copper coil
water
heating coil
air inlet →
fuel to be tested

is called the *specific heat capacity* of water, given the symbol *s*. Thus the energy supplied to the calorimeter is calculated by the formula:

energy supplied = mass of water × 4180 × rise in temperature

or, $E = msT$.

The problems with fossil fuels

There are two main problems with fossil fuels.

- We are using them up much more quickly than they can be replaced.
- Burning them produces waste gases which damage the environment.

How much fuel do we have?

Most of our coal was made during the long period in the Earth's history known as the Carboniferous Period (see page 245 in the 'Reference section'). This period lasted 65 million years. We have been using coal most heavily in the past 200 hundred years or so. In the past 50 years, oil has taken over as the main fuel we use. But oil takes just as long to make as coal – and there is less of it.

This diagram shows how long we expect fossil fuels to last. But the calculation assumes that we do not increase the rate at which we use the fuels. This has been true for the past ten years. But we have to bear in mind that most of the people on Earth use much less of these fuels than the people in Europe and North America. If everybody on Earth used as much as we do in Britain, the fuels would run out much more quickly.

Pollutant gases

Most natural fuels contain impurities. Coal and fuel oil contain sulphur, for example. But in practice much more sulphur is burnt with the fuel and goes into the air as *suphur dioxide*. This is an unpleasant, poisonous gas. But its main effect is that it causes *acid rain*.

All rain is slightly acid. Carbon dioxide from the air dissolves in water to make *carbonic acid*. But this is a weak acid compared with the *sulphuric acid* produced by sulphur dioxide dissolving in water.

$$2SO_2 + O_2 \longrightarrow 2SO_3$$

$$SO_3 + H_2O \longrightarrow H_2SO_4 \text{ (sulphuric acid)}$$

Nitrogen compounds in fuels produce *nitric acid*.

The effects of air pollution

The result of this kind of pollution is to make rain much more acid than normal. Many lakes and rivers in Britain and Europe are now so acid that fish cannot live in them. As many as half of Germany's trees are dying or dead because of the acid air and soil. Old and famous buildings are damaged as the acid rain eats away the stonework. In city centres the pollution from cars and industry may be enough to damage people's health. At certain times of the year, especially in hot summers, the air is

▼ The expected lifetimes of fossil fuels.

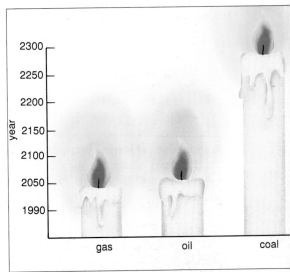

▲ Sulphur from burning coal and oil is released into the air. Here, we can see sulphur deposits on the chimney of the Drax B power station.

not really fit to breathe. Warnings about 'air quality' are broadcast on radio and TV weather forecasts.

Carbon dioxide pollution: the greenhouse effect

▲
When sunlight reacts with chemical pollutants in the air, a layer ofphotochemical smog is formed.

Carbon dioxide is essential for life on Earth. It does two main things for us:

- it is the main 'food' for plants, in photosynthesis, and,
- it acts as a blanket to help keep the Earth warm.

Photosynthesis is dealt with in Chapter Nine, *The green world*. Energy can only leave the Earth in the form of infrared radiation. This is an invisible form of electromagnetic radiation, like radio and microwaves. We can feel infrared radiation coming away from a warm object. It is quite easily absorbed by matter, which then heats up. This explains why infrared 'rays' are sometimes called 'heat rays'.

There is a range of infrared radiation just as there is a range of light or radio waves. Very hot objects give off shortwave infrared waves. Cooler objects give off longer waves. Carbon dioxide absorbs the long waves, but lets the short waves through.

There is not much carbon dioxide in the atmosphere – only about 0.03%, but it has a powerful effect. First, it allows the radiation from the hot sun to pass through to the ground. The warm ground also emits radiation. But this is the low-temperature radiation, with long waves. This is then *absorbed* by the carbon dioxide. The gas gets warmer. Later, it gives some of this extra energy back to the Earth, or to the air. Some radiation still gets away into space from the carbon dioxide. But the point is that the energy does not all escape into outer space.

The ordinary glass greenhouse works in the same way, with the glass doing the same job as the carbon dioxide. So the carbon dioxide is called a 'greenhouse gas', helping to produce the *greenhouse effect* on Earth.

▼
Carbon dioxide and the greenhouse effect. Carbon dioxide in the Earth's atmosphere does the same job as the glass in the greenhouse.

solar radiation

Earth radiation

the Sun's rays pass through the layer of gas

carbon dioxide in the air traps heat rays from Earth

radiation from warm plants, etc.

solar radiation from the hot Sun

glass

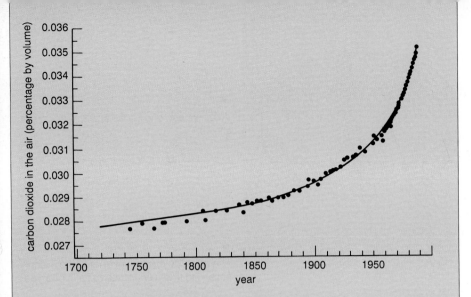

◄
The increase in carbon dioxide in the air since 1700.

Is the greenhouse effect increasing?

What is worrying scientists is that this blanketing may be getting too effective. The amount of carbon dioxide in the atmosphere is increasing. And the *rate* of increase is also rising. This is partly due to the extra fossil fuels that we have been burning for the past two hundred years.

But extra carbon dioxide is also caused by having more people and cows on Earth! People breathe out carbon dioxide, and so do cows. But cows also give out the gas methane as part of their digestive processes. Methane is an even better 'greenhouse gas' than carbon dioxide.

All over the world people are cutting down trees to make more agricultural land. Trees are actually *made* from carbon dioxide. They grow as their leaves take the gas out of the air. Cutting down the trees stops this natural soak-up of carbon dioxide. Burning them to clear forests releases the gas back into the air again.

The worry is that the temperature on Earth will increase. *Global warming* will occur. This does not necessarily mean that we will get sunnier summers. One effect may be more rain, with more winds and gales. The ice at the North and South Poles may melt. This will alter climate – and make sea levels rise. Low-lying land will be flooded. The most heavily populated parts of the World are near the seas. Major cities and agricultural areas would become unusable. Many other unpleasant changes might occur. Is there any evidence that this is beginning to happen?

Recent measurements have shown that the Earth is getting warmer. This is very likely to be due to the greenhouse effect. But the measurements are hard to make, and not all scientists agree that they are accurate. But the risk is too great to ignore. It could be time to say 'better to be safe than sorry'.

THE INDEPENDENT

Friday 11 January 1991

Pollution is blamed for warmest year on record

By Nicholas Schoon
Environment Correspondent

GOVERNMENT scientists said yesterday that there was now rea-

Bab

Average world temperatures for the last 140 years

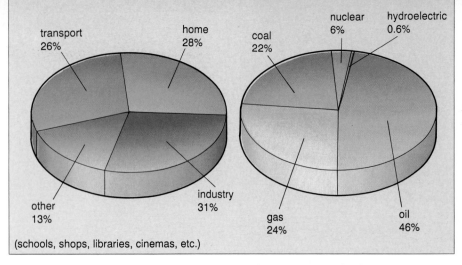

What we use energy for and where we get it from.

The average amount of energy that each person in these countries uses in one year.

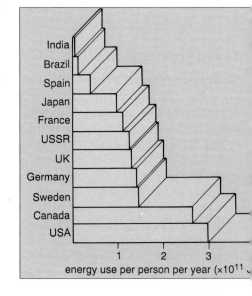

Can we solve the problems caused by fossil fuels?

A modern industrial society uses a lot of energy. This diagram shows how much energy is used in different parts of the world. The more economically developed nations are the big energy users. They have all agreed that they should reduce the bad effects of fossil fuels.

Short-term solutions mean removing the pollutant gases like sulphur dioxide from waste gases before they are pumped into the atmosphere. This is not cheap – it costs £350 million per power station. Most sulphur dioxide comes from power stations generating electricity, and in the next ten years it is planned to spend huge amounts of money on this. But it is not possible to remove carbon dioxide as easily.

Short-term solutions are not good enough. There are three important long-term solutions that are being tried:

- use less energy,
- use renewable, non-polluting energy sources,
- use nuclear energy.

Saving energy

There are plenty of ways to go about using less energy. We could take showers instead of baths, using less hot water. We could travel in buses and trains instead of in cars. We could wear more clothes in winter and live in cooler houses. The easiest way to make people do this would be to increase the price of fuel. This would not be a scientific decision, but a political one. And not a popular one at that!

A lot of energy is wasted through bad design. Houses are not well insulated, so that heating energy is lost to the outside. The British government spends over £40 million each year trying to persuade industry to save energy through better design of machines and processes. They hope to save £500 million worth of energy each year by 1995.

Clean energy?

What the world needs is a source of energy that is cheap, clean and *renewable*. 'Renewable' means that it will not run out like coal and oil will. There are plenty of sources of renewable energy: the Sun, wood and other forms of biomass, fast-flowing rivers, tides, energy from hot rocks, the wind, sea waves, hydro-electricity. These are all being used today. In the not too distant future there is the possibility of using *nuclear fusion*. Finally, there is a non-renewable source that will last very much longer even than coal: uranium used in *nuclear fission reactors*. This is already in use in nuclear power stations.

Energy from the Sun

The Sun is the main energy source for the Earth. It provides the energy for winds, waves and rivers, as explained in Chapter Seven, *Energy and the Earth*. It provides the radiation that plants need to grow as wood and make the leaves, seeds and fruit to feed animals. It makes the Earth warm enough to live on. Solar cells make it possible to change sunlight directly into electricity.

The problem with all these energy sources is that they are variable. The Sun does not always shine. The wind does not always blow. Sometimes the sea is calm. So each of these sources has to be linked to some kind of back-up system. This could be an 'energy store' or some other reliable energy source that we could switch in.

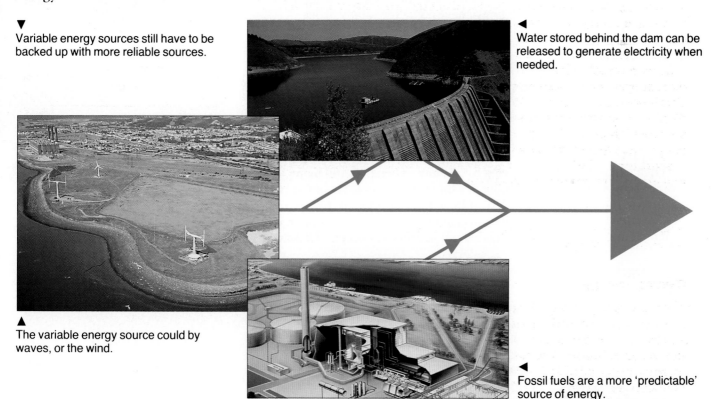

▼ Variable energy sources still have to be backed up with more reliable sources.

◄ Water stored behind the dam can be released to generate electricity when needed.

▲ The variable energy source could by waves, or the wind.

◄ Fossil fuels are a more 'predictable' source of energy.

For example, some of our electricity is generated by windmills. This is added to the electricity generated by nuclear and fossil-fuel stations. If the wind fails, the output from the other stations is stepped up. But if we relied on wind for more than about 25% of our electrical energy there would be problems. On calm days we would need to start up other power stations from scratch. This is slow and expensive at over £50 000 for each station.

There are similar problems with using wave power and solar cells. But the energy source is free and there is plenty of it. Many countries are spending money trying to make these alternative energy sources more practicable.

▲ Boiling water from deep inside the Earth is used to drive the turbines in Icelandic power stations. Icelanders claim that the water is pretty good for you too!

▲ A Turkish town covered in solar panels that are used to heat water.

Hydroelectric power stations are more reliable than wind and solar energy. They are mostly based on huge lakes of water held behind dams. They need a high rainfall. They also need to be in mountain areas – so that the water from the dam can flow downhill. As the water flows through turbine wheels it spins generators to make an electric current. Norway, with its high mountains and plenty of rain and snow, can make all of its electric power this way. In Britain we have a smaller supply, from hydroelectric power stations in Wales and Scotland.

Nuclear energy

Britain generates 20% of its electricity in nuclear power stations. France generates over 50% in this way. In theory, nuclear energy is non-polluting and cheap. In practice, it is proving to be quite expensive, and many people are scared by the possibility of a nuclear accident. The most famous such accident happened in 1986, in Ukraine. One of the reactors at the Chernobyl Nuclear Power Station caught fire. Radioactive material went high into the atmosphere and fell out in rain over much of Western Europe.

◄ Thousands of tonnes of sand and concrete were dropped onto the remains of the Chernobyl nuclear reactor to stop radioactive materials from getting into the air.

The following section explains how nuclear power stations work, and what it means to say that a substance is *radioactive*.

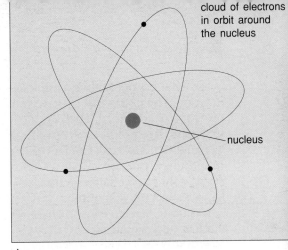

cloud of electrons
in orbit around
the nucleus

nucleus

▲
An atom (above); below, the nuclei of the elements get larger as you go along the periodic table.

Atoms and nuclei

An atom consists of a small central *nucleus* surrounded by a cloud of *electrons*. Atoms are very small, but can just about be 'seen' by special microscopes. The photograph on page 142 just shows the outermost part of the atom – the nucleus is even smaller. The atoms you can 'see' are mostly empty space, as shown in the diagram (right).

Electrons are even smaller than the nuclei, and weigh very little. Over 99.9% of the mass of a piece of material is in the nuclei of its atoms. The nuclei are made up of two kinds of sub-atomic particle: *protons* and *neutrons*.

Each proton has a positive charge. Protons and neutrons are almost the same, but neutrons are not charged. As a rule there are more neutrons than protons in the heavier nuclei. There is more about this in Chapter Five, *Chemical patterns*.

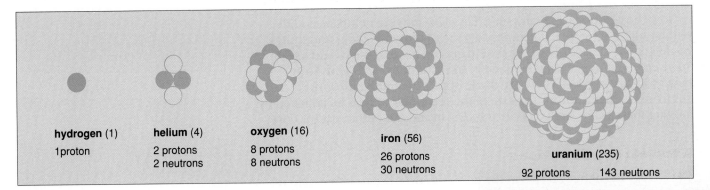

hydrogen (1)

1 proton

helium (4)

2 protons
2 neutrons

oxygen (16)

8 protons
8 neutrons

iron (56)

26 protons
30 neutrons

uranium (235)

92 protons   143 neutrons

Fission

The particles in a nucleus are held there by very strong forces. But if the nucleus gets too big then there is a chance that it will split into two parts. When this happens we call it *nuclear fission*. Heavier elements have large nuclei, and the nuclei most likely to split are those of the most massive natural element, uranium.

But even so, this does not happen very often. When it does, there is a large release of energy. One nucleus splitting gives out very little energy, but it is still a lot more than when one atom of carbon combines with two atoms of oxygen. Energy from nuclear changes is many times greater than the energy we can get from chemical changes.

The problem is to get a lot of nuclei to split at the same time. If too many split at once we have made an 'atomic' bomb – really a *nuclear bomb*. In a nuclear power station the *reactor* is designed to control the rate at which the nuclei split.

▲
Japanese children in front of a poster that shows what happens when nuclear energy is released in an uncontrolled way.

◀
The Dounreay nuclear power station. The fission reaction is contained in the sphere at the top of the picture.

So, what happens when a nucleus splits up? This is shown in the diagram. The new particles have movement energy, and some dangerous radiation is produced. The key effect that is used to control the reaction is that some *free neutrons* are produced when the nucleus splits.

These neutrons can trigger other nuclei to split. If they did not, the rate of splitting would be too slow to be useful. If they are too effective the result could be a chain reaction, resulting in an explosion. This is what happens in a nuclear bomb.

It is quite hard to cause a chain reaction, and *this* is not a danger in a nuclear power station.

The 'fuel' in a typical reactor is a type of uranium nucleus with 235 particles in it called uranium-235. It is made into *fuel rods* which can be moved in and out of the reactor core. The loose neutrons from the nuclei that do split move freely through the core, but they are moving too fast to be effective. They are slowed down by another rod, called a *moderator*. This is made of carbon.

Now the reaction can really start. The slow-moving neutrons collide with uranium-235 nuclei. This produces a lot more neutrons and things could get out of hand. The core would get too hot and we would have a 'melt-down'. This is what happened in the Chernobyl accident. So yet more rods are needed. These are made of an element that *absorbs* neutrons – usually boron. The rate of the reaction can thus be adjusted by moving these rods – called *control rods* – in and out of the reactor core.

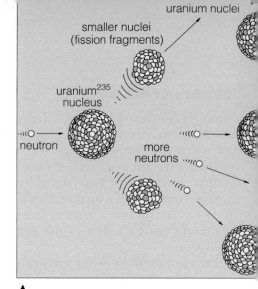

▲
A nuclear chain reaction.

A nuclear power station

The energy from the reaction in the core is transferred to movement of atoms. This internal energy is what we call 'heat' – the core gets very hot. This energy is carried away from the core in much the same way as energy is carried away from the furnace in a coal-fired generator. This may be by a gas or by a liquid. The fluid is heated by the reactor, keeping the reactor at its working temperature. The fluid is then piped to a heat exchanger connected to a steam-driven turbine. The turbines turn electrical generators.

Gas-cooled reactors use carbon dioxide as the working fluid; water-cooled generators use super-heated water or steam.

▼
How a nuclear power station is used to generate electricity.

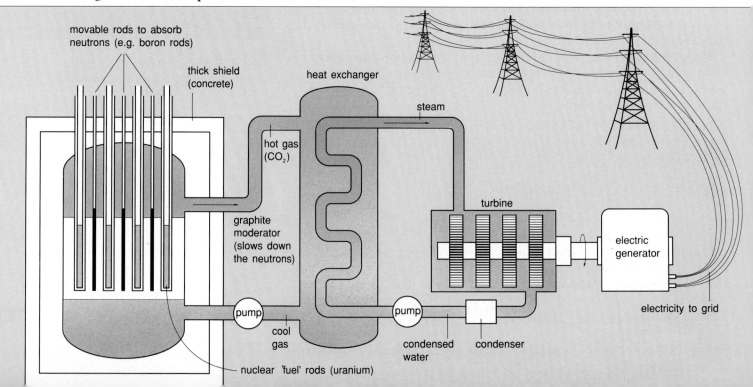

Worries about nuclear power

Nuclear power stations do not emit poisonous gases or gases that produce acid rain. But they do produce *nuclear waste*. This consists of radioactive materials produced in the reactor, and spent fuel and control rods. These are regularly removed and have to be treated and stored. But when the power station is closed down at the end of its working life most of the reactor's immediate surroundings will also have become radioactive.

The costs of nuclear energy have to allow for the safe treatment of these wastes. So what is radioactivity – and why is it so dangerous?

Radioactivity

Radioactivity was discovered almost a hundred years ago. This was long before nuclear fission was discovered. Like nuclear fission, the source of radioactivity is large nuclei. This time, instead of splitting into two roughly equal bits, the nucleus spits out smaller particles.

Ionising radiation

Radioactive substances emit three kinds of radiation, called *alpha*, *beta* and *gamma* radiation. They were named like this when they were first discovered, before scientists knew what they really were. All of them carry energy, and are powerful enough to knock electrons out of other atoms and molecules. This makes ions, so they are often called *ionising radiations*.

Properties of ionising radiations

Marie Curie, the discoverer of radium, with her husband and co-worker Pierre.

Name	Description	Range in air	Stopped by
alpha particle	very massive (2 protons with 2 neutrons); positive charge	4 – 10 centimetres	sheet of paper
beta particle	very light (electrons); negative charge	variable; up to about a metre	a few millimetres of aluminium
gamma ray	photons of electromagnetic radiation; not charged; travel at the speed of light	no limit	several metres of concrete

The dangers of ionising radiation

Living cells are damaged when some of their molecules are ionised. Sometimes they die as a result, but the most danger may come when they do not die. Instead, the cell changes to a cancer cell. This means that it carries on living and growing. It reproduces and makes more cells. But it is no longer controlled by the body. Cancer cells may then take over that part of the body at the expense of normal cells.

If cells in the reproductive system are affected by ionising radiation then the offspring may have *genetic mutations*. The genes that control development of children no longer work properly, and children may be born with various defects.

As people cannot see or feel these radiations they tend to be very frightened by all this. In fact, we are surrounded by radioactive materials. Every second each square centimetre of your body has one or two 'blips' of ionising radiation passing through it. This is known as *background radiation*. It comes from radioactive materials in the soil and rocks, in the food we eat and the air we breathe. Some comes from the Sun or from outer space.

Alpha particles carry the most energy and would cause most damage, but they are easily stopped. Gamma radiation can travel through most materials easily, but does not carry as much energy so cause less damage. Beta radiation is fairly penetrating and quite strongly ionising.

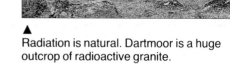

▲
Radiation is natural. Dartmoor is a huge outcrop of radioactive granite.

Radioactive decay

A uranium nucleus with 238 particles in its nucleus is unstable. When it sends out an alpha particle it loses two protons and two neutrons. This means that its atomic number (proton number) changes from 92 to 90. Chemically, it has become a nucleus of a different element – thorium. See Chapter Five, which explains how and why elements are different.

This kind of change is called *radioactive decay*. But the decay does not stop after a single change. The thorium is also radioactive. It decays by emitting a beta particle. This comes from the nucleus, where a neutron has changed into a proton. The extra charge on the nucleus means that it is now another different element – protactinium. In its turn, this changes to yet another element, and so on. These changes will continue, ending only when a stable form of lead is produced.

▼
Radioactive nuclei go through a series of changes as they decay.

Half-life

These changes do not happen at a constant rate. In fact, it all depends on chance. The bigger the chance of the nucleus decaying, the more will decay in a certain time.

Uranium-238 has a very small chance of decaying. Of all the uranium-238 that was on Earth when the Earth was formed, only about a half of it has decayed! The time it takes for half of the nuclei in a pure radioactive sample to decay is called the *half-life* of the nucleus.

The half-life of uranium-238 is 4.5 billion years. This is why there is still so much of it left on Earth. But thorium-234 decays with a half-life of only 24 days. When you plot half-life on a graph, you always get the same shape of curve.

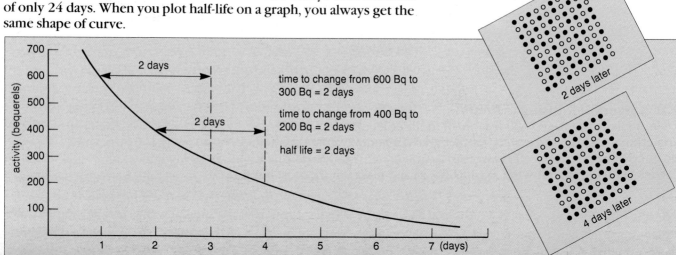

time to change from 600 Bq to 300 Bq = 2 days

time to change from 400 Bq to 200 Bq = 2 days

half life = 2 days

Half-life and nuclear waste

Nuclear wastes may have half lives of several thousand years. This means that they have to be stored for long times. They become *fairly* harmless only after about 10 half lives have passed. Nobody wants to have these wastes stored near them, even if they are put deep underground. The latest idea is simply to cover the wastes, and even the old worn-out power stations, under mountains of soil and concrete.

Where does nuclear energy come from?

The energy for nuclear fission and radioactive decay comes from a remarkable property of matter. This is that it can be destroyed and converted into energy. If we measure the mass of the uranium nucleus before it splits into two parts, we find that it weighs more than the smaller bits that it produces. The 'lost mass' has been converted to energy of radiation or of movement. The energy produced is given by one of the most famous equations ever written.

$$E = mc^2$$

E is the energy produced, m is the lost mass, and c is the speed of light. This explains why so much energy is produced – the speed of light is a very large number – 300 000 000 m/s.

Albert Einstein, who 'discovered' $E = mc^2$.

The laws of energy

The laws of energy are strict. We may be able to *save* energy, but the *First Law of Energy* says that you cannot *create* energy. You can only get it from something that already has it. Nuclear energy comes from the mass of the radioactive nucleus.

Equally, you cannot *destroy* energy. This sounds wonderful. Does it mean that we can use it again and again? Unfortunately, the answer is *no*. This is because of the *Second Law of Energy*.

This law tells us that whenever we use energy to do something useful – like a job of work – some of the original energy always becomes unusable.

Think of a car engine. To start with, we have a supply of energy in the 'petrol-and-air' system that drives the car. We hope to transfer this energy into movement of the car (kinetic energy). But car engines get hot. In fact, they will only work if they are hotter than the surrounding air. The result is that energy is 'lost' in heating the air. Even the best 'heat engines' lose about 65% of the input energy to the surroundings.

▼
The energy transfers through a car engine. This energy-flow diagram is called a Sankey diagram.

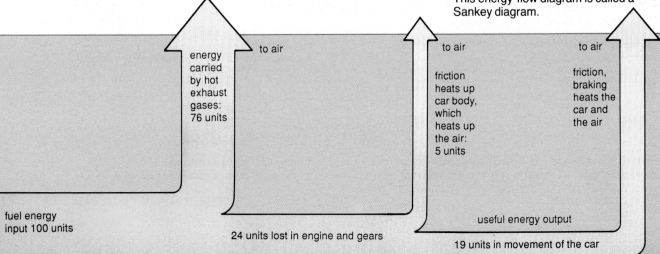

to air
energy carried by hot exhaust gases: 76 units

to air
friction heats up car body, which heats up the air: 5 units

to air
friction, braking heats the car and the air

fuel energy input 100 units

24 units lost in engine and gears

useful energy output

19 units in movement of the car

This general rule applies to all jobs where we do work. Most of the energy we use ends up warming the air. The energy is shared amongst billions and billions of air molecules, all moving a little faster. It is very hard to get this energy 'back together again'. See below for the efficiency of various energy-using devices. The figures tells us how much of the input energy gets to where we want it to go.

Energy in the future

There are signs that people are beginning to understand the need to use energy wisely. This is closely linked with the idea of looking after the world a lot better. But there are hard choices ahead.

Renewable energy sources are still too expensive or undeveloped to replace fossil fuels. As the fuels get scarcer, and their costs rise, we must either use less energy or make better use of the energy we have. For the past 50 years or so the hope has been that *nuclear fusion* can be made to work.

Nuclear fusion is the energy source that drives the stars – including our Sun. It is another example in which nuclear matter is converted to energy. In the centre of stars simple nuclei of hydrogen are *fused together* to make helium. The mass of the helium nucleus produced is less than the masses of the hydrogen nuclei that went into making it. The 'lost mass' appears as energy of movement or radiation.

Efficiency of some common devices

Device	Typical efficiency
steam locomotive	10%
car engine	25%
coal-fired power station	40%
diesel engine	40%
coal water heater	60%
oil water heater	70%
gas water heater	75%
electric locomotive	90%
hydroelectric turbine	90%

Activities

1 Make a survey of the fuels used by members of your class for heating their homes. Ask them to find the *main* reason why that fuel was chosen.
   Think of a good way of presenting your results (like a bar chart, pie chart, etc).

2 Use this book, especially the 'Reference section', and any other information that you can find, to tackle one of the following problems. Make sure that the information you use is up-to-date and that your ideas are clear and easy to follow.
   (a) Is there an 'energy crisis'?
   (b) Give ten energy-saving tips for either your home or your school.
   (c) Why we should use the idea of *combined heat and power* in generating electricity.
   (d) Give one page of clear advice to the Government on how to save energy, on a national scale, in transport.

3 Make a poster summarising the main points for and against using fossil fuels.

4 Imagine what would happen if *complicated* machines (like cars, lawn mowers, TV sets, power stations) all suddenly stopped working. What kind of energy would be most useful? How would it be best used? What difference would it make to the way we live? Are there any people on Earth who actually live in that kind of way at present? Discuss any of the above questions with your friends. Plan how you would survive.

5 Write a film script, radio broadcast or short play (or do a series of drawings) which gets across to people the ideas (which seem to contradict each other) that:
   ● energy cannot be created nor destroyed
   ● we are 'using up' the energy resources of the Earth.

6 Design an experiment to measure the efficiency of any simple (and safe) energy devices. You could try to measure the efficiency of:
   ● a small electric motor
   ● a wind-up toy car
   ● a simple machine (a pulley system or a car jack).

Questions

1 Two of the most important things that people need to know before deciding which fuel to use to heat their homes are:
   ● how much the fuel costs, and
   ● how much storage space the fuel needs.

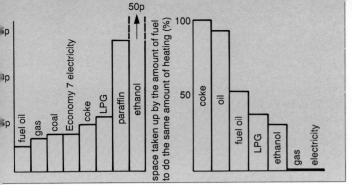

The costs of different fuels and the amount of space that they take up when stored.

The bar charts give information about this for some possible fuels, plus some information about electric heating.

Use the information given in the bar charts to answer the following questions.
(a) Which fuel is the cheapest?
(b) Which fuel takes up the most space?
(c) The chart does not give any 'space' value for gas and electricity. Give a reason for this.
(d) Apart from gas and electricity, which fuel would take up the least storage space in the home?
(e) Write a paragraph saying which fuel you would choose, giving reasons. (Remember that there are other reasons for choosing fuels, such as safety, ease of use, pollution, ash, etc.)

2 A group of students did a test of a number of substances that might be useful as fuels. They got the following results.

Possible fuel	Temperature rise of 100 g of water (°C)
charcoal	2
wood	3
ethanol	5
chopped straw	4

(a) Draw and label the kind of apparatus the students might have used to obtain these results.
(b) What important thing would they have to do to make sure that it was a *fair* test of the fuels?
(c) One student said that she thought the experiment was not accurate enough. She said that the temperatures rises they got were too small to measure properly. Give *two* things that they could do to get a bigger rise in temperature.
(d) In a more careful experiment the students found that 2 g (0.002 kg) of wood produced a temperature rise of 5.5 °C in 0.10 kg of water. They calculated that this meant that the water had absorbed 2.3 kJ of energy. Check their answer by using the formula:

$$\text{heating energy} = \text{mass of water} \times \text{temperature rise} \times \text{specific thermal capacity.}$$

(The specific thermal capacity of water is 4.2 kJ per kg per °C.)
(e) The students found a book that told them that 1 kg of the wood they used would transfer 12 MJ (12 million joules) of energy when it was burnt. Calculate how much energy 0.002 kg should produce. Compare this with the value they actually obtained. Can you think of a reason why the answers are different?

3 Here is a list of some energy sources: coal; oil; uranium; wind; tides; high-level dams; running water; geothermal (hot rocks); 'natural' gas; 'biogas'; wood.
(a) Which of these are *fossil fuels*?
(b) Which of them are in danger of being used up within the next 100 years?
(c) Which of them produce dangerous or polluting by-products when they are used?
(d) Three of them are the sources of nearly all the energy used in the UK. Name any two of the three.
(e) Name two of the sources that are *renewable*.
(f) *Electricity* is not included in the list – quite correctly. Why would it be wrong to call electricity an 'energy source'?

4 (a) Give three kinds of energy store.
(b) For each one, say: how the energy got into it; how the energy is got out of it and used.
(c) Which of the three examples you have given could store
(i) the *most* energy
(ii) its energy most *cheaply*.

5 Your family (or your village, street, school or commune) proposes that it should opt out of the national energy system (which provides coal, oil, gas and electricity) and 'go it alone'. Make a list of the energy sources that would then be available for you, giving a brief explanation of each. Would you support or oppose the decision? Give a reasoned argument for your point of view.

6 Use the diagram, which illustrates the energy flow through a coal-fired electrical power station, to draw, as accurately as you can, an energy flow-diagram (Sankey diagram) which shows what happens to the energy obtained from the combustion of the coal.

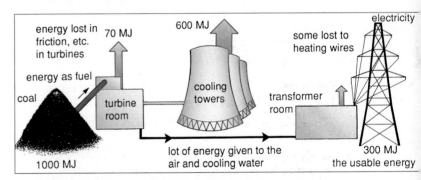

7 Use the information given in this chapter, and in the 'Reference section' to answer the following questions.
(a) From which source does Great Britain get most of its energy?
(b) What are alpha radiations, beta radiations and gamma radiations?
(c) What happens in nuclear *fission*?
(d) Give two problems that might be caused by the waste from nuclear power stations.

185

Checklist

These are the facts and ideas that you should have learned by studying this topic.

To succeed at Basic Level you should:

● know that people produce a lot of wastes and that even if the wastes decay it might take a long time
● know that getting and using fuels can affect the land, the air and water in rivers and the sea
● be able to describe a project to help improve your local environment

To succeed at Foundation Level you should:

● know that some wastes can be recycled
● be able to describe some of the sources of pollution, its effects and how it could be stopped or reduced
● know that making new materials needs chemical reactions
● know that fossil fuels, like coal and crude oil, come out of the ground, and have to be turned into everyday fuels like petrol, heating oil, diesel, paraffin, coke, propane, etc.
● understand that burning fuels need a supply of oxygen, and that oxides are produced
● understand why we should use fuels wisely (e.g. cost; fossil fuels take a long time to form; the Earth has a limited supply) and know some ways of doing this in the home
● know that a main use of fossil fuels is to generate electricity
● know how useful energy is, and that energy can be stored and transferred
● know that everything is made up of small particles called atoms
● know that some atoms break up and give out radiation; this radiation is useful but dangerous

To succeed at Merit Level you should:

● be able to identify the good and bad consequences of exploiting raw materials as fuels and give a balanced account of this
● know the meaning of *exothermic* and *endothermic* in describing chemical reactions and be able to relate these to temperature changes
● be able to construct simple word equations to describe reactions
● know how fossil fuels were made
● know which everyday fuels come from crude oil and coal
● understand that energy cannot be destroyed, but usually spreads out and becomes less useful when we transfer it
● be able to follow a sequence of energy transfers in the context of generating electrical power from fossil or nuclear energy sources
● understand that the Sun is the major energy source for the Earth
● know what efficiency means
● know that radioactive substances give out ionising radiations, which are always around us as background radiation

To succeed at Special Level you should:

● know that the main impact of human activity on the environment is fairly recent, and linked to population size, economic and industrial needs
● understand some major changes in the biosphere caused by human activity (e.g. acid rain, the greenhouse effect) and that such changes might take a very long time to reverse
● be able to select and analyse evidence to come to a reasoned judgement about some of these major ecological effects
● understand the long timescale associated with the formation of fossil fuels, and the implications of this
● understand that all energy transfers dissipate energy to heat the environment
● understand that using any energy source means making difficult choices about both the environment and the economy, and be able to use data to evaluate these
● be able to describe how electricity is generated from a variety of energy sources (fossil, nuclear and renewable)
● be able to describe the structure of the nucleus and relate it to radioactivity and nuclear fission
● know the three types of nuclear radiation and be able to describe their properties and effects
● be able to explain the meaning of half life and how it affects the use of radioactive substances
● be able to construct balanced symbolic equations in describing chemical reactions (in the context of fuel use)

Extension tasks

Things to read and do

Task 1
The greenhouse effect

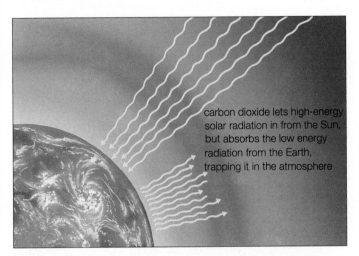

carbon dioxide lets high-energy solar radiation in from the Sun, but absorbs the low energy radiation from the Earth, trapping it in the atmosphere

Greenhouse gases allow the sun's rays to pass relatively freely through the atmosphere to warm the surface of the Earth, but they prevent the Earth's heat from being radiated back into space.

The greenhouse gases are carbon dioxide, the chlorofluorocarbons (CFCs), methane, nitrous oxide and, in the lower atmosphere, ozone. Carbon dioxide is the largest single contributor to the greenhouse effect, accounting for more than half the expected rise in temperature by the year 2030. The amount of CO_2 in the atmosphere has increased by more than a quarter since the late 18th century and the rate of increase is itself increasing – half the total increase has taken place since 1950. The combustion of fossil fuels and other industrial releases are now pumping more than 5 billion tonnes of CO_2 into the atmosphere each year.

This is more than three times the amount in 1950.

Most scientists now agree that if the CO_2 in the atmosphere doubled, it would cause a rise in temperature at the Earth's surface of between 1.5 °C and 5.5 °C. The last major change in temperature on Earth was at the end of the last Ice Age. That change was only 3–4 °C. The fear is that the rise due to the greenhouse effect will cause a complete change in the global climate.

No single nation accounts for the bulk of the world's production of CO_2, but the U.S.A., China and the U.S.S.R. together produce more than half of it. In Britain, generating electricity in power stations powered by fossil fuels produces 30 per cent of the carbon dioxide that the U.K. produces.

There are several mysteries about the greenhouse effect. One is that only about half the CO_2 pumped into the atmosphere stays there. We know that some of it is taken up by the surface waters of the oceans – but we do not know how much the sea could absorb, or exactly how it does it.

If the seas stay cool the air will not warm up very much. But if the seas warm up so will the atmosphere. And because of the inertia in the system, air temperatures will continue to rise for many years after any rise in ocean temperature.

Another unpredictable consequence is what effect warming up the sea will have on its ability to hold carbon dioxide. If this makes it give out some of its CO_2, then a small rise in temperature will lead to a vicious upward spiral in which the world gets hotter and hotter.

(Adapted from an article in *The Independent*, 17 October 1988.)

1 What gases are causing the greenhouse effect?

2 What part of the sun's radiation is the main cause of the heating effect?

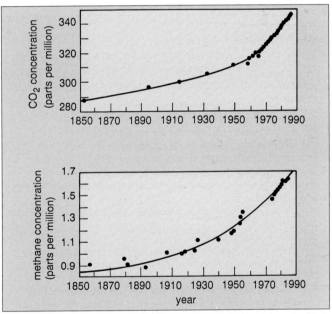

3 Why has there been such an increase in CO_2 emissions into the atmosphere since about 1950?

4 Plants are able to take in CO_2. They use it to help them grow, in turn giving out oxygen.
(a) What is this process called?
(b) What other human activity, not mentioned in the above passage, may be helping to increase the proportion of CO_2 in the atmosphere?
(c) What effects do living animals have on the CO_2/oxygen balance in the atmosphere?

5 Methane (CH_4) is a gas produced by the action of bacteria on waste organic material (decaying plants, etc.). Most of it comes from cows as part of their digestive process. Some comes from *termites* – insects that build large nests out of partly chewed wood.

Describe more fully what happens in *one* of these examples of methane production.

6 Explain what the author means by: 'a small rise in temperature will lead to a vicious upward spiral in which the world gets hotter and hotter'.

Task 2
Analysing movement

1 Checking the basics

Use the 'Reference section' to do the following:
(a) Write down the two things you would need to know to work out the *average speed* of a vehicle during a journey.
(b) Write down the formula that would help you work out:
(i) the final speed after a vehicle has been steadily accelerating for a few seconds,
(ii) how far it would have travelled whilst it was accelerating.
(c) (i) What does acceleration mean?
(ii) What are the two main things that decide the rate at which a vehicle (or any movable object) accelerates?

2 Using the ideas

In testing a new model of car, the following measurements were taken.

Time in seconds from start to finish	0	2	4	6	8	10	12	14	16
Speed in metres per second	0	6	12	18	24	28	30	30	30

(a) Draw a graph of speed against time.
(b) Mark on your graph:
(i) the part which shows a steady acceleration.
(ii) the part which shows a steady speed.
(c) Use the table, or the graph, to work out:
(i) the change in speed in the first 6 seconds,
(ii) the rate (in metres per second per second) at which the car accelerated.
(d) A car is designed so that it can *decelerate* faster than it can *accelerate*.
(i) Give a reason for this.
(ii) Is the force that can be exerted by the car's brakes larger or smaller than the force that the engine can produce? Give a reason for your answer.
(iii) The test car had a mass of 800 kg. Use the value of the acceleration calculated in c(ii) above to work out the effective force produced by the engine. (*Note*: force = mass × acceleration.)
(iv) The designers want the brakes to stop the car from a speed of 30 m/s in a time of 3 seconds. Work out the braking force that this would need.
(v) Would it be safer to design the car so that it could stop from this speed in a time of 0.5 seconds? Give reasons for your answer.
(e) (i) Give two safety features you would look for in a well-designed car.
(ii) Explain, using your knowledge of physics, how any one of the features helps to make the car safer.

Task 3
Problems of pollution

Some students were carefully monitoring the effects of untreated sewage being pumped into a stream. They had samples from various points along the river. The map below shows the sample points and the results are shown on the table.

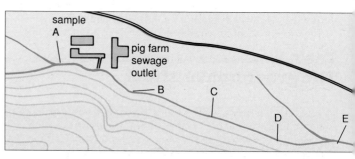

Water content	Station				
	A	B	C	D	E
Number of animals in standard sample					
trout	2	0	0	0	0
mayfly	60	0	0	0	41
stonefly	19	0	0	0	12
water louse	15	0	243	512	50
shrimps	40	0	0	4	28
Tubifex (bloodworm)	0	958	472	153	6
Physical components of the sample					
suspended solids (mg)	8	16	9	8	6
dissolved oxygen (100 is the maximum)	100	31	62	87	95

1 Find out as much as you can about each of the animals found at Station A. Work out if each one is a carnivore, herbivore or omnivore.

2 Draw up a possible food web based on this information.

3 Plot a graph or a series of graphs to represent what is happening along this stretch of river.

4 The local water authority wishes to build a new sewage-water treatment plant to reduce the problems of pollution in the river.
   Imagine that you are the River Authority Ecologist. Prepare a booklet explaining:
(a) how pollution in the river is investigated,
(b) the amount of pollution in the river,
(c) how building the sewage plant will help.

Task 4
Plant growth hormones

Plants need light to drive the reactions of photosynthesis. Plant stems will grow towards a light source, and leaves are positioned so as to collect as much sunlight as possible. This 'movement' of plants towards light is called *phototropism* (from the Greek, *photo* for light and *tropo*, movement). It is easy to observe such a thing happening, but very difficult to discover how this works.

The mechanism of phototropism was revealed over a span of almost 50 years. The work was done by several scientists, each designing new experiments that built on the research of earlier workers. The history of studying plant tropisms is a very good example of how the results of investigations can be added together over a period of time to produce a final, accepted theory.

Each of the scientists used the same plant — the young growing shoots of grass seedlings. This shoot consists of the developing leaves wrapped in a tough sheath, called the *coleoptile*. The coleoptile is the basis of all the experiments that follow.

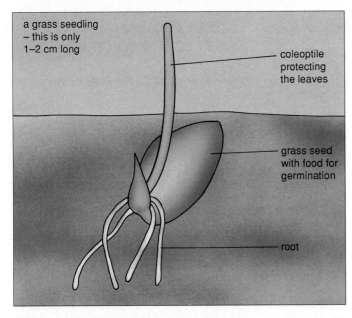

A grass seedling within its protective coleoptile.

1880 – Charles Darwin
Darwin is most widely known for his theory of evolution, *The Origin of Species*. But he was also a good experimenter. Darwin proved that it was only the tip of the shoot that was sensitive to light. When the tips were covered with a cap, the shoots did not bend towards the light.

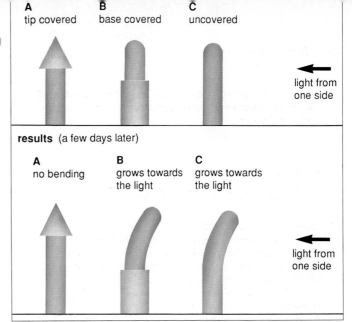

Charles Darwin proved that it is the *tip* of the coleoptile that responds to light.

1910 – Peter Boysen-Jensen
Thirty years after Darwin's work, the Dutch biologist Boysen-Jensen solved the problem of how the growing tip passed on the information about the direction of light to the rest of the plant. He suspected that the plants used chemical messengers. This diagram shows his first set of experiments.

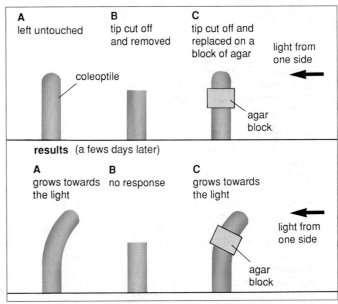

The results proved that the instruction from the shoot tip must be a chemical one because it could pass through an agar-jelly block. Agar is mostly water and so the message must be able to move through water. Like Darwin, Boysen-Jensen showed that the message must come from the tip, because shoots did not bend towards the light if their tips were removed.

The chemical messenger is called *auxin*. This comes from the Greek word *auxein*, to grow. By using slithers of mica, Boysen-Jensen showed that the auxin passed only down the 'dark' side of the shoot. Auxin cannot pass through mica. The shoots only bent towards the light when auxin could pass down the dark side of the shoot.

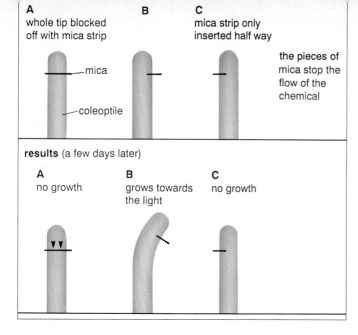

A
whole tip blocked
off with mica strip

B

C
mica strip only
inserted half way

mica

coleoptile

the pieces of
mica stop the
flow of the
chemical

results (a few days later)

A
no growth

B
grows towards
the light

C
no growth

1926 – F. W. Went

Went showed that the auxin could be collected in the agar blocks. He used this to show that auxin makes stem cells grow longer. So the side of the plant that gets most auxin will grow the most.

It is now clear that light, coming from one direction, causes auxin to move to the shaded side of the plant. This was discovered by using radioactive-labelled auxin. The auxin was traced because the radiation shows up on photographic plates.

Roots respond differently to auxin. High concentrations of auxin in a root cause cells to *stop* elongating. This causes negative phototropism: roots grow away from light. Scientists are still not sure how root cells and shoot cells can respond differently to the auxin.

Several other plant hormones have been discovered. They have various effects on the growth and development of plants. Some are involved in germination, others affect growth in height. Hormones control dormancy, fruit-ripening, and leaf fall. The life cycle of the plant is co-ordinated by the chemicals that it makes.

1 Describe Darwin's experiment that showed that it is the *tip* of the shoot that is sensitive to light. Give your answer as if you were Darwin, writing up your laboratory notes.

2 How did Peter Boysen-Jensen prove that the messenger chemical (auxin) passed down the dark side of the shoot?

3 (a) Auxin makes a plant cell grow. Explain how this can result in a shoot turning *towards* the light.
(b) How is it that roots move away from the light (showing negative phototropism)?

4 Auxin is a *hormone*. Write a paragraph or two about any other hormone that you have learned about. Say what it does, and why it is important in the life of the organism that makes it.

A good theory explains why things happen, or why things are the way they are. Newton's *theory of gravity* helped to explain why the planets move in their orbits around the Sun. Darwin's *theory of evolution* explained why there are so many different kinds of plants and animals on Earth. The kinetic theory helps to explain why gases expand, how they exert pressure and how substances change from solid to liquid to gas.

But to be scientific, a theory has to do more. First of all, there has to be good evidence for it. This is usually obtained by doing experiments. But the theory also has to *predict* something.

And a theory has to pass yet another test. It has to convince other experts that it is a *good* theory. This isn't always easy to do, even if the theory has been backed up with a great deal of evidence. Even good scientists find it hard to change their ideas. Sometimes a new theory is not accepted until all the old experts have retired — or died.

Scientists have to be cautious about new theories and results. Look at the people on page 000 who claimed to have carried out a fusion reaction in a test tube. If all the world's scientists had accepted their results, then some wrong results would have been accepted as fact.

Scientists can also be reluctant to accept new theories if they have come from people who they think do not really understand what they are talking about.

But he's only a meteorologist!

The theory of *continental drift* is a good example of the problems that theories have in getting accepted.

The idea that the continents drift about the surface of the Earth and are not fixed in their places came to a German scientist, Alfred Wegener, as he was looking at a map of the surface of the Earth. Others had had the same idea before, and since. Look at a map of the Earth. It seems obvious that the continents on either side of the Atlantic could fit together. The bit that sticks out of the side of South America matches the bit of Africa that curves in; and North Africa looks as if it could slot in to the space between North and South America.

Alfred Wegener was born in Berlin in 1880. He was interested in the weather and in astronomy. He qualified as a meteorologist and took part in many expeditions to the Arctic. He died in 1930 on an expedition to Greenland.

Wegener's theory

Wegener published a book describing his ideas on continental drift in 1924. He said that many features on Earth could be explained if the major continents had drifted across the surface of the Earth. He said that the shapes of the continents supported this idea. They would all fit together perfectly well, especially if you looked at the shapes 100 m below the present-day sea levels. Not only that, but he pointed out that the mountain chains in western Africa had 'twins' on the other side of the Atlantic. The rocks in both ranges were the same and of the same ages.

The rocks even had the same fossils in them. And, to cap it all, the fossils were of land animals — they were not of animals that could have swum across!

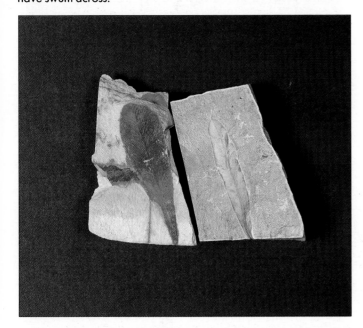

These are fossils of leaves. they are the same age and are from the same species of tree. But one was found in North America and the other in Africa.

The animals that we find in South America today are very different from African animals. But Wegener argued that when the continents had all been together, the animals had all been the same. The drifting continents had kept the species apart, which had then evolved differently.

He pointed out that there was coal in Siberia — the coldest place on Earth. No trees of the kind that had made the coal could possibly have survived if Siberia had always been so close to the North Pole, Siberia must have been nearer to the equator at some time in the past.

Wegener said that his theory also explained how mountains were built. Look at the Himalayas, he said. The rocks had obviously been pushed together by a huge force. Many hundreds of kilometres of rock had been pushed sideways into less than half that distance, so that they were all folded up and had been pushed up to a height of tens of kilometres above sea level. This had been done by the land mass of India crashing, very slowly, into Asia.

All this sounded very reasonable. In fact, he *was* right. But all his facts were already known. And geologists had already produced explanations for them.

The 'twin' mountains that spanned the Atlantic. This was explained by the theory of a 'land bridge'. Once upon a time, argued the geologists, the mountains did extend across the Atlantic — they had been worn away by the sea.

The land animals were the same in America and Africa 100 million years ago. Of course they were — up until then they could walk across the land bridge.

Coal in Siberia. The climate was better in those days — and quite small trees could die, decay and end up turned into coal.

Building the Himalayas. The Earth was shrinking! As we all know, claimed the theory of the day, the Earth is losing a lot of heat and so must be cooling down inside. As it cools, it shrinks. More land has to squash into a smaller space. It does this at weak spots — like the Himalayas.

Anyway, Wegener was a meteorologist. What did *he* know about geology!

Wegener's theory was argued for nearly 50 years. In the end it was proved by more detailed *evidence*, backed up by careful *measurements*:

- there was a better knowledge about the fossils on each side of the Atlantic and other places where oceans were widening;
- more accurate map measurements showed that the continents did actually move (including, eventually, photographs taken from satellites);
- magnetic measurements each side of the mid-Atlantic Ridge that showed rocks getting older as you went away from the ridge — the Atlantic Ocean had been getting wider for 100 million years;
- more accurate measurements about the radioactivity of rocks that showed there was enough energy to power these incredible movements.

Once the theory became 'respectable', more scientists became interested in it and started to do their own research. For example, they made *predictions* about the kind of fossils that they might find in an area based on where the continents were millions of years ago. Not many scientific theories are accepted straight away. But Alfred Wegener's was unluckier than most.

1 What do the following scientists study: (a) meteorologists (b) geologists?

2 Name two scientific *theories* that you know about that are *not* mentioned in this article.

3 What are the basic qualities of a good theory?

4 How did the geologists of Wegener's time explain:
   (a) How the mountains on each side of the Atlantic were so similar?
   (b) Why the fossils in South America and Africa were of the same kind of animals?

5 The article names four pieces of modern evidence that make scientists now believe that Wegener was right. Choose one of these and explain it in more detail. You may need to use reference books.

6 Some scientific theories are no longer believed in, although they were thought to be correct at one time.
   (i) Name one theory that is now known to have been 'wrong'.
   (ii) Explain why it was a good theory for its time.
   (iii) Explain why no one now believes in this theory.

Task 6
The rock cycle

Use the large diagram about the rock cycle on page 247 in the 'Reference section', and Chapter 7, *Energy and the Earth* to help you to answer the following questions.

1 What are sedimentary rocks?

2 What are igneous rocks?

3 How are metamorphic rocks made?

4 What part does the Sun play in helping to make new rocks?

5 Where do volcanoes get their energy from?

6 Explain the difference between *erosion* and *transport* as parts of the rock cycle.

7 Why are these processes called a *cycle*?

Task 7
A mixed bag

Use the Index and the 'Reference section' to help you to answer the following questions.

1 Some students were investigating what happens when an acid is added to an alkali. They used acid in a burette.

They added the acid slowly to the alkali, 5 ml at a time. They stirred the mixture and took the temperature after each 5 ml was added. This table shows the results that they got.

Volume of acid added (ml)	0	5	10	15	20	25	30	35	40	45
Temperature of liquid in flask (°C)	20	22	24	26	28	30	32	31	30	29

(a) Draw a graph of these results.
(b) Estimate the volume of acid needed to completely neutralise the alkali.
(c) What makes the temperature increase in the first part of the experiment?
(d) Why does the temperature fall after 30 ml of acid has been added?
(e) If you have not done so in your answer to part (c), use the idea of making and breaking chemical bonds to explain the results of this experiment.

2 What are the main types of pesticides? Why are they used and what are the possible dangers if they are over-used?

3 (a) What happens in photosynthesis?
(b) Here is some data about the production of oxygen by some algae (small water plants) at a range of light values ('lux' is a measure of how strong the light was) at two different temperatures.

Light value (lux)	Oxygen production in mg per m² per hour 8 – 10°C	18°C
25 500	226	361
16 700	200	331
11 400	180	439
7 400	201	182
4 300	121	208
2 150	133	58
1 180	42	59
620	44	−62

Plot a graph of these results (both graphs on the same axes). Which is the better temperature for oxygen production? Can you think of a reason?
(c) Describe in a sentence or two how the oxygen produced depends on the amount of light falling on the plants. Comment on any unusual features.
(d) What do you think is the cause of the negative value for oxygen production at low light levels in the second column?

4 Draw diagrams showing:
(a) How a prism can act as a mirror.
(b) How molecules are arranged in a plastic material.
(c) A circuit in which two lamps can be connected to the same power supply and be controlled separately by two switches.
(d) The differences between arteries and veins.
(e) How the populations of greenfly and ladybirds might change together over a fairly long time if there was a sudden increase in the numbers of greenfly to start with (*hint:* ladybirds eat greenfly).
(f) The arrangements of molecules in a dilute solution compared with a strong solution.

5 How does *electroplating* work?

6 Why does your heart beat faster when you run?

7 Why do some things bounce, while others do not?

8 Why do some trees lose their leaves in the winter? How can other trees keep theirs without coming to any harm?

9 How did nitrates get into the soil (for growing crops) *before* the large-scale factory production of nitrates, which only began about 60 years ago?

Task 8
Creating life

Mix some tap water and dead grass in a bottle. Leave it in a warm place for a few days. If you then look at a drop of the water under a microscope you will see that it is teeming with tiny life-forms. The water contains many thousands of protozoa, a Greek word meaning 'early life'. A dead animal, left lying, will soon be full of maggots. Old biscuits may become filled with weevils — the only really fresh food the old-time sailors ever ate!

We now believe that these small animals do not just appear from nowhere. The protozoa came from dried 'spores' that are everywhere in the air or in the soil. These are already alive, and are

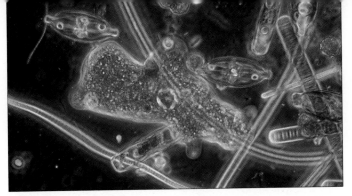

The life in a sample of pond water. These organisms have not generated from the water, but grown from spores that cannot be seen by the naked eye.

just waiting for the right conditions for them to become active, grow and reproduce. Maggots and weevils are the larvae of insects, hatched from small eggs laid by the adult insects, perhaps a long time before. But it is not easy to prove this. It needed careful detective work to show that life can only come from already existing life.

The greatest scientist of his day was Aristotle. He was a Greek who lived at the time of Alexander the Great, over two thousand years ago. He wrote books about everything, from biology to astronomy, drama, poetry and philosophy. What he wrote was so good, clear and sensible and his reputation so great that people believed him — even when he was wrong. And they kept on believing his view about creating new life for two thousand years.

'. . . everything comes into being not only from the mating of animals but also from the decay of the earth. Plants are the same, some come from seeds, but others arise from decaying earth, by natural forces, as it were by *spontaneous generation*.' The Greeks believed that rats generated from dirt and rubbish.

Spontaneous generation

The idea that life, if only of a very simple kind, could come from nowhere had a long run. It was not until 300 years ago that anybody even questioned this 'fact'. It was done by an Italian doctor, Francesco Redi (1626–1697). Redi was a doctor to the Dukes of Tuscany, but he had many other interests. He was an expert in language and a poet — and he was one of the first of a new type of scientist: the kind who actually did experiments.

Redi thought, for example, that a dead animal did not *create*

In the seventeenth century, scientists began to do proper experiments. They planned, designed and used controls. This man is weighing himself to see if all of the weight of the food that he eats is added to his own weight.

maggots from its flesh. It was the place where flies happened to lay their eggs. He did an experiment to test this idea:

'In the middle of July, I put a snake, some fish, some eels and a slice of milk-fed veal into four large, wide-mouthed flasks. I closed them well and sealed them. I then filled the same number of flasks in the same way, only leaving these open.'

He found that the meat and fish in the second set of flasks became 'wormy'. He saw that flies were going in and out of them. He showed that the maggots indeed turned into flies.

But there were no maggots in the flesh in the sealed flasks. He said this proved his theory. Indeed, he had carried out the very first experiment in biology that used a 'control'. No one else did this for 200 years.

He wrote about this and other experiments in a book. Lots of scientists read this book, but most of them still preferred Aristotle's ideas. Sometimes it takes more than a good experiment to change people's minds about something they have believed in for years!

Redi would have noticed that the flesh in the sealed jars would soon become bad, in a hot July in Italy. His experiment was not sterile, and the flesh and the flasks would be covered with bacteria.

New invention backs Aristotle!

This could have been a 17th century newspaper headline. During Redi's lifetime a Dutchman called Antonie van Leeuwenhoek invented the microscope. Surprisingly, this did not help Redi's theories. Using it, scientists could see that 'clean' water, gravy, wine or milk would grow tiny 'animals', too small to be seen with the naked eye. These must, they said, have 'generated spontaneously' from nothing. In some experiments, the tiny animals appeared even when boiled water, or boiled gravy, were put into 'clean' flasks which were then tightly stoppered. But other scientists seemed to get opposite results when the liquids were boiled for longer.

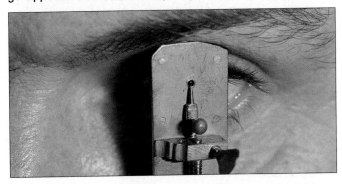

This is Leeuwenhoek's first microscope. The sample is placed on the needle point and then viewed through the tiny lens.

The death of the theory of spontaneous life

Scientists were still deeply divided about this in the middle of the last century. The argument got quite violent. In the end, the French Academy of Sciences offered a prize for anybody who could settle the argument, one way or the other. It was won in 1862 by Louis Pasteur. Pasteur was an expert in solving the problems caused by 'germs', the bacteria that cause disease, fermentation and decay.

Pasteur designed experiments that showed that even Leeuwenhoek's 'tiny animals' could not come 'on their own'. They had to come from somewhere else. His experiments were simple and elegant. He had perfected a sterile technique for keeping germs away. He showed that the germs were carried by dust in the air. This diagram shows his apparatus. Even after this, it took some time for all biologists to stop believing in spontaneous generation. Good 'wrong' ideas take a long time to die.

1 Where do you think the tiny animals on dried grass, in dust, etc., actually came from?

2 What features of Redi's experiments were a 'control'?

3 What does *spontaneous generation* mean?

4 Why did the invention of the microscope mean a set-back for the theory that 'life can only come from life'?

5 Why do you think some of the experiments with boiled gravy produced microscopic 'animals', while others did not?

6 One explanation of 'spontaneous generation' was that ordinary air (or perhaps the 'life-giving oxygen' in it) could create life. How did Pasteur's experiments disprove this as a possible explanation.

7 How did Pasteur's experiments show that (i) spontaneous generation did not occur and (ii) that life could not be created from thin air?

8 The Earth is about 4.5 billion years old. There was certainly no life on it to start with.
(i) How might (a) Aristotle and (b) Pasteur explain the origin of life on Earth?
(ii) How do you think life began on Earth?

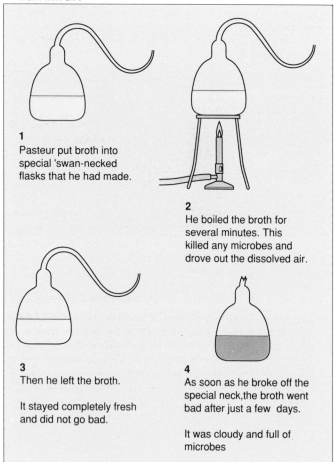

1
Pasteur put broth into special 'swan-necked flasks that he had made.

2
He boiled the broth for several minutes. This killed any microbes and drove out the dissolved air.

3
Then he left the broth.

It stayed completely fresh and did not go bad.

4
As soon as he broke off the special neck, the broth went bad after just a few days.

It was cloudy and full of microbes

Reference section

How to find what you want

This part of the book is arranged in six sections.

- *Laboratory skills*
  Using equipment and instruments to investigate, measure and test
- *Biology: data store*
- *Chemistry: data store*
- *Physics: data store*
- *The Earth: data store*
  All the main facts you need to follow this course are arranged in topics. You can learn a lot by just browsing through this.
- *Index*

But if you want to look something up, think of a *key word* that is to do with what you want to know. For example, you might want to find out how to test plants for starch. The key word would be 'starch': look this up in the Index on page 252 and it will refer you to the page that describes how to test plants for this. The key words are listed in alphabetical order. If you know about computer data bases, you may have used key searches already.

Some details that are given in the topic chapters are not repeated. Just use the Index to find them.

Reference

▽ Safety rules

1 **Think safe!**

2 **Read/listen to instructions.**

3 **Move carefully.**

4 **Beware of poisons. Do not eat or drink in laboratories.**

5 **Save eyes. Wear eye protection whenever you handle chemicals.**

6 **Work cleanly. Mop up spillages and do not put solids or paper into sinks.**

7 **When in doubt, check!**

This section covers the basic investigating, measuring and testing skills that are useful in any kind of practical science. It also includes some more advanced techniques which have special uses.

INVESTIGATING

▽ Techniques for investigations on plants

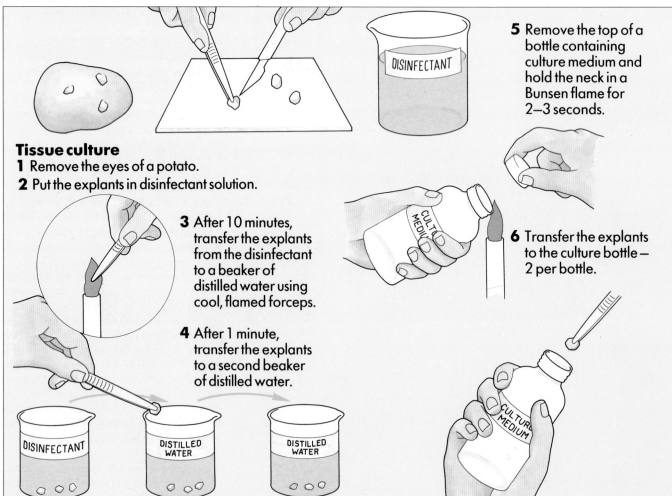

Tissue culture
1 Remove the eyes of a potato.
2 Put the explants in disinfectant solution.

3 After 10 minutes, transfer the explants from the disinfectant to a beaker of distilled water using cool, flamed forceps.

4 After 1 minute, transfer the explants to a second beaker of distilled water.

5 Remove the top of a bottle containing culture medium and hold the neck in a Bunsen flame for 2–3 seconds.

6 Transfer the explants to the culture bottle — 2 per bottle.

DISINFECTANT

DISTILLED WATER

DISTILLED WATER

DISINFECTANT

CULTURE MEDIUM

CULTURE MEDIUM

Reference

Detecting starch in leaves

1 Dip a leaf in boiling water for about a minute.

2 Turn off the Bunsen flame.

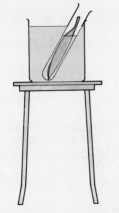

3 Put the leaf into a test tube containing ethanol.

4 Put the test tube into the hot water.

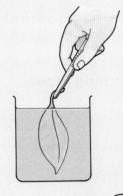

5 Remove the leaf from the ethanol and wash it in the hot water to make it softer.

6 Carefully spread the leaf out on a white tile and then put dilute iodine solution all over it.

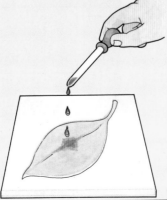

7 The parts that turn blue contain starch.

▽ Ecology field work

When you consider a particular habitat you need to look at the physical features of the habitat as well as the organisms that live there. Depending on your investigation there are a wide range of meters available to help you measure different physical factors. Your teacher will tell you about these.

Always write down as much information as possible about the site you are studying, and the weather at the time. Some of the things you should record are:

1 The nature of the rock, soil, stream bed, etc. that you are collecting from.
2 If the ground slopes, the way it faces (e.g. south-facing).
3 Drainage – does water run off easily?
4 Temperature and pH of soil, water or air.
5 Cloud cover – whether it is raining or not.
6 Light level (open or shaded, or a reading from a light-meter).
7 Humidity of the air.
8 Wind speed and direction, or water speed in a river.
9 Time of day and date.

Factors such as light, pH, and temperature can be measured by using special environmental probes. Often these probes allow you to record changes in your habitat over a period of time.

When you are collecting organisms, remember the following rules.

1 Observe the country code.
2 Obtain permission from the landowner before starting to study a particular area.
3 **Never** take organisms away, or destroy them needlessly.
4 Replace stones, logs, etc. that you have moved.
5 If you must take specimens away take as few as possible, and try to return them when you have finished.
6 Keep your animals in separate pots, or you could end up with *one* well fed predator!

Reference

Collecting insects

Beating tray
This is a standard-sized sheet or tray which is held under a tree or a bush which is then shaken. Small creatures fall onto the sheet and can be collected. A pooter is a useful tool to collect them.

A pooter
The large tube is held over an insect; the other is used to suck up the insect.

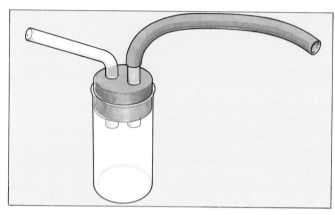

Pitfall trap
Used to collect ground insects. Sink a clean jam jar into the ground so that the top is level with the soil. Cover the mouth of the jar with a stone or wood roof to keep the rain out of the jar. You can bait this jar with meat to attract scavengers. Inspect the trap regularly.

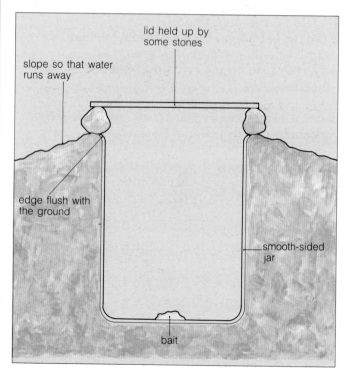

slope so that water runs away

lid held up by some stones

edge flush with the ground

smooth-sided jar

bait

Tullgren funnel
This is used to collect small soil animals. A soil or leaf-litter sample is placed on a sieve under a lamp. The heat from the lamp drives the animals through the sieve down a funnel into a pot containing 60% ethanol. The ethanol kills the animals, so stopping the carnivores from devouring the rest.

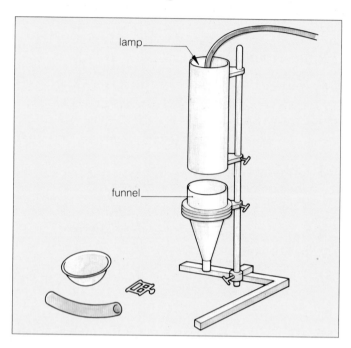

lamp

funnel

Sweep net
Used to catch small flying insects. You use a sweep net by waving it to and fro in front of you over the plants. Check the net regularly to see what you have caught.

Sampling plants

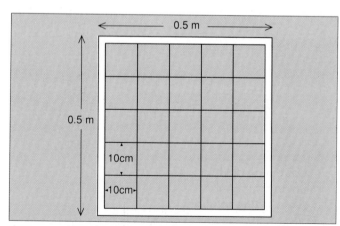

0.5 m

0.5 m

10cm

10cm

To compare different areas, you must take a standard sample. The type of sample depends on the nature of the area. The standard sample is taken by using a *quadrat*. This is a square metal or wooden frame, usually 0.25 m^2 or 1 m^2, but the quadrat can be bigger — it depends on what you are studying. A tree survey requires at least a 10 m^2 quadrat; an investigation into daisies on the lawn would need a 0.25 m^2 one.

Often the quadrat is used at random — throwing it into a general area. Sometimes you want to study along a line through an area. Then, the quadrat can be placed at regular intervals along this line to sample the vegetation and animal life.

Kick sample
This special net is used to take a sample of the wildlife from a stream bed.

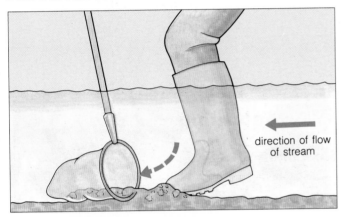

direction of flow of stream

▽ Collecting gases

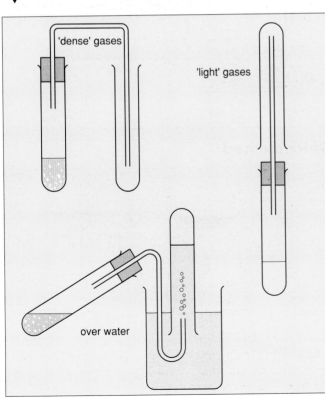

'dense' gases

'light' gases

over water

▽ Titration

Add the acid a little at a time, whilst shaking the flask to make sure the chemicals mix. Carefully watch the colour of the indicator in the flask. The reaction is complete when the indicator shows that the liquid in the flask is neutral pH.

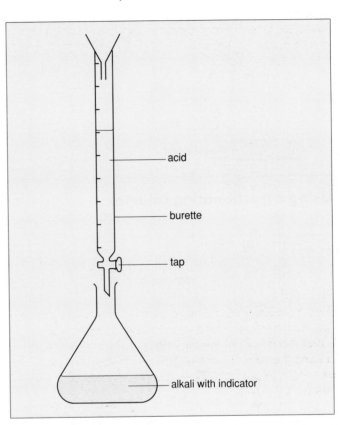

acid

burette

tap

alkali with indicator

▽ Distilling

Distilling is a way of separating a mixture of two or more liquids. It relies on the fact that the liquids will boil at different temperatures.

Simple method

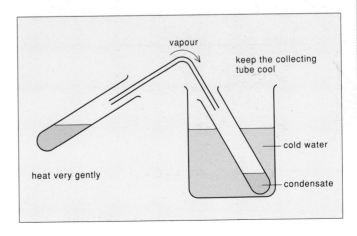

vapour

keep the collecting tube cool

cold water

condensate

heat very gently

More complicated method using a still/condenser

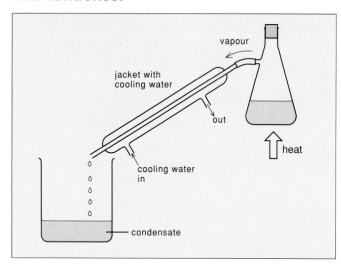

Using a fractionating column

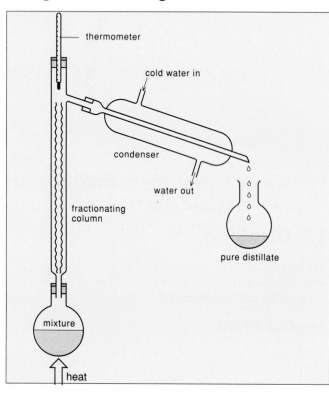

▽ Adding liquids safely to solids or other liquids

Dropping funnel

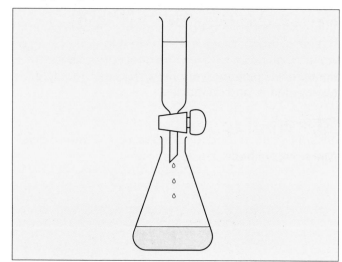

▽ Evaporating

Slow method

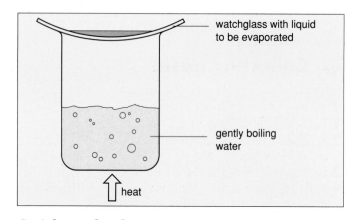

Quick method

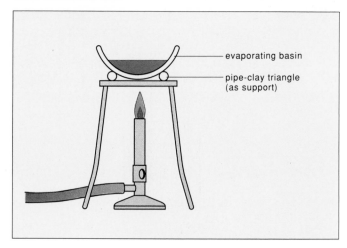

Reference

MEASURING

▽ Temperature

Use the right kind of thermometer; *glass* thermometers are useful for liquids and the air, but should not be pushed into the soil.

A *maximum-and-minimum* thermometer can record the highest and lowest temperatures reached during a period of time.

▽ Wind speed

Measured with an anemometer.

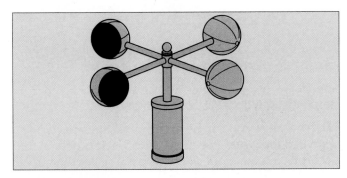

▽ Acidity

Measured with either a *pH meter* or by using indicator (solution or paper). A simple test for the pH of soil:

1 Take a small sample of soil and dry it carefully.
2 Put the dry soil into a test tube, add distilled water and shake.
3 Let the solid settle until the water is clear.
4 Add indicator solution (or use paper) and compare the colour with a pH chart.

(Note: For a more accurate result use a special Soil Testing Kit.)

▽ Turbidity

1 Place a cross painted on a white metal disc at the bottom of a large measuring cylinder.
2 Pour in water until you *just* can't see the cross.
3 The higher this water level, the clearer the water must be.

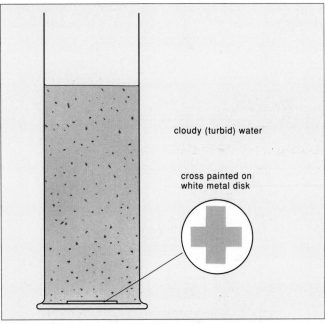

cloudy (turbid) water

cross painted on white metal disk

▽ Measuring water use by leaves (transpiration)

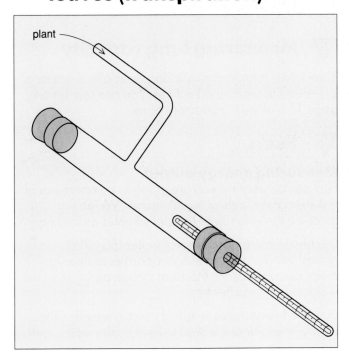

plant

A sealed system on a top-pan balance

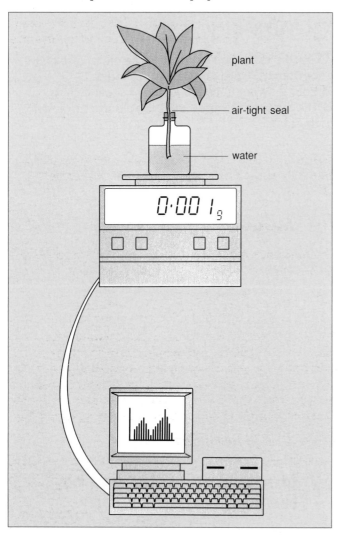

plant

air-tight seal

water

Measuring lung capacity

Blow into a rolled-up plastic bag, specially made as a cylinder and marked off in litres. You can see this on page 156 of the Introductory book.

Fuels

Measuring energy output
First decide whether you are going to compare equal *volumes* of the fuels or equal *masses*. Weigh or measure the volumes of the fuel samples accordingly.

Decide on a standard mass of water (50–200 grams) which is placed in a standard container (a metal can or beaker). Measure the temperature of the water before you heat it.

Burn the fuel samples, in turn, in such a way that the energy they release is used to heat up the water, and measure the *final* temperature the water reaches after all the fuel is burned.

Calculate the *rise* in temperature produced by burning the fuel. The larger the temperature rise, the more energy the sample of fuel was able to provide.

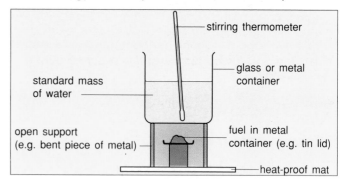

stirring thermometer

glass or metal container

standard mass of water

open support (e.g. bent piece of metal)

fuel in metal container (e.g. tin lid)

heat-proof mat

A rough value for the energy supplied by the fuel, in joules, can be calculated using the formula:

$$\text{energy supplied} = \text{mass of water (in grams)} \times \text{rise in temperature} \times 4.2$$

Note: Unless you can be sure that *all* the energy went into the water, the comparison is not very accurate. It is quite difficult to stop the surroundings being heated by the fuel.

Measuring voltage and current

The diagram shows how the instruments are placed in a circuit to measure the resistance of a lamp (in *ohms*) and the power (in *watts*) that the lamp needs to make it work.

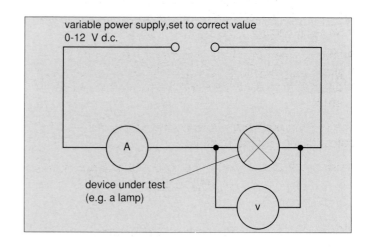

variable power supply, set to correct value 0-12 V d.c.

device under test (e.g. a lamp)

Measuring resistance

$$\text{resistance} = \frac{\text{voltmeter reading}}{\text{ammeter reading}} \qquad R = \frac{V}{I}$$

 ## Measuring power

$$\text{power} = \text{voltmeter reading} \times \text{ammeter reading}$$

For example, if the voltmeter reads 6 V and the ammeter 0.5 A:

$$\text{resistance} = \frac{6}{0.5} = 12 \text{ ohms,}$$

$$\text{power} = 6 \times 0.5 = 3 \text{ watts.}$$

 ## Measuring energy

Electrical energy
Use the formula:

$$\text{electrical energy} = \text{voltage} \times \text{current} \times \text{time}$$
$$E = VIt$$

(E in joules, V in volts, I in amperes and t in seconds.)

By definition, a *volt* is the potential difference between two points when a current of 1 ampere flowing between them produces 1 joule of energy each second. In most applications, this is produced as heating energy.

 ## Measuring work and energy

Work and energy are measured in the same unit: the *joule*.

The word *work* is used scientifically to mean the quantity of energy transferred by means of applying a force, such as

- lifting something against the force of gravity,
- slowing a bicycle by using the force of the brakes,
- accelerating a car by using the force from its engine.

The work done for the energy transferred is calculated using the formula:

$$\text{work} = \text{force} \times \text{distance moved in the direction of the force}$$
$$W = Fd$$

W is in joules, F is in newtons and d in metres.

 ## Measuring power

Power is the rate at which work is done, or the rate at which energy is being used. It is calculated by dividing the work done by the time taken to do it:

$$\text{power} = \frac{\text{work done}}{\text{time taken}}$$

$$P = \frac{W}{t}$$

Power is measured in *watts*, if work is in joules and time is measured in seconds: work = joules per second.

Measuring efficiency

The efficiency of a system measures how good it is as an energy converter:

$$\text{efficiency} = \frac{\text{energy output}}{\text{energy input}} \times 100\%$$

No system, machine or process has an efficiency greater than 100%. That would mean that energy had been created. That can't be done. Energy can only be transferred from something else that already has energy. The energy output cannot be greater than the input (see the laws of energy on page 183).

Some typical efficiencies:

System	Efficiency (%)
car engine	25%
steam engine (train)	10%
diesel engine	40%
electric motor (large)	90%
power station	33%
human muscle	85%
bicycle	27%
central heating:	
— gas-fired boiler	75%
— oil-fired boiler	70%
— coal-fired boiler	60%
plants (photosynthesis converts light energy to chemical):	
— wheat	1%
— sugar cane	2.5%
food animals (plant biomass to animal biomass)	
— beef cattle	0.6%
— fish	20%

▽ Work

Work done (or energy transferred) =
   force × distance
Lifting — doing work against the force of gravity

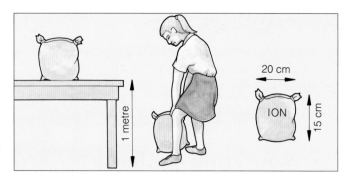

Measuring forces

The standard way is to use a *newton meter*, but remember that a 1-kilogram mass provides a force of almost exactly 10 newtons, due to the pull of gravity.

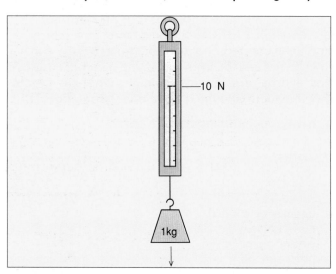

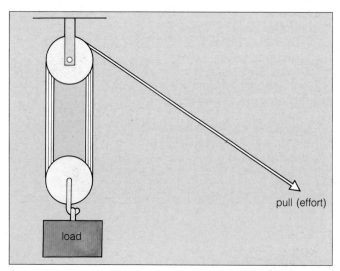

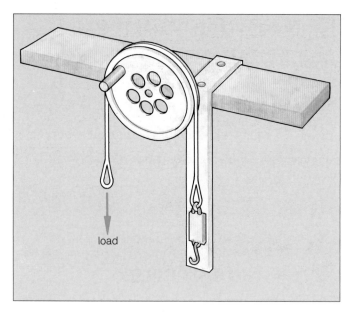

1 Read the force
2 Turn the handle and count the number of turns of the 1 m circumference wheel.
3 Take the difference in the force readings
4 Work = force applied × number of turns

Friction

Energy used in working against friction in heating the surroundings.

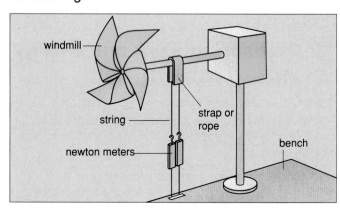

Both meters should be under tension before the windmill starts turning.

Heating energy
Use the formula:

heating = mass × temperature × specific heat
energy   rise   capacity

$$H = mTS$$

The energy needed to heat an object depends on its mass (how much of it there is), the rise in temperature produced, and the substance the object is made of.

Some materials need more energy to heat them through 1°C than others, e.g. for a standard mass of 1 kilogram heated through 1°C, water needs 4.18 kilojoules (kJ), while copper needs only 400 joules. This quantity is is called *specific thermal capacity*.

substance	specific heat capacity (J/kg K)
water	4180
aluminium	900
copper	400
iron	475
polystyrene	1300
glass	600

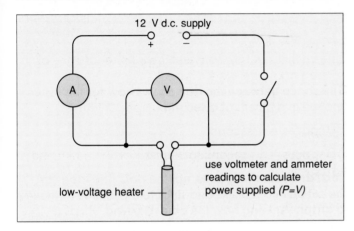

use voltmeter and ammeter readings to calculate power supplied *(P=V)*

▽ Measuring power

Power is the *rate* of using energy or doing work:

$$\text{power} = \frac{\text{work done}}{\text{time taken}}$$

$$= \frac{\text{energy used}}{\text{time taken}}$$

$$P = \frac{E}{t}$$

(*P* is in watts, *E* in joules, *t* in seconds.)

Use any of the methods for measuring energy described above, time the process in seconds and use the formula to calculate power.

▽ Detecting radioactivity

The standard way is to use a *geiger counter*. For safety reasons this equipment may not be used by students under 16 years old.

▽ Measuring stress

When a force or load is applied to a structure, the force is shared out over the area involved. Thus a useful idea is *stress*.

$$\text{stress} = \frac{\text{force}}{\text{area}} \quad or \quad \frac{\text{load}}{\text{area}}$$

$$S = \frac{F}{A}$$

Measure force as above, then measure or calculate the area (*A*) on which the force acts:

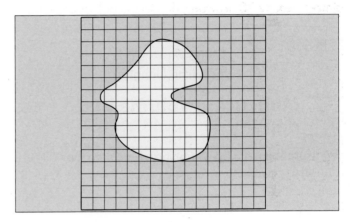

1 Trace outline.
2 Count the squares: e.g. 60 squares, each square 1 cm^2 ∴ area = 60 cm^2.

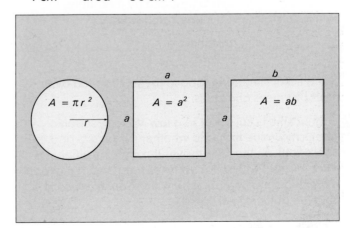

3 Circle
4 Square
5 Rectangle

Measuring strain

Strain measures the effect of a stress, e.g. the change in length per unit length, the angle bent or twisted through per unit length.

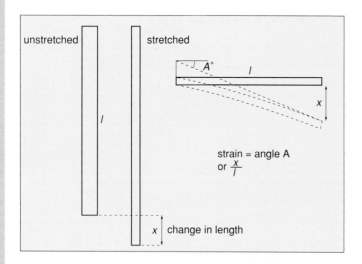

unstretched   stretched

$A°$ l

x

l

strain = angle A
or $\frac{x}{l}$

x change in length

$$\text{strain} \ = \ \frac{\text{change in length}}{\text{unstretched length}} \ = \ \frac{x}{l}$$

 Measuring volume and density

Measure the mass (by weighing). Calculate the density by using the formula:

$$\text{density} \ = \ \frac{\text{mass}}{\text{volume}}.$$

 Measuring speed

You can measure *average* speed by measuring the time taken to cover a measured distance:

$$\text{speed} \ = \ \frac{\text{distance}}{\text{time}}.$$

Use a ticker-timer and tape to measure speed over short distances and times.

Connect the ticker-timer to a low-voltage supply (check the value first, and whether it is an a.c. or d.c. operation). As the tape moves through the timer, the timer marks it with a dot 50 times a second. If the tape is fixed to a moving object, it will produce a record of how the object moved.

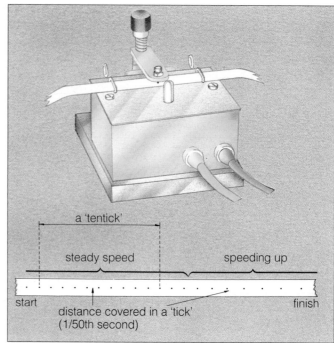

a 'tentick'

steady speed   speeding up

start   finish

distance covered in a 'tick'
(1/50th second)

The *space* between the dots shows how far the tape moved in a fiftieth of a second.

50 spaces = 1 second

10 spaces = ⅕ second (a 'tentick')

Note: Count the *spaces*, not the *dots*. The tape can be cut up into tenticks and stuck to a baseline to make a graph showing how the object moved. This is a *speed–time* graph.

 Measuring acceleration

You need to measure two speeds, each one over a fairly short time interval. Measure one at the beginning and the other near the end of the movement. Subtract one from the other to find the *change in speed*. Divide this by the time elapsed between taking the two speeds. The result is the acceleration (the *change in speed in a certain time*).

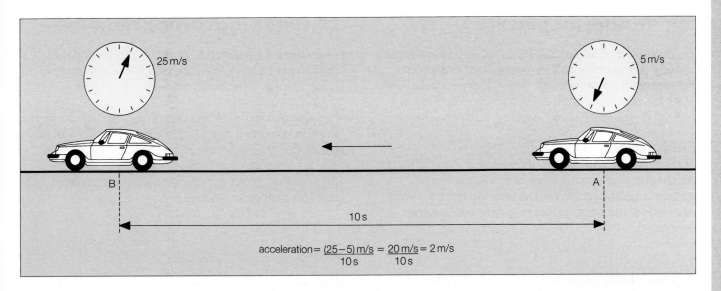

$$\text{acceleration} = \frac{(25-5)\,\text{m/s}}{10\,\text{s}} = \frac{20\,\text{m/s}}{10\,\text{s}} = 2\,\text{m/s}$$

TESTING

▽ Identifying metals

You can use a flame test or the sodium hydroxide tes

Flame test
Dip a splint into the solution or powder being tested. Put the dipped end into a clear blue Bunsen flame, near the bottom. The flame will become coloured, and the colour produced shows what metal is present.

metal	colour
calcium	brick red
copper	green
potassium	lilac
sodium	yellow

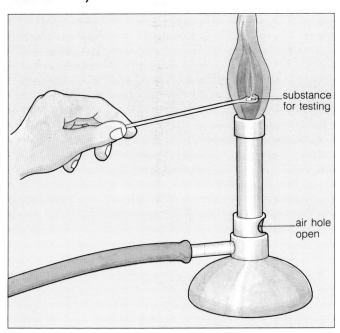

Sodium hydroxide test for metals in compounds

Dissolve the metal compound and put some of the solution in a test tube. Add one or two drops of sodium hydroxide solution. Note the colour of any precipitate that may be formed. Then add more sodium hydroxide ('to excess'). Use the table below to work out what metal was in the compound.

Colour of precipitate after adding 1 or 2 drops of sodium hydroxide	Effect of adding more sodium hydroxide	Metal in compound (metallic ions)
pale blue	no change	copper
green	no change	iron (II)
brown	no change	iron (III)
white	no change	calcium
white	dissolves to colourless solution	zinc, lead or aluminium

▽ Detecting water

The simple tests for water are:
- For large quantities: measure the boiling point (100°C for *pure* water).
- For small quantities: touch the liquid with dry cobalt chloride paper; this will change from blue to pink if water is present.

▽ Testing for plastics

Modern plastics and plastic objects can be made from a mixture of plastics, so it isn't very easy to find out exactly what an object is made of. These tests will only work for objects or samples containing one kind of plastic.

Safety note:
Burning plastic can be dangerous — the fumes may be poisonous, and there is a risk of starting a fire or getting a 'plastic scald'. Do the burning test only with permission, use small pieces of plastic and a fume cupboard.

▽ Detecting carbon dioxide

- For samples expected to contain a lot of carbon dioxide: add calcium hydroxide to the gas sample in a test tube. If the solution turns milky, carbon dioxide was present.
- For samples expected to contain a small amount of carbon dioxide: keep bubbling the sample through a bicarbonate indicator solution. This may need a 'recycling' circuit with a pump. If carbon dioxide is present the colour of the indicator changes from reddish-orange to yellow.

Simplified methods of identifying common plastics

Plastic type	Physical test (for solid articles)				Burn test (for film and solid articles)	
	Try to cut a thin slice off. You get:	Drop on hard surface	Scratch with fingernail	Place small sample in water	Appearance of flame	Smell on extinguishing
low density polyethylene (LDPE)	coherent sliver	dull sound	scratches easily	floats	pale blue flame, yellow edge	very waxy (like candle wax)
high-density polyethylene (HDPE)	coherent sliver	dull sound	scratches to some degree	floats	pale blue flame, yellow edge	very waxy (like candle wax)
polystyrene (PS)	coherent sliver	metallic sound	does not scratch	sinks	very sooty flame	distinctive styrene smell
acrylonitrile butadiene styrene (ABS)	coherent sliver	metallic sound	does not scratch	sinks	very sooty flame	distinctive styrene smell plus smell of rubber
polypropylene (PP)	coherent sliver	dull sound	does not scratch	floats	pale blue flame, drops hot molten polymer	waxy
unplasticised polyvinyl chloride (uPVC)	coherent sliver	dull sound	does not scratch	sinks	won't burn; smoulders	very acrid
plasticised polyvinyl chloride (PVC)	coherent sliver		scratches easily	sinks	smoky flame	very acrid
cellophane					burns rapidly	like paper
thermosetting plastics	powdery chips	depends on type	does not scratch	sinks	difficult to burn	fishy smell or distinctive phenol smell

▽ Electrolysis

This key shows what happens when different ions are present in a solution of a compound being electrolysed.

Remember: the *anode* is the *positive* electrode and the *cathode* is the *negative* electrode.

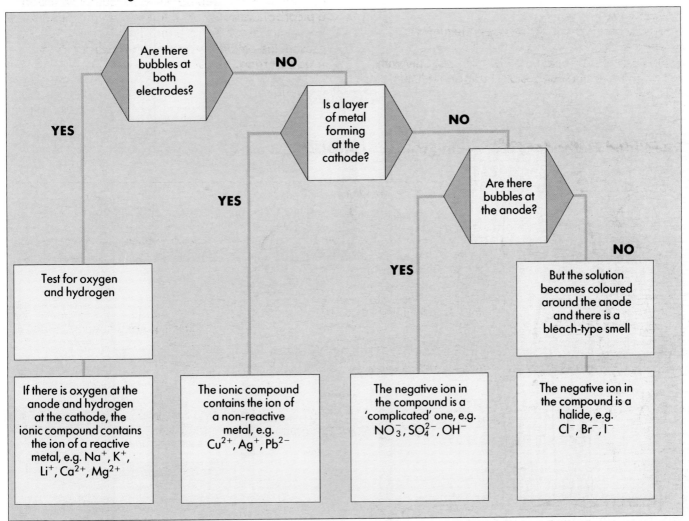

▽ Testing for hardness of water using soap solution

Use a burette and flask as shown in the Laboratory Skills section. Put 100 ml of the water to be tested in the conical flask. Add some soap solution from the burette, take the flask well away and gently shake it to try to make some bubbles (lather). If none are made the water is hard. Add some more soap solution and repeat the shaking. Repeat this until bubbles are produced. Measure and note down how much soap solution was needed. The harder the water the more soap is needed to produce a lather.

Notes:
(i) To ensure that the test is fair you should use the same concentration of soap solution for each water sample.
(ii) For accuracy you should add only small volumes of soap solution each time — but if the added volumes are *too* small it will take too long to do the experiment.

▽ The cardiovascular system

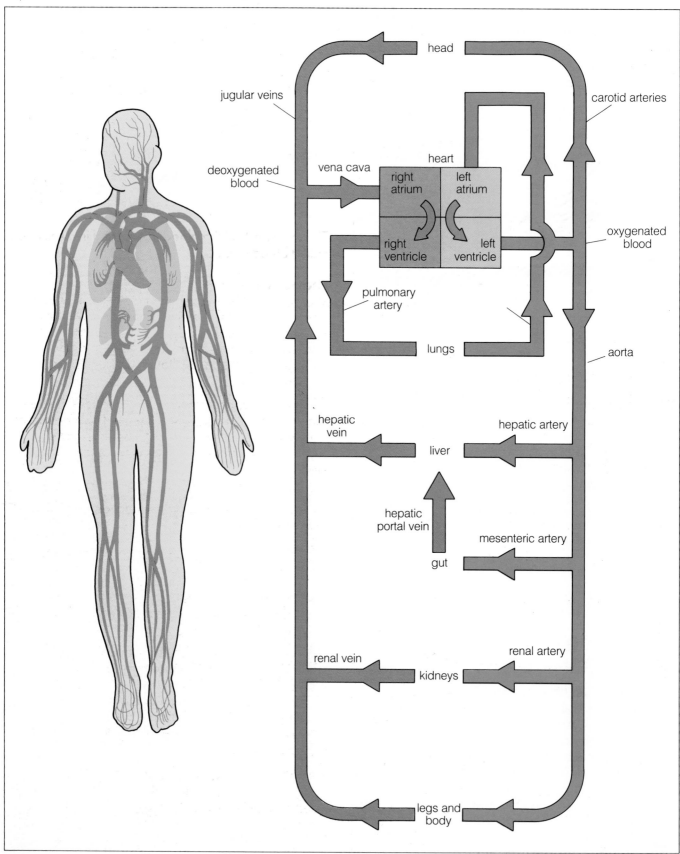

▽ The heart

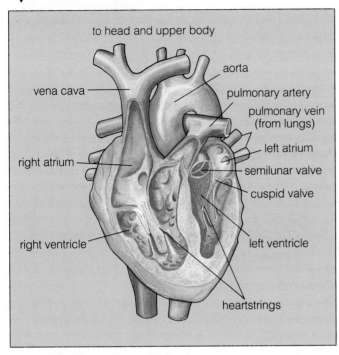

to head and upper body

aorta

vena cava

pulmonary artery

pulmonary vein (from lungs)

right atrium

left atrium

semilunar valve

cuspid valve

right ventricle

left ventricle

heartstrings

▽ Arteries, veins, capillaries

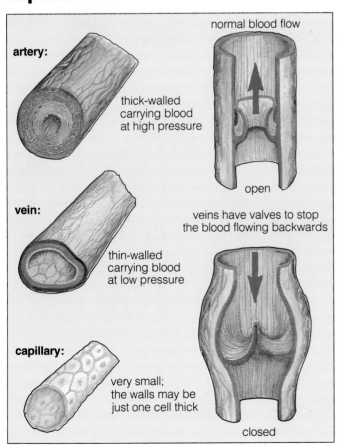

normal blood flow

artery:

thick-walled carrying blood at high pressure

open

vein:

veins have valves to stop the blood flowing backwards

thin-walled carrying blood at low pressure

capillary:

very small; the walls may be just one cell thick

closed

▽ Blood

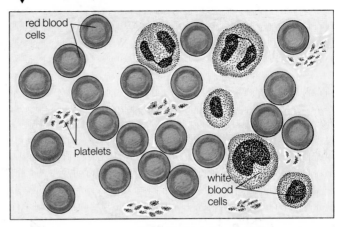

red blood cells

platelets

white blood cells

The main parts of the blood are carried in a salty fluid called blood plasma.

Blood clotting

The clotting of blood involves a series of complex chemical changes. The process must not be allowed to happen inside the body. A clot, or *thrombosis*, formed inside one of our blood vessels might block the supply of blood to a vital organ — with fatal consequences.

To stop this happening, our blood contains chemicals that prevent clotting. These are called *anticoagulants*. They are given to patients who are undergoing surgery. One commonly used anticoagulant is Heparin.

The clotting process begins when the platelets are exposed to the air at the site of a wound. The platelets break open to release thromboplastins.

In the presence of vitamin K and calcium ions, the thromboplastins cause a blood protein called *prothrombin* to become activated — it is converted into its soluble form, *thrombin*.

This acts on yet another soluble plasma protein, *fibrinogen*, which also changes into a soluble form, *fibrin*.

A network of fibrin threads at the site of the wound traps passing red blood cells, which then dry out to form a clot.

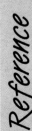

Reference

▽ Human senses

Stimulus	Sense organ	Sense
light	eyes	sight
sound	ears	hearing
pressure, temperature (hot/cold), pain	receptors in the skin	touch
chemicals in the air	receptors in the nose	smell
chemicals in food	taste buds on the tongue	taste

All information from our senses is sent to the brain as minute electrical impulses. The brain then translates these impulses into sensations of sight, touch, etc. So, we do not see with our eyes. We see with our brains. The eyes change light signals into electrical signals that the brain can 'understand'.

▽ Reflexes

These are simple, rapid reactions to stimuli. They work by means of a *reflex arc*. The illustration shows the reflex arc that operates when a baby's foot is tickled. Receptors in the skin of the baby's foot send impulses into the spinal cord along a sensory nerve. A relay nerve inside the cord passes the information on to a motor nerve across two nerve junctions or *synapses*. (Another nerve passes information up to the brain to keep it informed of what is happening.) The motor nerve sends a message to the muscles in the baby's foot which then contract causing the foot to curl up. Reflex arcs make our hands move away from very hot objects to stop our skin being burned.

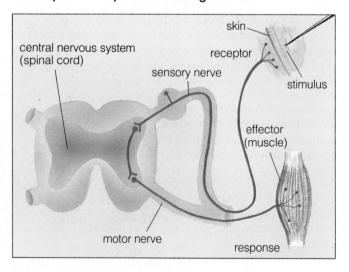

Conditioned reflexes

These are reflex actions triggered off by a 'learned' stimulus. They are the basis for 'training' in animals, and in humans.

Conditioned reflexes were first discovered by a Russian scientist called Ivan Pavlov in 1902. He knew that dogs always salivate (produce saliva) when they see or smell food and that this was a normal reflex. Every time Pavlov fed the group of dogs in his laboratory he rang a bell. After much repetition the dogs would salivate at the sound of the bell. There was no need for food to be present at all. Pavlov had set up a conditioned reflex in the dogs. They had become *conditioned* to salivate on hearing the bell.

▽ Control, co-ordination and communication

Central nervous system

The human body is controlled, in part, by the central nervous system (CNS). This consists of the *brain* and *spinal cord*.

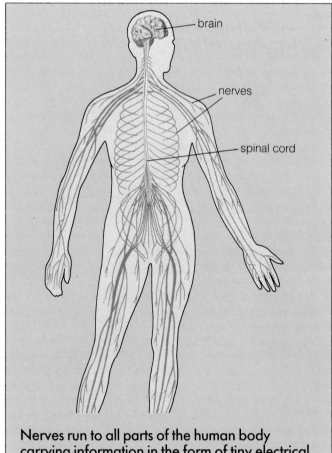

Nerves run to all parts of the human body carrying information in the form of tiny electrical impulses to and from the brain and spinal cord (CNS).

Communication between the body and the CNS is done through *nerves*. You can see the main layout of the human nervous system in the illustration.

Cranial nerves are attached directly to the brain and serve the head and face. Spinal nerves are joined to the spinal cord and communicate with the rest of the body. These large nerves contain many smaller nerve *fibres* conducting impulses in different directions. Nerves inside the spinal cord relay information to and from the brain.

Types of nerve fibre

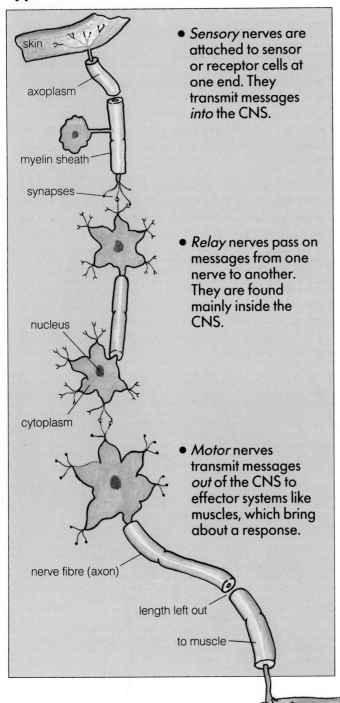

- *Sensory* nerves are attached to sensor or receptor cells at one end. They transmit messages *into* the CNS.

- *Relay* nerves pass on messages from one nerve to another. They are found mainly inside the CNS.

- *Motor* nerves transmit messages *out* of the CNS to effector systems like muscles, which bring about a response.

Passing messages on

Nerve impulses or signals move from one nerve fibre to another across small gaps called *synapses*. The signal is carried across the gap as a tiny amount of chemical. The chemical causes the second nerve cell to fire off electrical pulses along its fibre to the next nerve cell in the chain.

Each nerve cell is linked at the synapse with several other nerve cells, so that if one system fails there are others to carry the message on. The synapse also helps to 'damp' the system. If insufficient chemical is released across the gap at the synapse, the second nerve cell fails to respond. The message is not passed on and so unimportant information is therefore 'filtered out' of the system. We would not want to respond to every stimulus we receive!

The human brain

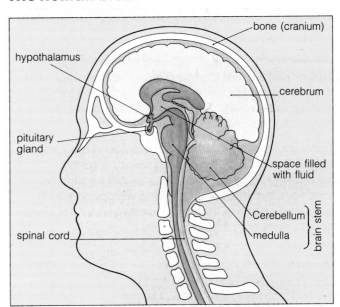

The brain is made of several distinct parts that do different jobs. The brain is protected by the cranium or skull, in which it floats in a special fluid.

- *Medulla* — controls important but basic and automatic functions, e.g. the control of breathing and heart-rate.
- *Cerebellum* — controls and co-ordinates movement and balance. Much of this is automatic but we also have to *learn* how to do it properly, for example in walking, or riding a bike, or playing a sport. Some people are better at this than others. The cerebellum co-ordinates fast, accurate movements.
- *Hypothalamus* — a small part of the brain that seems to control some basic body needs, such as thirst and hunger. It is also the control centre for some of our emotional behaviour, e.g. anger and sexual drive.

213

Reference

• *Pituitary gland* — this small lobe at the base of the brain controls the release of special chemicals called hormones from other organs and tissues of the body.

• *Cerebrum* or *cerebral hemispheres* — the largest part of our brains.

The surface of the cerebrum is full of grooves and cracks to increase its surface area. Most of the 14 billion cells of the nervous system are located here and each of these cells is able to link up with 25 000 other nerve cells! No computer yet built — or even planned — has a relay capacity as large as this.

The cerebrum is the seat of consciousness, it deals with our senses, it controls speech, holds our memory, and enables us to *think*. It is the site of intelligence.

The cerebrum is made of two parts, the left and right cerebral hemispheres. The right half of the brain controls the left half of the body and the left half deals with the right side.

Different parts of the hemispheres carry out different jobs or functions as you can see in the illustration. The speech centre, for example, is located in the left hemisphere, whereas the centre that responds to music is found on the right-hand side.

Complex learning behaviour is located in the surface of both hemispheres called the cerebral *cortex*. Surprisingly, a lot of the brain does not seem to be used for anything, which explains why people with quite large parts of their brain damaged by accident or injury appear to function quite normally.

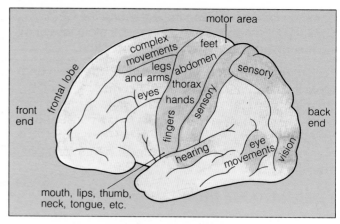

▽ **Biological control — homeostasis**

The skin and temperature regulation

The skin is the largest (in area) of the organs in the human body. It protects us from the outside world, keeps the insides from falling out, and senses touch, temperature and pain. It also helps to control body temperature.

Humans are 'warm-blooded' animals. This means that their inside body temperature stays the same whether the outside temperature is hot, cold, or changing from one to the other. An Artic explorer and a sun-bather on the beach will have the same core body temperature — about 37 °C.

If this internal temperature rises too high because we cannot lose heat, or falls too low because we cannot gain or save heat, we will die. Making sure that the body temperature stays at the correct level is one of the skin's main jobs.

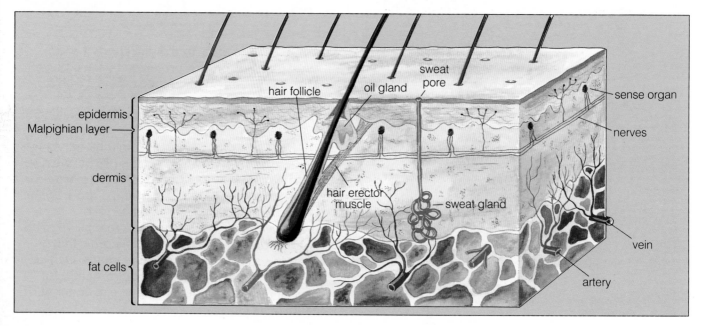

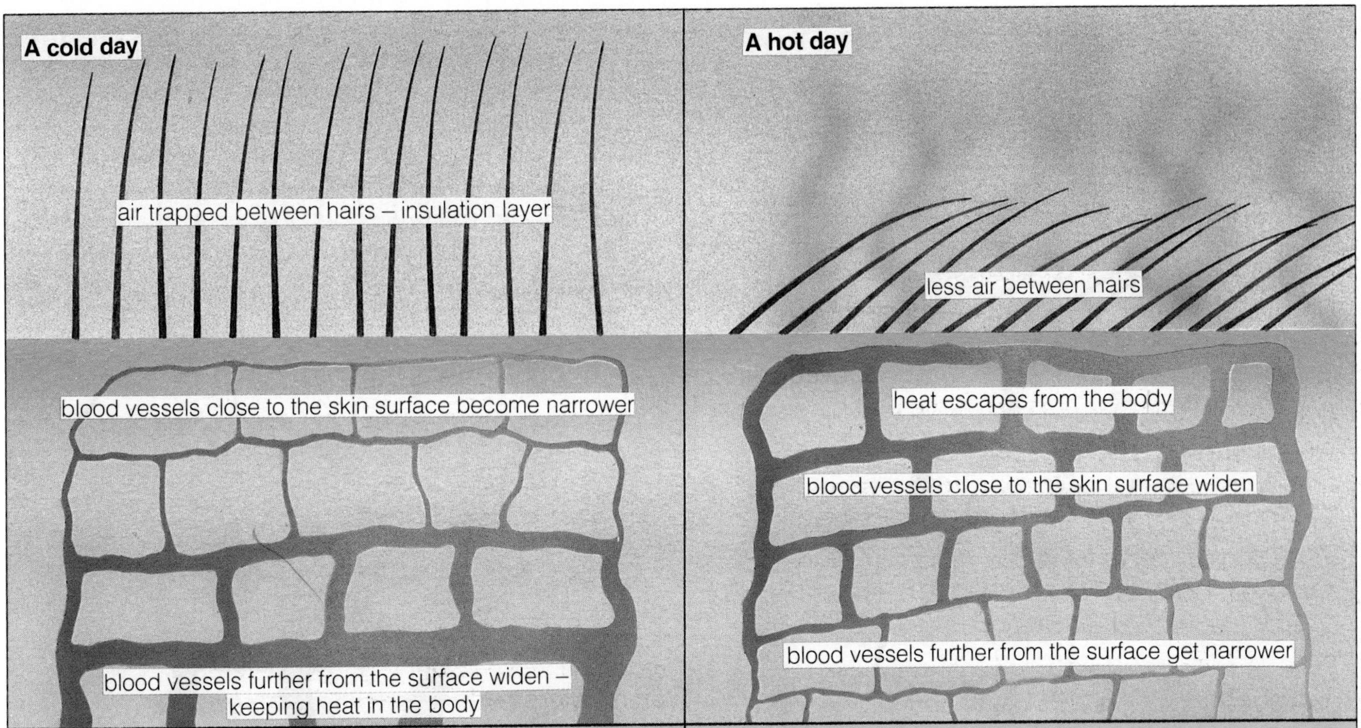

A cold day

air trapped between hairs – insulation layer

blood vessels close to the skin surface become narrower

blood vessels further from the surface widen – keeping heat in the body

A hot day

less air between hairs

heat escapes from the body

blood vessels close to the skin surface widen

blood vessels further from the surface get narrower

TOO HOT:

Hair muscles relax.
Hair lies flat.
Less air trapped, so more heat lost.

Blood vessels near the surface of the skin get wider: Vasodilation. More blood is brought to the skin surface and so more heat is lost from the body.
You appear 'red'.

Sweat glands release sweat.

The sweat takes heat from the skin when it evaporates into the air and so cools the body down.

No shivering.

TOO COLD:

Hair muscles contract.
Hair stands up trapping a layer of air between the skin and the outside world. Air is a poor conductor of heat and so the layer of air insulates against heat loss.
Humans do not have much body hair and use clothing to trap layers of air instead.

Blood vessels near the surface of the skin get narrower: Vasoconstriction. Less blood is brought to the skin surface and so less heat is lost from the body.
You appear 'white'.

No sweating

Muscles under the skin contract in spasms – we shiver.

As the muscles contract, more heat is released to keep us warm.

A layer of fat beneath the skin may also insulate us from the cold.

Animals like seals and whales living in very cold climates have a thick layer of blubber to insulate them against the cold water.

▽ Exposure and hypothermia

Exposure to extreme cold can cause hypothermia. If the core body temperature falls, the person soon becomes unconscious and goes into a coma. This fall need only be 1.5–2.0 °C. Without treatment, death will follow fairly quickly. Very young and very old people are most at risk because they are less efficient at controlling their body temperatures.

Reference

215

▽ Infectious diseases

Disease	Cause	How prevented	How transmitted
measles	virus	immunisation	through the air
chicken pox	virus	immunisation	through the air
tetanus	bacterium	immunisation	cuts
whooping cough	bacterium	immunisation	through the air
diphtheria	bacterium	immunisation	through the air
polio	virus	immunisation	through the air; drinking-water
German measles	virus (*Rubella*)	immunisation	through the air
TB	bacterium	immunisation	through the air
AIDS	virus	no method known	body fluids; sexual intercourse
food poisoning	bacterium (*Salmonella*)	antibiotics	eating contaminated food
sore throat	bacterium	antibiotics	through the air
blood poisoning	bacterium	antibiotics	cuts
pneumonia	bacterium	antibiotics	through the air
sexually transmitted diseases (STD)	bacteria and viruses	antibiotics	sexual intercourse

▽ Immunisation: the discovery of vaccines

Some harmless form of the disease, or disease-causing micro-organism must be injected into the human body to stimulate the production of antibodies which then give protection against the disease. This is done in three ways.

- *Injecting toxoids* – the poisons or toxins released from the harmful microbes are extracted and made harmless chemically. Only these chemicals need then be injected to bring about antibody production and immunity. Diphtheria vaccine is made this way.
- *Injecting dead microbes* – the microbes are killed, again with a chemical (formaldehyde) and injected into the blood. They cannot reproduce inside the body but the correct antibodies are formed against them and so immunity is gained. The polio virus, was first treated in this way.
- *Injecting weakened living microbes* – the harmful microbes are grown or cultured in an animal and

then weakened with chemical treatment, but not killed. When injected, they no longer cause the symptoms of the disease but they do promote antibody production and immunity. Examples include BCG vaccination against the bacteria that cause tuberculosis (BCG, Bacille Calmette-Guerin, named after Calmette and Guerin, the two French scientists who discovered it), and the modern poliomyelitis vaccine.

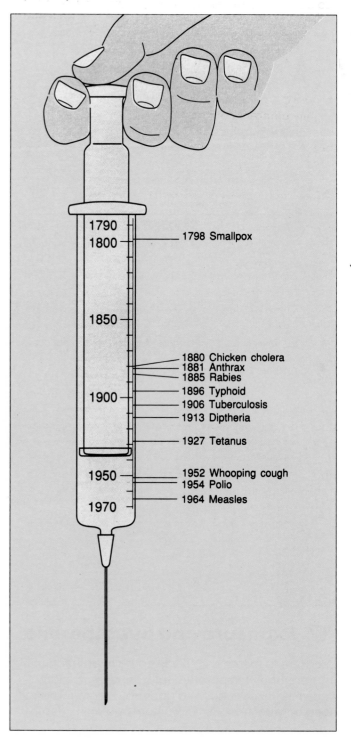

1798 Smallpox
1880 Chicken cholera
1881 Anthrax
1885 Rabies
1896 Typhoid
1906 Tuberculosis
1913 Diptheria
1927 Tetanus
1952 Whooping cough
1954 Polio
1964 Measles

Colds and influenza

If scientists have been so successful in producing vaccines against serious illnesses like diphtheria and smallpox, why is it that they still cannot protect us from simple diseases like the common cold and flu?

The answer lies in the nature of the viruses which actually cause colds and flu. They are constantly changing or *mutating*. Every time you catch a cold or go down with influenza, the virus causing your illness will be slightly different to the one that caused it the last time. This is why you suffer from these illnesses again and again. You have to make new antibodies each time a new form of the virus gets into your body. For the same reason it has proved impossible to produce a vaccine that will protect us against ALL the slightly different cold and flu viruses that already exist, as well as those that will make us ill in the future. We are lucky indeed that other harmful microbes cannot change or mutate so quickly.

AIDS (Acquired Immune Deficiency Syndrome)

The virus that causes AIDS is different from any other disease-causing microbe known. The virus of AIDS attacks the cells that produce antibodies, so that the body is no longer able to defend itself against other disease causing organisms. The immune system becomes 'deficient'. Eventually, people with AIDS are killed by other viruses, bacteria and cancers.

The immune system does produce some antibodies against the AIDS virus, and it might be that many people whose bodies contain the virus are successfully fighting it off. There are certainly many more people with the antibodies in their blood than there are people dying as a result of the disease. But nobody knows how long these people will live before acquiring the deficiency syndrome which will mean that they have lost their natural ability to fight off disease organisms.

▽ Growth and development

Human growth data

This table gives information about the average weight and height of boys and girls of different ages.

Age	Boys		Girls	
	mass (kg)	height (cm)	mass (kg)	height (cm)
at birth	3.4	50.6	3.36	50.2
1 year	10.07	75.2	9.75	74.2
2 years	12.56	87.5	12.29	86.6
3 years	14.61	96.2	14.42	95.7
4 years	16.51	103.4	16.42	103.2
5 years	18.89	110.0	18.58	109.4
6 years	21.9	117.5	21.09	115.9
7 years	24.54	124.1	23.68	122.3
8 years	27.26	130.0	26.35	128.0
9 years	29.94	135.5	28.94	132.9
10 years	32.61	140.3	31.89	138.6
11 years	35.2	144.2	35.74	144.7
12 years	38.28	149.6	39.74	151.9
13 years	42.18	155.0	44.95	157.1
14 years	48.81	162.7	49.17	159.6
15 years	54.48	167.8	51.48	161.1
16 years	58.3	171.6	53.07	162.2
17 years	61.78	173.7	54.02	162.5
18 years	63.05	174.5	54.39	162.5

▽ What plants are made of

Plants, like animals, are made up of living cells. Cells of a similar type are grouped into tissues. Different tissues are grouped into organs. All the organs of the plant work together to keep the plant alive.

The five main organs of a flowering plant are shown in the illustration.

Buds
● Buds are the growing points on the stem of a plant.
● *Flower buds* will open and produce flowers.
● Buds on the tip of a stem are called *terminal buds*.
● Buds between a leaf stalk or petiole and the stem are called *lateral buds*.

Reference

217

Flowers
- Flowers contain the reproductive structures of the plant.

Leaves
- Most of the food is made and stored by a plant in its leaves.

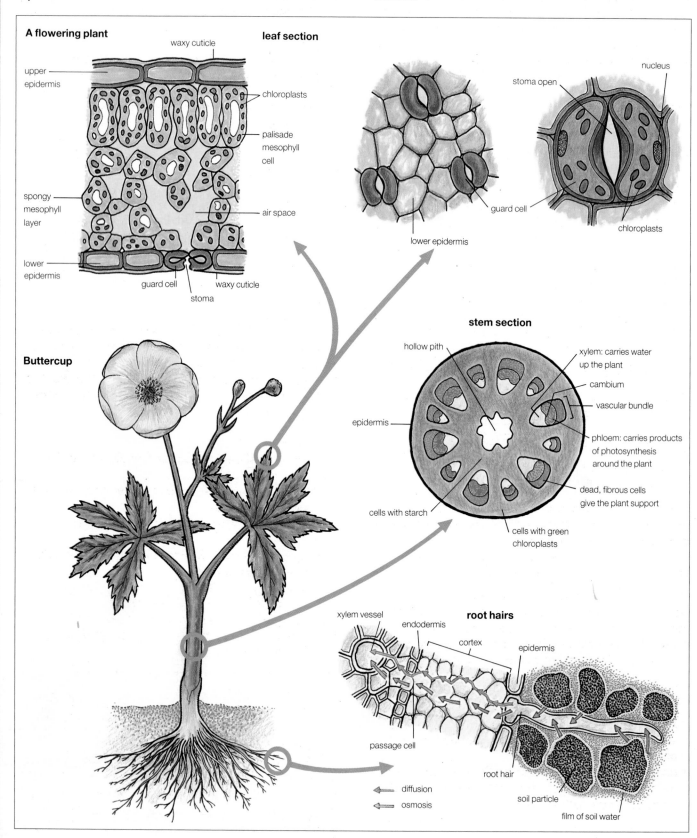

A flowering plant

leaf section

waxy cuticle

upper epidermis

chloroplasts

palisade mesophyll cell

spongy mesophyll layer

air space

lower epidermis

guard cell

waxy cuticle

stoma

stoma open

nucleus

guard cell

chloroplasts

lower epidermis

Buttercup

stem section

hollow pith

xylem: carries water up the plant

cambium

vascular bundle

epidermis

phloem: carries products of photosynthesis around the plant

dead, fibrous cells give the plant support

cells with starch

cells with green chloroplasts

root hairs

xylem vessel

endodermis

cortex

epidermis

passage cell

root hair

soil particle

film of soil water

diffusion

osmosis

- Leaves are flat, broad, and thin. This gives them a large surface area for absorbing sunlight.
- Leaves have veins or vessels. Some of these vessels carry water and mineral salts up to the leaves from the roots. Other tubes take food away to different parts of the plant.
- Leaves have pores called stomata. These pores allow gases to move into and out of the leaf.

Stem
- The stem supports the structures of the plant above ground — the leaves and flowers.
- Different tubes and vessels inside the stem carry water, mineral salts, and food to all parts of the plant.
- In trees, the stem becomes woody. This gives the added strength to support a tall structure.

Roots
- Roots anchor the plant in the ground.
- Roots absorb water and mineral salts from the soil.
- Roots contain vessels to transport the water and salts up the stem to the leaves. They also have tubes bringing them food from the leaves.

▽ The plant transport system

When you pick or cut a plant, the stem will bleed sap. What is this sap, and where does it come from?

Although you cannot see it happening, substances are constantly on the move inside a plant. Sugars are being transported from the leaves, and water is moving up the stem from the roots.

This important job of moving substances is carried out by the veins or *vascular bundles*. This system of vessels and tubes reaches every tissue and organ of the plant. You can see how the vascular bundles are arranged in the section through a stem.

The sap which leaks out of a cut stem consists of the water, sugars, and salts normally inside the vascular bundles. These tubes can be seen clearly in a stalk of celery. The 'stringy' bits that get caught in your teeth are the vascular bundles of the celery stem.

There are two main types of tube or vessel in the vascular bundles:

- *xylem vessels*, which carry water and mineral salts such as nitrates from the roots up to the leaves. They also support the plant;
- *phloem tubes*, which transport the products of photosynthesis (sugars) from the leaves to all other parts of the plant that need them.

▽ Agrochemicals

These are the chemicals used in modern agriculture and horticulture. There are four main types.

Pesticides
These are used for killing the insect pests that eat crops growing in the fields, and also food in storage. They are usually sprayed onto crops from tractors or aircraft. Persistent pesticides stay in the soil for a long time. They are not easily broken down into harmless substances by soil bacteria. Persistent pesticides can be dangerous because of their long-term effects on the environment.

Herbicides
These are used for killing weeds. The weeds would otherwise compete with the food crops for light, water, and mineral salts from the soil. The yield of crop plants would be smaller. Herbicides can also be applied by spraying.

Fungicides
These are used to stop diseases on crop plants caused by fungi. Common types of fungal diseases are mildews, blight, and rusts. They spread quickly and can wipe out an entire crop. Seeds are often treated by fungicides before they are planted to stop them rotting in the soil.

Fertilisers
These consist of extra minerals that plants need for healthy growth.
- *Nitrates* are needed to make proteins for growth, especially of leaves.
- *Phosphates* help to make roots grow and function properly.
- *Magnesium* is important for making chlorophyll, vital for photosynthesis.

Using fertilisers — the benefits
Average yields of wheat and potatoes from a field
Different parts of the field were given different amounts of fertiliser.

Nitrogen added	Phosphorus added	Potassium added	Yield: (tonnes per hectare)	
(kilograms per hectare)			Wheat	Potatoes
0	0	0	1.69	8.47
96	0	0	3.68	8.30
0	77	107	2.04	16.63
96	77	107	6.60	38.57

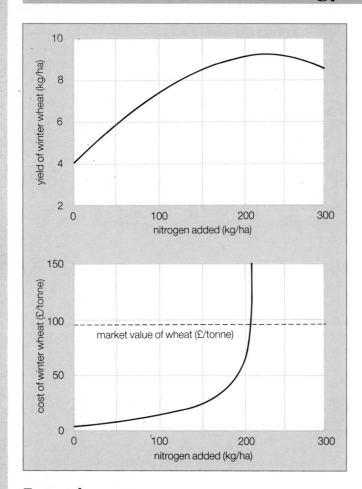

▽ What do plants need to grow?

The key chemical nutrients

Major plant nutrients
Nitrogen (N) — making leaves add to sandy soils; rainy areas
Phosphates (P_2O_5) — making roots add to sandy soils
Potash (K_2O) — making flowers and fruits add to sandy soils

Intermediate plant nutrients
Calcium (Ca) add to acid soils; potash-rich soils
Magnesium (Mg) add to sandy soils; peaty soils; potash-rich soils
Sulphur (S)

Trace elements
Iron (Fe) add to chalky soils
Manganese (Mn) add to chalky soils
Molybdenum (Mo) add to acid soils
Boron (B) add to sandy soils
Zinc (Zn) add to sandy soils
Copper (Cu) add to sandy soils

Trace elements

As well as the three minerals shown in the chart above, plants also need other substances or elements to grow properly. Only very small amounts of these are needed and so they are called *trace elements*. They include sodium, chlorine, copper, and aluminium and are taken in by the plant as mineral salts dissolved in the water from the soil.

Using fertilisers — the dangers

Artificial fertilisers, spread onto the land, can cause serious problems of pollution. The minerals may be washed out of the soil by rainwater. This is called *leaching*.

The mineral-rich water then drains into nearby rivers and lakes. The nitrates and phosphates help the growth of water plants, especially the green algae, which reproduce in vast numbers. This algal 'blooming' clogs up the waterways, making it difficult to purify the water for drinking.

When the algae die in winter, colonies of bacteria feed on them, using up oxygen in the water. The fish and other forms of animal life will also die and decay, leaving putrid, poisonous ponds and streams.

Reference

Biology: data store

Plants most in need	Signs of shortage	How to avoid shortage	
Large amounts required for satisfactory plant growth			
• Grass • Vegetables grown for their leaves • Root-bound plants	• Stunted growth • Small, pale green leaves • Weak stems	• Apply before sowing or planting • In spring and summer, add a nitrogen-rich	fertilizer. Repeat, as quick-acting nitrogen is rapidly leached by rain.
• Young plants • Root vegetables • Fruit and seed crops	• Stunted roots and stems • Small leaves with a purplish tinge • Low fruit yield	• Apply bone meal or a compound fertilizer with a high P_2O_5 content	• Use a compound fertilizer when top dressing plants
• Fruit • Flowers • Potatoes	• Edges of leaves turn yellow and then brown • Low fruit yield; fruit and flowers poorly coloured • Low disease resistance	• Apply a compound fertiliser with a high K_2O content	• Use a compound fertiliser when top dressing plants
Moderate amounts required for satisfactory plant growth			
• Fruit • Flowers • Vegetables	• Similar to nitrogen shortage – stunted growth and pale green leaves	• Apply lime	• If the soil is very alkaline, use gypsum instead of lime
• Roses • Tomatoes	• Yellow or brown patches between the veins of older leaves • Young leaves may fall	• Apply a compound fertiliser containing magnesium	
• All plants	• Similar to nitrogen shortage – stunted growth and pale green leaves	• No action is necessary if a sulphur-containing product is used during the year	
Minute amounts required for satisfactory plant growth – application of large amounts can lead to damage			
• Rhododendrons • Azaleas • Camelias	• Yellowing of younger leaves	In good growing conditions no action is required. Use humus-makers in the usual way and these, together with the impurities present in fertilisers, will provide sufficient trace elements required for satisfactory growth.	On *chalky*, peaty, very light and distinctly acid soils, one or more trace elements, e.g. iron and manganese, may be short due to lock-up by calcium. Growth of some plants is difficult or impossible in such situations.
• Rhododendrons • Azaleas • Camellias	• Yellowing between the veins of older leaves		
• Brassicas	• Narrow leaves		
• Root vegetables	• Brown heart		
• Fruit • Vegetables	• Dieback		
• Fruit • Vegetables	• Leaves start to die • Brown spots on leaves		

▽ **Biological recycling**

In the natural world, substances are being re-cycled all the time. The oxygen you breathe in will have come from a plant feeding by photosynthesis. Other plants will take up the carbon dioxide you breathe out.

Human beings and the things they do, may change or interfere with these natural cycles.

- Intensive farming may release all sorts of harmful chemicals into the soil.
- Burning fossil fuels in our power stations puts millions of tonnes of carbon dioxide and other gases into the air every year.
- Cutting down the rain forests at a rate of one hundred acres a minute could change the weather patterns of the world.

It is important to understand exactly how natural recycling works if we are to keep our planet fit to live on.

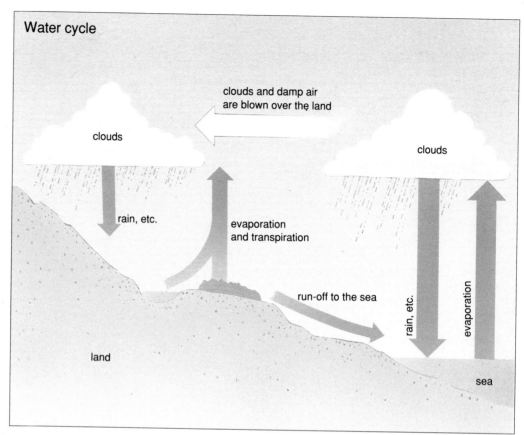

Water cycle

clouds and damp air are blown over the land

clouds

clouds

rain, etc.

evaporation and transpiration

run-off to the sea

rain, etc.

evaporation

land

sea

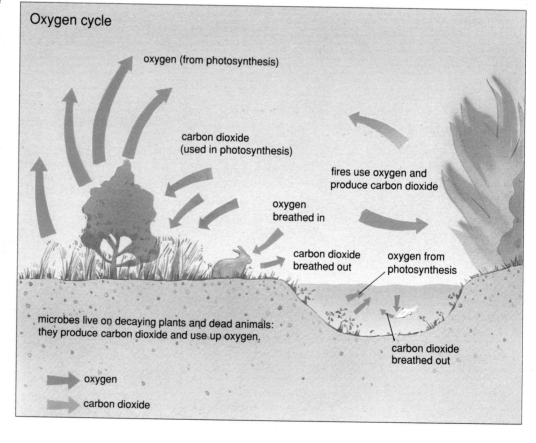

Oxygen cycle

oxygen (from photosynthesis)

carbon dioxide (used in photosynthesis)

fires use oxygen and produce carbon dioxide

oxygen breathed in

carbon dioxide breathed out

oxygen from photosynthesis

microbes live on decaying plants and dead animals: they produce carbon dioxide and use up oxygen.

carbon dioxide breathed out

oxygen

carbon dioxide

Carbon cycle

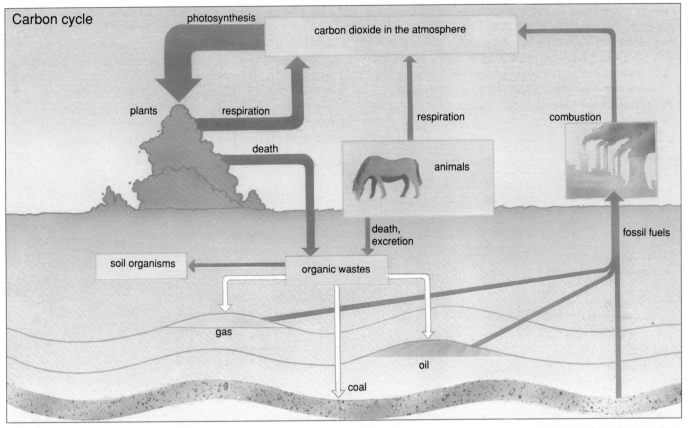

Nitrogen cycle

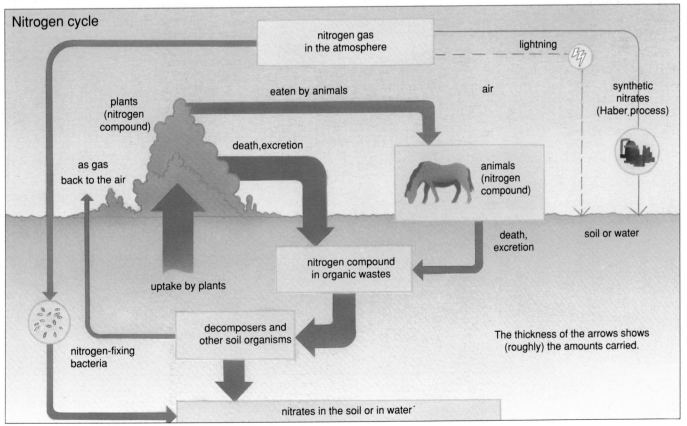

The thickness of the arrows shows (roughly) the amounts carried.

▽ Ecology

Ecology is the study of living organisms and how they cope with the world in which they live. There are several special terms that ecologists use.

- An *ecosystem* is the term used to describe a habitat and the community of living organisms living in it.
- The *habitat* is where an organism lives, obtains its food and shelter, reproduces and so on.

- A *community* is all the plants and animals in a particular habitat.
- The *environment* is everything around a living creature that could possibly affect it. The habitat of a rabbit for example is grassland, but its environment would include the weather, the nature of the soil and so on.
- A *food chain* is a simple way of showing the feeding relationships within a community. Every food chain begins with plant material, followed by the animals that feed on the plant and so on.

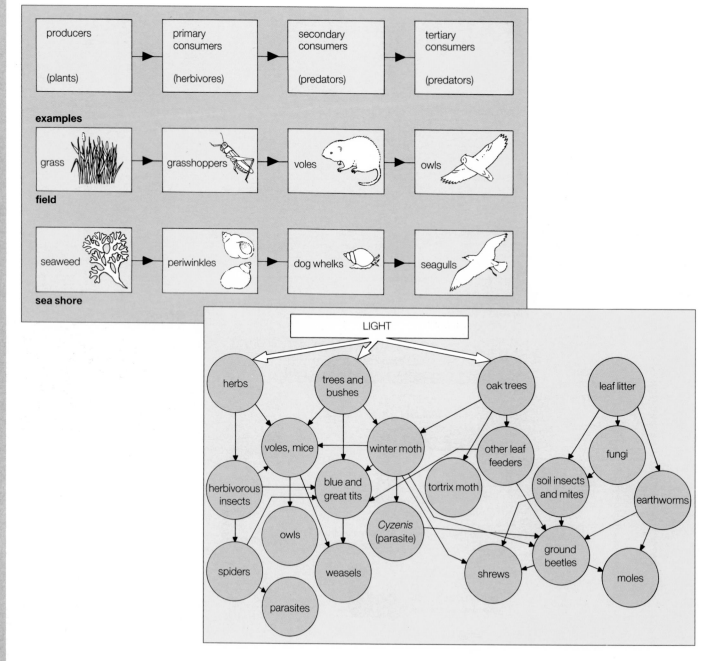

- A *food web* shows all the feeding relationships in a community.

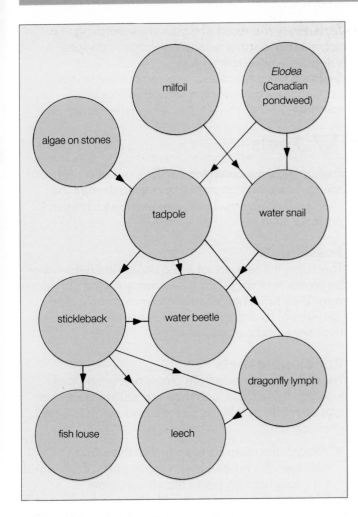

- A *pyramid of biomass* shows the mass of the organisms at each stage in the food chain.

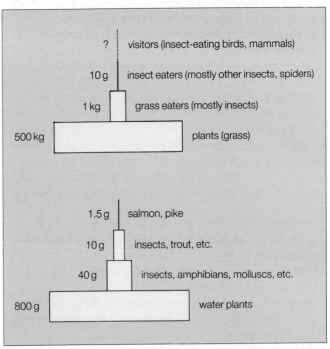

- A *pyramid of energy* shows how much energy is in each part of a food chain.

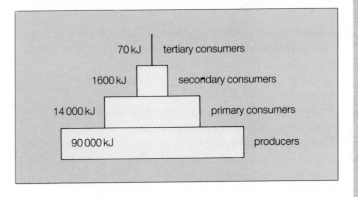

- A *pyramid of numbers* shows the number of animals and plants at each stage in the food chain.

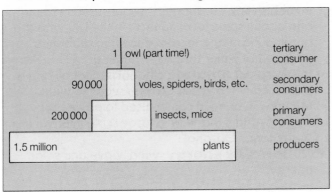

▽ Useful words in chemistry

Alloy: a mixture of metals.

Atom: the smallest particle of an element; the smallest particle that can take part in a chemical reaction.

Bond: the force holding atoms together inside molecules.

Catalyst: a substance that will help speed up the reaction. It is the same at the end of a reaction as it was at the start.

Compound: a pure substance made up of different kinds of atoms (from more than one element), joined together. Examples of compounds are sodium chloride, water, ammonia and chlorofluorocarbons (CFCs).

Concentration: a measure of how much of one substance is dissolved in a certain volume of another (e.g. grams per litre).

Electron: a negatively charged particle that is the smallest part of an atom.

Element: a pure chemical substance that can't be broken down into other substances. They contain only one kind of atom.

Ion: a charged atom or group of atoms.

Molecule: a group of atoms (of the same element or of several elements).

Neutron: the neutral (unchanged) particle found in the nucleus.

Nucleus: the centre of an atom, where most of the atom's material is, packed into a small charged mass, consisting of protons and neutrons.

Oxide: a compound of oxygen and another element.

Polymer: a large molecule made up of smaller repeating 'units' of groups of atoms.

Polymerisation: joining groups of atoms together to make a large molecule (polymer).

Proton: the positive particle found in the nucleus.

Reaction: a chemical change that happens between chemicals.

Reaction rate: how fast the change happens.

Relative atomic mass: the mass (or average mass) of an atom compared with a standard atom (e.g. carbon 12).

Salt: a compound, usually of a metal with other elements, held together by ionic bonds; a compound made when an acid is neutralised; 'common salt' is sodium chloride.

Solubility: a measure of how well a substance dissolves.

Solute: a substance that is dissolved in a solvent, e.g. copper sulphate is the solute in copper sulphate solution.

Solution: the result of dissolving something in a solvent (e.g. copper sulphate solution – copper sulphate dissolved in water).

Solvent: a substance which can dissolve other substances, e.g. water is a solvent for copper sulphate.

▽ Fuels

Fuels are chemicals which can be used as a source of energy – the energy is usually released when the chemicals are burned with oxygen. (See Chapter 12, page 171.)

Fossil fuels

These are the remains of living organisms (which may be plants or animals) that lived many millions of years ago. They have been converted into complicated mixtures of *hydrocarbons*, which are compounds of hydrogen and carbon.

Renewable fuels

These are fuels made from plants or from animal wastes. Unlike fossil fuels they are not 'used up', but can be made as long as animals and plants live and grow on Earth.

- **Wood**: the main cooking fuel of the world. Although it is renewable, in many parts of the world it is being used up faster than it can grow.
- **Biogas**: this is methane, CH_4. It is produced by the action of bacteria, causing decay on many organic wastes, such as agricultural waste (e.g. sugar-cane leaves), animal and human dung, household waste in rubbish tips, etc. Biogas is widely used in China, and also in some local councils in the UK, who are burning the methane from decaying rubbish to provide hot water for district heating.
- **Biological ethanol**: ethanol is alcohol, and is produced when yeasts grow in sugar solution. Mixed with petrol it can be used to power car engines, and is made on a large scale in Brazil from sugar cane, 'Gasohol'.
- **Renewable energy**: wind, wave and solar energy.

Nuclear fuels

These are radioactive elements that provide energy in power stations (and nuclear bombs) as a result of physical changes deep inside the atom (in the nuclei). They are not 'fuels' in the ordinary chemical sense, there is no combination with oxygen or any other kind of chemical reaction. The elements used in power stations are plutonium and uranium.

Fuels and pollution

All fuels cause pollution when used. The chemicals produced when hydrocarbon fuels (coal and oil) are burned are water and carbon dioxide. If the fuels contain other substances (such as sulphur) then other polluting substances are released (such as sulphur dioxide, which dissolves in water to make sulphuric acid – and so 'acid rain'). Water is harmless, but carbon dioxide is building up in the atmosphere. The result will be a gradual warming up of the Earth due to the *greenhouse effect*.

- **Carbon monoxide** is a deadly poisonous gas produced when a fuel is not properly burned. If there is a shortage of oxygen, the hydrocarbon fuel will produce carbon monoxide (CO) instead of carbon dioxide (CO_2).

▽ Dates of discovery of the elements

B.C.
Carbon	C
Copper	Cu
Gold	Au
Iron	Fe
Lead	Pb
Mercury	Hg
Silver	Ag
Sulphur	S
Tin	Sn
Zinc	Zn

A.D. 1200–1300
Arsenic	As

1500–1600
Bismuth	Bi
Antimony	Sb

1600–1700
Phosphorus	P

1700–1760
Platinum	Pt
Cobalt	Co
Nickel	Ni

1761–1780
Hydrogen	H
Fluorine	F
Nitrogen	N
Chlorine	Cl
Manganese	Mn
Oxygen	O

1781–1790
Molybdenum	Mo
Tellurium	Te
Tungsten	W
Uranium	U
Titanium	Ti
Zirconium	Zr
Strontium	Sr

1791–1800
Yttrium	Y
Chromium	Cr
Beryllium	Be

1801–1810
Niobium	Nb
Tantalum	Ta
Cerium	Ce
Palladium	Pd
Rhodium	Rh
Iridium	Ir
Osmium	Os
Potassium	K
Sodium	Na
Barium	Ba
Boron	B
Calcium	Ca
Magnesium	Mg

1811–1820
Iodine	I
Cadmium	Cd
Lithium	Li
Selenium	Se

1821–1830
Silicon	Si
Aluminium	Al
Bromine	Br
Thorium	Th
Vanadium	V

1831–1840
Lanthanum	La

1841–1850
Erbium	Er
Terbium	Tb
Ruthenium	Ru

1861–1870
Caesium	Cs
Rubidium	Pb
Thallium	Tl
Indium	In
Helium	He

1871–1880
Gallium	Ga
Ytterbium	Yb
Holmium	Ho
Samarium	Sm
Scandium	Sc
Thulium	Tm

1881–1890
Neodymium	Nd
Praesodymium	Pr
Dysprosium	Dy
Gadolinium	Gd
Germanium	Ge

1891–1900
Argon	Ar
Krypton	Kr
Neon	Ne
Polonium	Po
Radium	Rd
Xenon	Xe
Actinium	Ac
Radon	Rn

1901–1910
Europium	Eu
Lutetium	Lu

1911–1920
Protactinium	Pa

1921–1930
Hafnium	Hf
Rhenium	Re

1931–1940
Technetium	Tc
Francium	Fr
Astatine	At
Neptunium	Np
Plutonium	Pu

1941–1950
Americium	Am
Curium	Cm
Berkelium	Bk
Californium	Cf

1951–1960
Einsteinium	Es
Fermium	Fm
Mendelevium	Md

1961–1970
Nobelium	No
Lawrencium	Lr

▽ Common chemicals

This table shows some commonly found chemical compounds. It gives their 'household' names and their formulae.

Name	Common name	Formula
aluminium oxide	alumina	Al_2O_3
ammonia		NH_3
ammonium chloride		NH_4Cl
ammonium nitrate	'Nitram' (fertiliser)	NH_4NO_3
calcium carbonate	limestone, chalk	$CaCO_3$
calcium chloride		$CaCl_2$
calcium hydroxide	slaked lime	$Ca(OH)_2$
calcium oxide	quicklime	CaO
carbon monoxide		CO
carbon dioxide		CO_2
cobalt (II) chloride		$CoCl_2$
copper (II) chloride		$CuCl_2$
copper (II) oxide		CuO
copper (II) sulphate		$CuSO_4$
hydrogen chloride	hydrochloric acid	HCl_g
hydrochloric acid		HCl_{aq}
hydrogen fluoride		HF_g
hydrogen peroxide		H_2O_2
hydrogen sulphide		H_2S
iron (II) oxide		FeO
iron (III) oxide		Fe_2O_3
magnesium carbonate		$MgCO_3$
magnesium chloride		$MgCl_2$
magnesium oxide	magnesia	MgO
manganese (IV) oxide	manganese dioxide	MnO_2
nitric acid		HNO_3
nitrogen monoxide		NO
nitrogen dioxide		NO_2
potassium chloride		KCl
potassium hydroxide	caustic potash	KOH
potassium manganate (VII)	potassium permanganate	$KMnO_4$
potassium nitrate	saltpetre	KNO_3
silicon (IV) oxide	silicon dioxide, silica	SiO_2
sodium carbonate	soda ash (washing soda)	Na_2CO_3
sodium chloride	salt	$NaCl$
sodium hydrogen-carbonate	sodium bicarbonate	$NaHCO_3$
sodium hydroxide	caustic soda	$NaOH$
sodium nitrate		$NaNO_3$
sodium sulphate		Na_2SO_4
sulphur dioxide		SO_2
sulphur trioxide		SO_3
sulphuric acid		H_2SO_4
zinc oxide		ZnO
water		H_2O

Alkanes

The alkanes are a group of carbon compounds of the general formula C_nH_{2n}.

Name	Formula	Melting point (°C)	Boiling point (°C)
methane	CH_4	−182	−161
ethane	C_2H_6	−183	−88
propane	C_3H_8	−188	−42
butane	C_4H_{10}	−138	−1
pentane	C_5H_{12}	−130	36
hexane	C_6H_{14}	−95	69
heptane	C_7H_{16}	−91	99
octane	C_8H_{18}	−57	126
nonane	C_9H_{20}	−51	151
decane	$C_{10}H_{22}$	−30	174
dodecane	$C_{12}H_{26}$	−10	216
eicosane	$C_{20}H_{42}$	37	344

Activity series of common metals

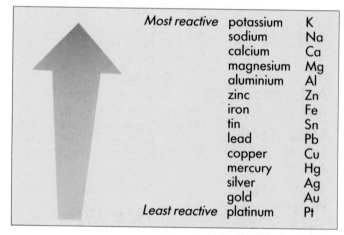

Most reactive	potassium	K
	sodium	Na
	calcium	Ca
	magnesium	Mg
	aluminium	Al
	zinc	Zn
	iron	Fe
	tin	Sn
	lead	Pb
	copper	Cu
	mercury	Hg
	silver	Ag
	gold	Au
Least reactive	platinum	Pt

▽ A simple model of an atom

Atoms consist of a central nucleus of protons and neutrons, and a set of electrons that orbit this nucleus.

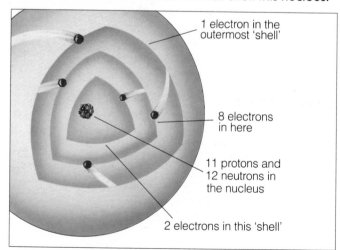

1 electron in the outermost 'shell'

8 electrons in here

11 protons and 12 neutrons in the nucleus

2 electrons in this 'shell'

The electrons in atoms are more like fuzzy clouds than neat points. They do not circle the nucleus in neat orbits, but a drawing of three fuzzy clouds would be very confusing.

▽ Drawing chemical structure

Atoms are held together in molecules by bonds. The bonds can be shown in different ways. The drawings show four representations of an ethane molecule (C_2H_4).

Structural formula

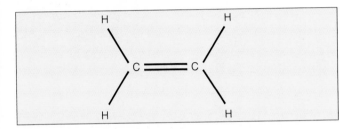

Simple diagram

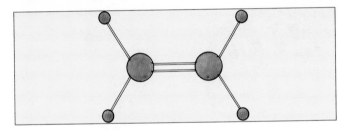

'Ball-and-stick' model
But the sticks don't really exist of course! A more realistic model is 'space filling'.

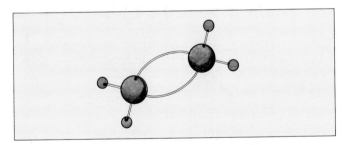

Solid models

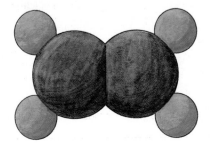

▽ Ions

An electron has a negative charge and a proton has a positive charge. A neutron has no charge at all. If these positive and negative charges are not balanced out in a molecule or atom, it will have extra positive or negative charges(s). This is called an ion. The table shows the charges on some ions.

Positive ions (cations)		Negative ions (anions)	
ammonium	NH_4^+	bromide	Br^-
hydrogen	H^+	chloride	Cl^-
copper (I)	Cu^+	iodide	I^-
potassium	K^+	hydroxide	OH^-
sodium	Na^+	nitrate	NO_3^-
silver	Ag^+	carbonate	CO_3^{2-}
calcium	Ca^{2+}	oxide	O^{2-}
magnesium	Mg^{2+}	sulphate	SO_4^{2-}
copper (II)	Cu^{2+}	sulphite	SO_3^{2-}
iron (II)	Fe^{2+}	sulphide	S^{2-}
zinc	Zn^{2+}	phosphate	PO_4^{3-}
aluminium	Al^{3+}		
iron (III)	Fe^{3+}		

Cations are usually metals and anions are usually non-metals.

▽ Bonding

Covalent bonding
The particles are held together by electric forces caused by sharing electrons, e.g. water.

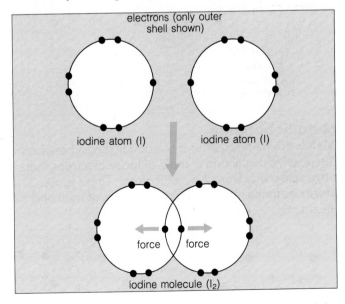

electrons (only outer shell shown)

iodine atom (I)   iodine atom (I)

force   force

iodine molecule (I_2)

The 'lone' electrons are shared. The molecule is held together by the attraction forces between the shared electrons and the positive nuclei of *both* atoms.

Ionic bonding

Charged particles (the ions) are held together by electric forces caused by transferring electrons, e.g. sodium chloride (NaCl), salt.

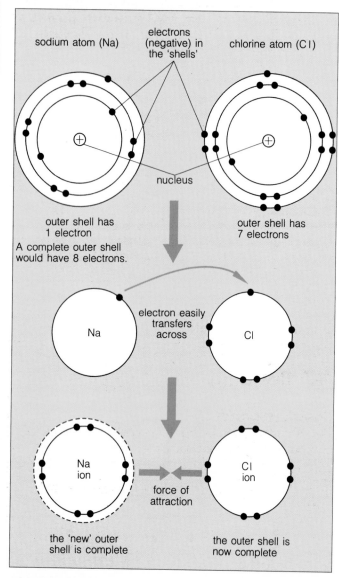

Metallic bonding

Metals are held together by electrical forces between the positive nuclei and a 'mob' of loose electrons that have split away from the metal atoms. These loose electrons make metals good conductors of heat and electricity.

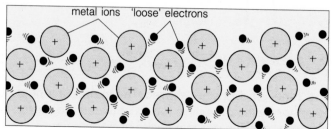

▽ Solid, liquids, solutions and gases

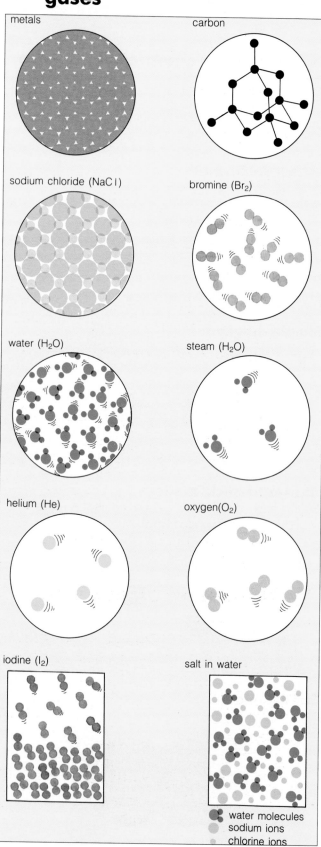

metals

carbon

sodium chloride (NaCl)

bromine (Br$_2$)

water (H$_2$O)

steam (H$_2$O)

helium (He)

oxygen(O$_2$)

iodine (I$_2$)

salt in water

water molecules
sodium ions
chlorine ions

Reference

▽ Minerals

Mineral	Formula	Main product	Annual production (ktonnes in 1986)
haematite (iron ore)	Fe_2O_3	steel	715 000
impure aluminium oxide (bauxite)	complex hydrocarbons, various sulphides	aluminium	15 300
porphyry copper (pyrites, borite, chalcopyrite)	CuS, Cu_5FeS_4, $CuFeS_2$	copper	8200
sphalerite (zincblende)	ZnS	zinc	6800
galena, cerussite	PbS, $PbCO_3$	lead	3200
cassiterite	SnO_2	tin	180
limestone	$CaCO_3$	cement, aggregate	
clay	complex hydrosilicates	bricks, cement	

▽ The uses of crude oil

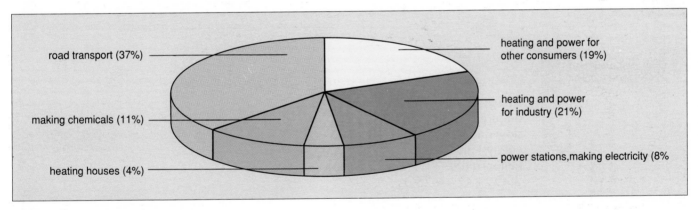

road transport (37%)

making chemicals (11%)

heating houses (4%)

heating and power for other consumers (19%)

heating and power for industry (21%)

power stations, making electricity (8%)

▽ The lifetime of resources

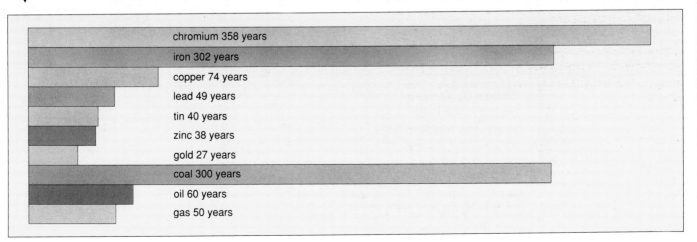

chromium 358 years
iron 302 years
copper 74 years
lead 49 years
tin 40 years
zinc 38 years
gold 27 years
coal 300 years
oil 60 years
gas 50 years

▽ Making sulphuric acid

Sulphuric acid is widely used in industry. More sulphuric acid is made than any other chemical.

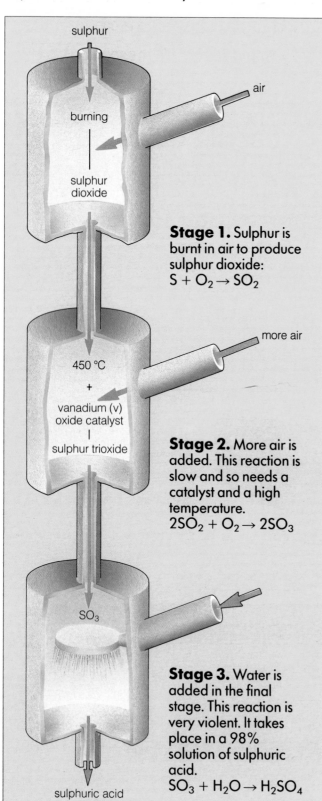

sulphur

air

burning

sulphur
dioxide

Stage 1. Sulphur is burnt in air to produce sulphur dioxide:
$S + O_2 \rightarrow SO_2$

more air

450 °C
+
vanadium (v) oxide catalyst
|
sulphur trioxide

Stage 2. More air is added. This reaction is slow and so needs a catalyst and a high temperature.
$2SO_2 + O_2 \rightarrow 2SO_3$

SO_3

Stage 3. Water is added in the final stage. This reaction is very violent. It takes place in a 98% solution of sulphuric acid.
$SO_3 + H_2O \rightarrow H_2SO_4$

sulphuric acid

▽ The Haber process – making ammonia

Reaction 1: producing hydrogen:

methane + steam →
          carbon monoxide + hydrogen

$CH_4 + H_2O \rightarrow CO + 3H_2$

Reaction 2: uses oxygen from the air to help remove carbon in a complicated set of reactions which can be summarised as:

carbon monoxide + oxygen → carbon dioxide

$2CO + O_2 \rightarrow 2CO_2$

The carbon dioxide is taken out by a 'scrubbing' process (it is dissolved in water).

Reaction 3: the ammonia cycle:

nitrogen + hydrogen → ammonia

$N_2 + 3H_2 = 2NH_3$

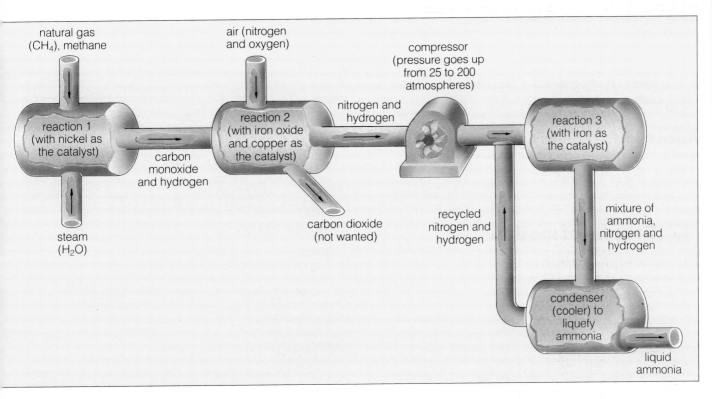

▽ Making fertilisers

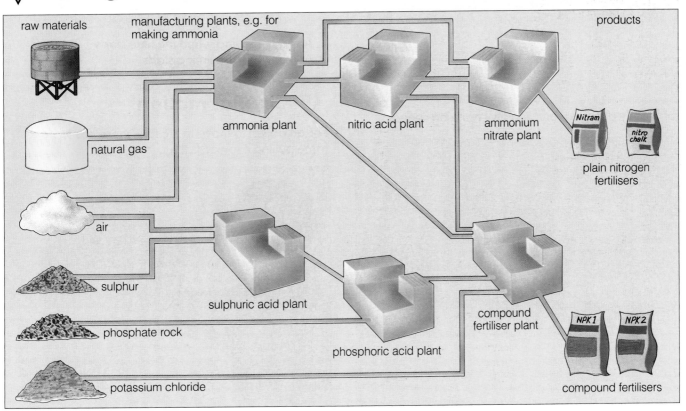

Physics: data store

▽ Equations of motion

average speed = $\dfrac{\text{distance covered}}{\text{time taken}}$

$$v = \frac{d}{t}$$

final speed = starting speed + (acceleration × time)

$$v = u + at$$

To find the distance covered, if you know the starting speed, acceleration and time of travel:

distance $d = ut + \frac{1}{2}at^2$

▽ Graphs of motion

Distance–time graphs
The steepness shows the speed.
(a) Steady speed.

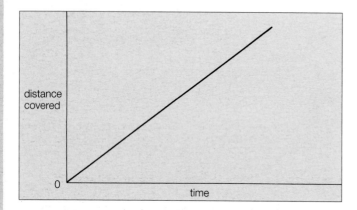

(b) Steady acceleration (steadily changing speed).

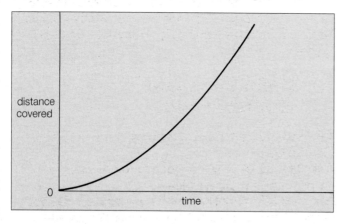

Speed–time graphs
The steepness shows the acceleration.
(a) Steady speed.

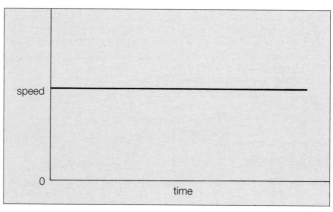

(b) Steady acceleration.

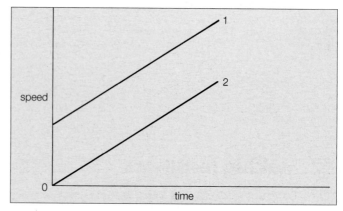

1. Already moving when the time starts.
2. At rest when the timing starts.

▽ Circular motion

For an object to move in a circle, there has to be a force pulling it towards the centre.

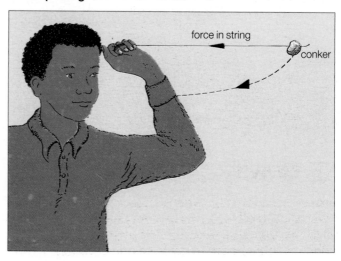

Reference

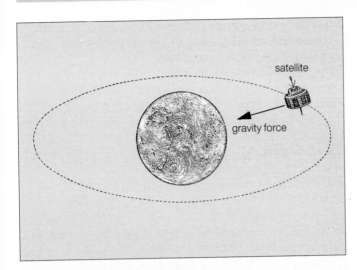

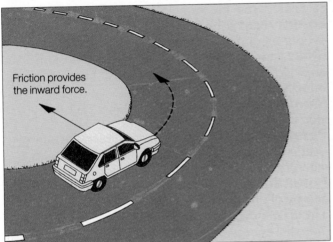

Friction provides the inward force.

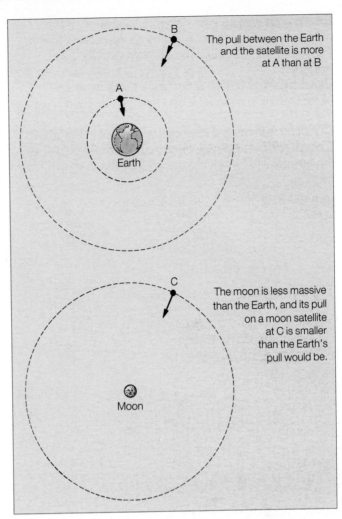

The pull between the Earth and the satellite is more at A than at B

Earth

The moon is less massive than the Earth, and its pull on a moon satellite at C is smaller than the Earth's pull would be.

Moon

On an icy road there is no friction and no circular motion.

The Earth and the satellite pull on each other. This force gets smaller the further the satellite is away from Earth. The force between the Moon and the satellite is smaller than that between the Earth and the satellite, even when the distances between them are the same, because the moon is less massive than the Earth. The force of gravity between objects depends on their masses.

 ## Gravity

Gravity is the force between masses that pulls them towards each other. It acts on everything, and can act through empty space. The force gets less, the further the objects are away from one another.

▽ Definitions and explanations

a.c. and **d.c.**: alternating and direct current (see Chapter 00).
Acceleration is the rate of change of velocity (velocity change per unit time).
Acceleration of free fall is the rate of increase of speed by an object falling freely under gravity.
Braking distance is the distance a vehicle moves before the brakes bring it to a stop, after they have been applied.
Brittle: Breaks by shattering into pieces, like glass.

Reference

235

Centre of mass is the 'point of balance' of an object, the place where all of its weight seems to act. This is sometimes called its centre of gravity. See *stability*.

Centripetal force is the force that makes an object move in a circle; it acts towards the centre of the circle.

Compression is a change (decrease) in length.

Conduction, convection and radiation are the three ways by which energy travels from hot objects.

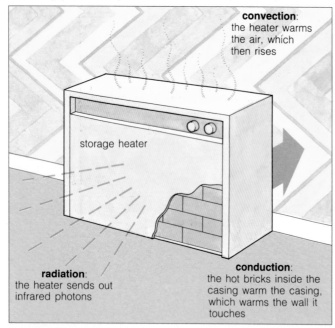

convection: the heater warms the air, which then rises

storage heater

radiation: the heater sends out infrared photons

conduction: the hot bricks inside the casing warm the casing, which warms the wall it touches

Crumple zone is the part of a car that has been designed to protect the passengers and crumples up in an accident.

Current is the rate at which electrical charge flows, measured in amperes (amps).

Deceleration is the rate of change of velocity whilst an object is slowing down.

Density: The density of a material is the mass, in grams, of 1 cm^3 of the material. (Sometimes you will see it worked out as the mass, in kilograms, of 1 m^3 of material.) To work out the density of a sample of the material, divide its mass by its volume.

Efficiency:

$$\text{Percentage efficiency} = \frac{\text{useful energy transferred}}{\text{total energy put in}} \times 100\%$$

$$\left(\text{or } \frac{\text{output}}{\text{input}} \times 100\%\right)$$

No system, machine or process can have an efficiency greater than 100%. That would mean that energy had been created, which is impossible. Energy can only be transferred from one system to another.

Elastic: when a force changes its shape or size, an elastic material will go back to its original shape and size when the force is removed.

Elastic deformation is the change in size or shape of an elastic object caused by a force.

Elastic energy is the energy stored in an object that has been stretched, squashed or twisted by a force.

Evaporation is a liquid changing to a gas (vapour) without actually boiling.

Extension is a change (increase) in length.

Friction is the force between two surfaces that resists movement.

Force is the cause of a change in velocity (equals the rate at which momentum changes).

Kinetic energy is the energy of movement, calculated from the formula $E = \frac{1}{2}mv^2$.

Latent heat is the energy needed to make a liquid evaporate or a solid melt.

Mass (inertia) is the natural 'unwillingness' of an object to be affected by a force (i.e. to have its velocity changed).

Momentum is the name for 'mass × velocity'; an idea used in collision studies.

Potential difference is a measure of the energy needed to drive electric charge through an object, measured in volts.

Potential energy: the gravitational potential energy of an object is the energy that is transferred to it from whatever lifts it. It is often just called the potential energy.

Potential energy = mass × height lifted × g, where g is the gravitational field strength of the planet you are on. On Earth, g is 9.8 newtons per kilogram.

Power is the rate of using energy or doing work, measured in watts (or joules per second).

Pressure: pressure = force ÷ area

$$p = \frac{f}{a}$$

Pressure has units of newtons per square metre (N/m^2) but these are sometimes given the name Pascals, Pa. 1 N/m^2 = 1 Pa.

Resistance is a measure of how hard it is for electric charge to flow through an object, measured in ohms.

Specific heat capacity is the heating energy needed to warm 1 kilogram of a material by 1°C.

Speed is the rate of movement (distance per unit time).

Stability is about how easy or difficult it is to knock things over. The two things that decide it are:
- the area of the supporting base,
- the position of the centre of mass ('where the weight is').

The further an object can be tilted before the centre of mass is outside the base, the more stable it is.

Small base — easy to tip over

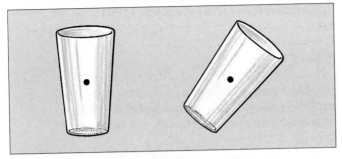

Larger base — harder to tip over

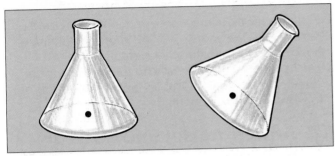

Chair made of light material

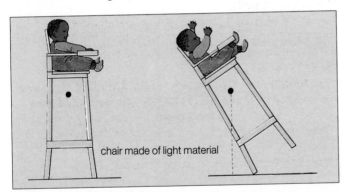

Chair with bottom part made of denser material. Note how this lowers the centre of mass.

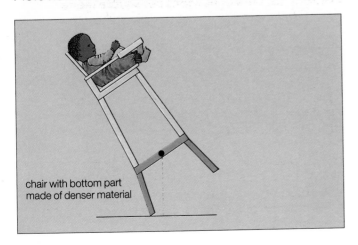

Stiffness/flexibility is a measure of how much a material changes shape or size when a force is applied.

Thermal capacity is the heating energy needed to warm an object by 1 °C.

Thinking distance is the distance a vehicle moves whilst the driver reacts to a signal to start braking.

Toughness is a measure of how much a material can be deformed by a force without breaking.

Velocity is the rate of movement with direction included.

Work is the energy transferred when a force is applied to move something (work = force × distance moved along the direction of the force).

▽ **Falling**

An object in free fall has an acceleration, g.
For an object falling from rest:
distance fallen in time t, $h = \frac{1}{2}gt^2$
speed after time t, $v = gt$.

A 1 kg brick falls from a 20 m building:

giving, $v^2 = 2gh$.

So, v is the speed reached by an object falling h metres.

$V^2 = 2 \times 9.8 \times 15$
$= 294$
$V = 17$ m/s

Reference

▽ Laws of motion ('Newton's Laws)

1. A force is needed to change the movement of an object; otherwise the object will keep still or keep moving steadily in a straight line.
2. If an unbalanced force does act on an object, it will make the object accelerate and/or change its direction of movement.
3. Two objects are always needed to produce a force, and the force acts equally on both.

The formulae
Force = mass × acceleration
$F = ma$

Impulse = change of momentum
$Ft = mv$

(F = force (N), t = time (s), a = acceleration (N/kg), m = mass (kg), v = change in velocity (m/s)).

▽ Laws of flotation (Archimedes' Principle)

When an object is put in a gas or liquid, it displaces its own volume of these fluids. If the displaced fluid weighs more than the object, the object will float; if it weighs less, the object will sink.

▽ Hooke's Law

An object obeys Hooke's law if it is elastic and stretches (or compresses) evenly with force, i.e. if the change produced is proportional to the applied force.

▽ Ohm's Law

An object obeys Ohm's law if its electrical resistance stays the same whatever the current that flows through it (assuming that the object doesn't get hotter).

▽ The laws of energy

1 The conservation law: energy cannot be created or destroyed — the energy we find in one system must have come from some other system.
2 The 'spreading out' law: whenever we use energy, some of it becomes unusable because it spreads out to warm up the surroundings.

▽ Atoms, nuclei and nuclear energy

Practically all the mass of an atom is in its nucleus. An atom is electrically *neutral* — it has the same number of positive charges (on protons) in the nucleus as

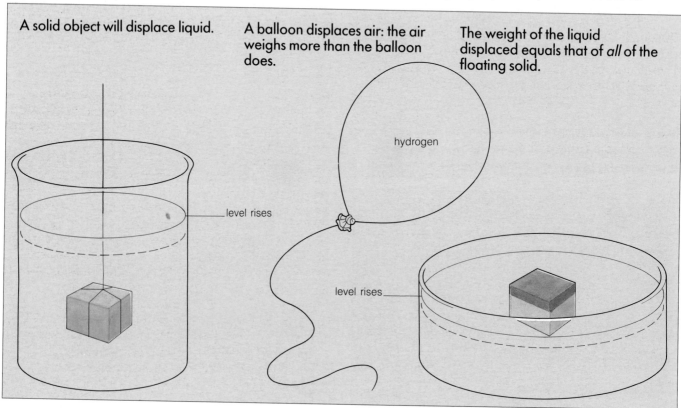

A solid object will displace liquid.

A balloon displaces air: the air weighs more than the balloon does.

The weight of the liquid displaced equals that of *all* of the floating solid.

level rises

hydrogen

level rises

there are negative charges surrounding the nucleus (on electrons). The nucleus also contains unchanged (neutral) particles called neutrons, these are as big as the protons.

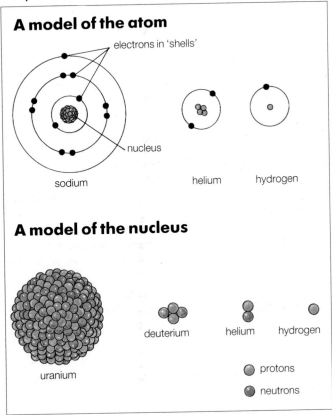

A model of the atom

electrons in 'shells'

nucleus

sodium   helium   hydrogen

A model of the nucleus

uranium

deuterium   helium   hydrogen

○ protons
● neutrons

The number of protons is the same for all atoms of one element, but is different for the different elements. Some nuclei of the *same element may have different numbers of neutrons*. They are called *isotopes* of that element.

Some examples are below — more may be found in a good Periodic Table of the elements.

Element	Number of protons	Number of neutrons	Mass number (total number of neutrons and protons)
hydrogen	1	0	1
helium	2	2	4
carbon	6	6	12
carbon*	6	8	14
nitrogen	7	7	14
oxygen	8	8	16
chlorine	17	18	35
chlorine*	17	20	37
uranium	92	146	238
plutonium	94	148	242

*radioactive isotope

Radioactivity

Some nuclei are *unstable*, and there is a chance that they may give out energy by sending out a small part of themselves, either as particles of matter or as electromagnetic radiation. The particles of matter they emit are:

- *alpha particles* – a package of two protons and two neutrons;
- *beta particles* – a single electron.

The electromagnetic radiation is of very short wavelength (high photon energy), called *gamma radiation*. Gamma radiation is even more penetrating and harmful to living cells than X-rays.

Properties of the radiations

Name	Description	Range in air	Stopped by
alpha	very massive (2 protons with 2 neutrons); positive charge	4–10 centimetres	sheet of paper
beta	very light (electrons); negative charge	variable up to about a metre	a few millimetres of aluminium
gamma	photons of electromagnetic radiation; not charged; travel at the speed of light	no limit	several metres of concrete

Half-life

Radioactive elements that give off the radiations described above change into new elements in doing so. This change is called nuclear *decay*. The nuclei do not all change at the same time, they change at random so that it is impossible to predict when a given nucleus will change. But there are so many nuclei in even a very small sample of the element that the laws of chance ensure that for a given radioactive element *half* of the nuclei will have decayed in a certain time. This time is called the *half-life* of that element. Because some elements have isotopes (nuclei with the same number of protons but differing in the number of neutrons) we should use this word rather than 'element' when discussing radioactivity. Some isotopes are radioactive, others are not. For example, carbon can have eight isotopes, only two of which are not radioactive – carbon-12 and carbon-13. Ordinary carbon is a mix of carbon-12 (98.89%), carbon-13 (1.11%) and carbon-14 (a trace).

Reference

239

Examples of radioactive isotopes

Isotope	Radiation emitted	Element it decays to	Half-life of element
carbon-14	beta	nitrogen	5739 years
uranium-235	alpha	thorium	713 million years
caesium-137	beta and gamma	barium	30 years

The half-life of carbon 14 is used in *radiocarbon dating* in archaeology.

Nuclear energy

Nuclear power stations use the nuclei of certain very massive elements as the energy source (i.e. instead of coal, oil or gas). The elements used are selected isotopes of uranium and plutonium. The energy does not come from the chemical reaction of combustion (burning in air) but from the splitting of the heavy nuclei into two roughly equal parts. This happens naturally when the nuclei have the right mix of protons and neutrons, and are collected together in large enough amounts.

If too many nuclei are close enough together, the splitting-up reaction runs away with itself in a *chain reaction* — as happens in nuclear bombs. When the nuclei split up, some neutrons are also given off and they can trigger off the splitting up of other nuclei. The reaction can be controlled by altering the number and speed of these neutrons. This is done by using *control rods*, which absorb and slow down the neutrons as required. The active elements are contained in *fuel rods*.

The energy from the splitting nuclei is used to heat water and change it to steam, which is then used in turbine-generators as in an ordinary power station.

Nuclear waste

The reactions that occur inside the fuel elements in a nuclear power station produce new elements and new isotopes. Even the material that the containers are made from may change. Generally, the new isotopes are themselves radioactive. When parts of the reactor are replaced the old parts may be dangerously active, emitting alpha, beta and gamma radiations that can harm living things. Some parts of this waste have very short half-lives, and are effectively stable after a few months or even days. But some have longer half-lives, for example, plutonium-239, half life 24 000 years. These have to be stored away from living things, perhaps for thousands of years. The best way to do this is continually updated.

▽ Power rating of some common devices

A *unit* of electrical energy is 1 kilowatt-hour (3.6 megajoules).

Device	Typical power rating	What you get for 1 unit
one-bar electric fire	1 kW	1 hour's heating
radiant heater	3 kW	20 minutes' heating
kettle	2 kW	10 litres of boiling water
lamp	100 W	light for 10 hours
TV set (colour)	160 W	6 hours' use
cassette player	50 W	a day's play
hi-fi system	100 W	10 hours' listening
electric iron	500 W	2 hours' use
food mixer	100 W	60 cake mixes
toaster	900 W	70 slices of toast
refrigerator	200 W	about a day's use
vacuum cleaner	500 W	2 hours' cleaning
instant shower	3 kW	1 shower

▽ Wiring a plug

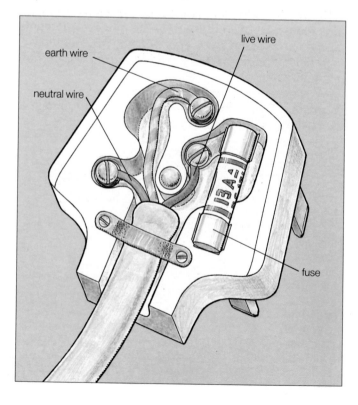

earth wire

live wire

neutral wire

fuse

▽ **The gas laws**

If you hold your finger over the end of a bicycle pump that has been 'pulled open' ready to pump, and then push the plunger, you reduce the volume of air inside, and can feel that the pressure has increased.

If a volume of gas is heated, the gas expands or its pressure increases.

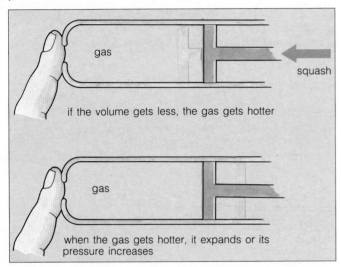

gas

squash

if the volume gets less, the gas gets hotter

gas

when the gas gets hotter, it expands or its pressure increases

These results are described by the gas formula. It says that for a fixed volume of gas:

$$\frac{PV}{T} = \text{constant}$$

(*P* is pressure, *V*, volume and *T*, temperature in kelvin. Kelvin temperatures start at absolute zero ($-273\,°C$)).

The pressure, volume and temperature of a gas are inter-related.

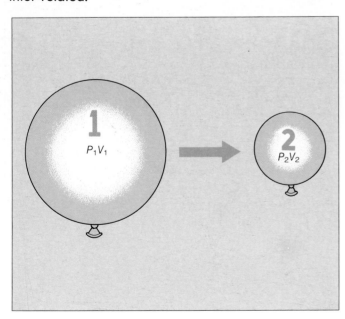

At a *constant temperature*, the volume of a gas is inversely proportional to its temperature. Thus, when changing a gas from condition 1 to condition 2:

$$P_1 \times V_1 = P_2 \times V_2$$

At *constant volume*, the pressure of a gas is proportional to its temperature in K (kelvin).

When changing a gas from condition 1 to condition 2:

$$\frac{P_1}{T_1} = \frac{P_2}{T_2}$$

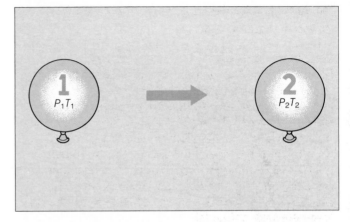

At *constant pressure*, the volume of a gas is proportional to its temperature in kelvin. Now when changing a gas from condition 1 to condition 2:

$$\frac{V_1}{T_1} = \frac{V_2}{T_2}$$

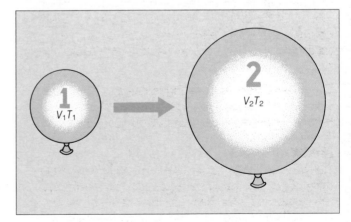

Physics: data store

▽ The properties of some useful materials

Metals

Metal	Melting point (°C)	Density (g/cm³)	Elasticity (relative)	Strength (MN/m²)	Conductivity (relative)		Hardness (relative)
					electric	thermal	
aluminium	659	2.7	35	70	40	24	23
chromium	1903	7.2	—	80	8	9	70
copper	1083	8.9	65	220	64	40	60
gold	1063	19.3	—	170	49	31	50
iron	1539	7.9	—	210	11	8	variable
lead	328	11.4	8	15	5	4	10
magnesium	650	1.7	—	150	26	15	40
tin	232	7.3	—	10	7	6	5
titanium	1677	4.5	—	230	2	2	—
tungsten	3377	19.4	—	120	20	20	225
zinc	420	7.3	—	140	18	11	—
aluminium alloy	variable	—	35–45	100–400	—	12	—
steel	variable (about 1600°C)	—	100 (high tensile)	240–340	—	7	—

Building materials

brick	—	1.7	3.5	depends on joints	—	0.12	variable
concrete	—	2.2	20	cracks	—	0.2	variable
glass	—	2.5	33	very variable; cracks	—	—	about 100
glass-reinforced plastic	—	1.9	37	220–300	—	—	—
wood	—	0.2–0.8	3–5	—	—	0.02	variable

Reference

Plastics

All plastics are poor electric and thermal conductors

Plastic	Density (g/m^3)	Strength (MN/m^3)	Elasticity (relative)
acrylic (e.g. Perspex)	1.2	13	1.5
PVC	1.3	4–12	1.25
polythene (low density)	0.92	3	0.1
polythene (high density)	0.96	6	0.5
polypropylene	0.9	7	0.6
polystyrene	1.05	8	17.0
phenolic resin (e.g. Bakelite)	1.4	10	3.5

▽ Structures

Forces acting on solid structures

Compression forces are the ones that squash an object, making it smaller.

Tension forces try to pull the object apart.

These act directly in line with a main dimension of the object. Other forces may bend or twist an object.

In bending, both compression and tension forces are brought into play. Structures or parts of structures that have to withstand bending forces are called beams or cantilevers.

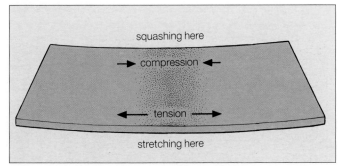

squashing here
compression
tension
stretching here

▽ Scaling up and down

In a scale model, all dimensions (length, breadth, thickness) are changed by the same factor, e.g. made one-tenth the size.

Effects of changing scale

(Assuming that the same materials are used in the model and the real structure.)

Scale factor	Effect on area	Effect on volume	Effect on mass (weight)
doubled (×2)	more than doubled (×4)	more than doubled (×8)	more than doubled (×8)
trebled (×3)	×9	×27	×27
×4	×16	×64	×64
×n	×n^2 (squared)	×n^3 (cubed)	×n^3 (cubed)

Types of structure

- simple beams (one- and two-end support)
- pillars (hollow and filled) – compressions
- 'guys' – solid, for tension
- arches
- triangular structures
- combinations of triangles
- 3-dimensional arches (domes)
- triangles and domes (geodesic domes)

All these types of structures are illustrated in Chapter 11.

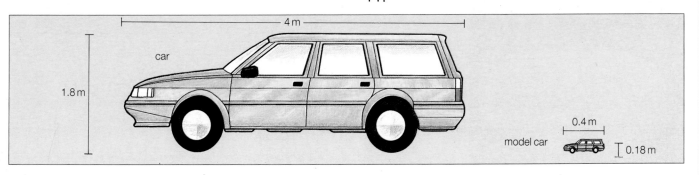

4 m
car
1.8 m
0.4 m
model car
0.18 m

The history of the Earth

The continents have moved . . .   Plants and animals have changed . . .

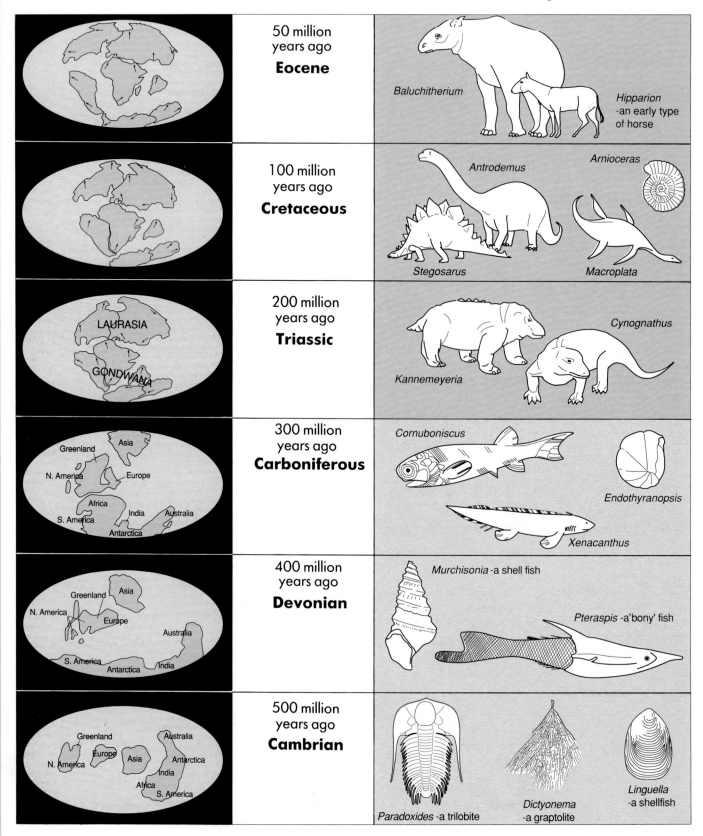

	50 million years ago **Eocene**	*Baluchitherium* — *Hipparion* -an early type of horse
	100 million years ago **Cretaceous**	*Antrodemus* — *Arnioceras* — *Stegosarus* — *Macroplata*
	200 million years ago **Triassic**	LAURASIA — GONDWANA — *Kannemeyeria* — *Cynognathus*
	300 million years ago **Carboniferous**	*Cornuboniscus* — *Endothyranopsis* — *Xenacanthus*
	400 million years ago **Devonian**	*Murchisonia* -a shell fish — *Pteraspis* -a 'bony' fish
	500 million years ago **Cambrian**	*Paradoxides* -a trilobite — *Dictyonema* -a graptolite — *Linguella* -a shellfish

The Earth: data store

The time-scale down the centre of the chart is in millions of years.

Era	Period	Epoch	Time	Events
Cenozoic The Earth's climate became colder, resulting in Ice Ages. This is the age of the mammals, but also of insects and flowering plants Opening of North Sea			Now	Early Egyptians cities, etc
	Quaternary	Holocene	0.01	
		Pleistocene	2	Many Ice Ages Humans migrate over Asia
	Tertiary	Pliocene	7	First human beings (Africa)
		Miocene	26	India meets Asia, Himalayas form
		Oligocene	38	First deer, monkeys, dogs, cats Africa, Europe and Asia collide, Alps form
		Eocene	54	First rodents, elephants, horses
		Paleocene	65	Extinction of dinosaurs
Mesozoic This was the age of the dinosaurs The great southern continent of Pangaea broke up, forming most of our modern continents The Earth's climate was warm and pleasant almost everywhere	Cretaceous		136	Final break-up of Pangaea Sea flooded to cover more land, Formation of chalk over much of what is now Europe First flowering plants and modern types of insect
	Jurassic		190	Beginning of the Atlantic Ocean First birds and mammals
	Triassic		225	Many new species Sea levels fall all over the world
Paleozoic At the beginning, most life was in the sea. Plants colonised the land in the Silurian era, followed after a few million years by amphibians. Towards the end of this period the first reptiles appeared, as land animals.	Permian		280	Rise of the reptiles Formation of Pangaea, the greatest continent ever
	Carboniferous		355	Britain at the Equator; coal laid down in many parts of the world. Age of amphibians. First reptiles.
	Devonian		395	Age of the Amphibians First fish, first flying insects Animal life moves on to the land
	Silurian		440	Plants move on to the land
	Ordovican		500	sea covers many continents
	Cambrian		570	most life in the sea, as shellfish and floating plants
Precambrian This covered a huge period of time — over 4000 million years. It began with the formation of the Earth and ended with the first many-celled organisms. The first green plants appeared in the sea — and began to put oxygen into the atmosphere				First multicellular organisms
	Proterozoic		2500	
	Archaean		4600	? First free oxygen in atmosphere ? First living organisms — single celled plants and animals 3960 — Age of oldest known rocks Earth cooling down; formation of tectonic plates

Meteorology – some key words and ideas

Low
A block of low-pressure air, typically about 300 – 500 km across, consisting of warm air that originated in the tropics. It usually reaches Britain across the Atlantic, and so is called *tropical maritime* air. It contains a great deal of water vapour, and so produces cloud and rain. See page 96.

High
A block of high-pressure air, consisting of cold air that flows down from polar regions. It is usually dry and dense and so has little cloud and causes a high pressure. This usually brings cold dry winter weather and hot dry summer weather. See page 99.

Front
A boundary between polar air and tropical air. A *warm front* leads the block of tropical air in a low; it is followed by the *cold front* as the low moves away. An *occluded front* on a weather map shows where these two fronts merge as the low is lifted off the ground. See page 98.

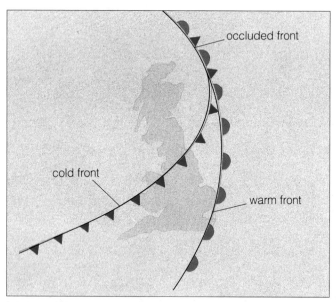

Jet stream
A stream of air moving at high speed. Usually found at the boundary between the main convection cells in the atmosphere. Britain is just underneath the normal path of the *Polar jet stream*, which travels west-to-east at over 200 km/hour at a height of 10–12 kilometres. The air moves in a wavy path dragging lows and highs with it. Transatlantic planes use the jet stream when flying west-to-east. This makes the eastbound journey an hour shorter than the westbound trip.

Blocking pattern
An effect caused by the jet stream staying fixed on one pattern for some time, with a high permanently based over northern Europe. This pushes lows well to the south of Britain, and can produce long periods of fine, dry weather.

Precipitation
Anything that 'falls' – rain, hail and snow – can be classed as precipitation.

Clouds and types
Clouds are small drops of water or ice crystals. They are small enough to be kept in place by air currents. The main cloud types are illustrated on page 97.

Weather-map symbols

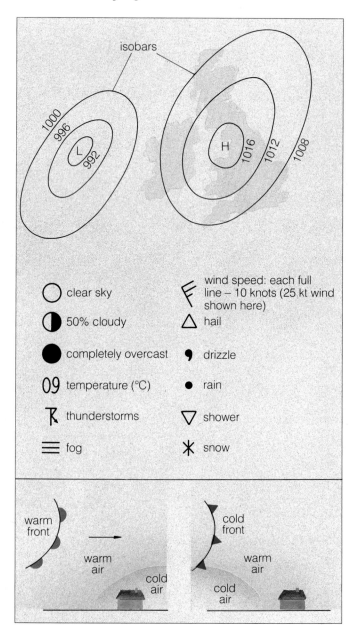

▽ Geology

The major types of rock

Sedimentary rocks

These are made from particles eroded from other rocks that have been deposited, usually in sea water, where rivers that carried the particles ended. Some were laid down in lakes, others in deserts as wind-blown sediments. (See the summary diagram on page 111.)

Sedimentary rocks often contain fossils. These are the remains of an animal or plant that has been preserved in the rock. The original material has usually been changed chemically so that wood, bones, flesh, shells, etc. have been changed into a mineral of some kind.

Igneous rocks

Igneous rocks were formed from a hot liquid material called *magma* that comes from deep inside the Earth. Surface flows of magma are called *lavas*. Magma that cooled inside the Earth formed rocks that have unique properties (e.g. large crystals). Associated landforms are *sills, dikes* and *bosses*. Volcanoes also produce material that is thrown into the air, forming piles of material that may eventually form hard rock. See page 111 for a summary.

Metamorphic rocks

These are rocks that have been changed, usually by high temperatures and pressures when igneous material flowed over or through them. They are explained on page 112.

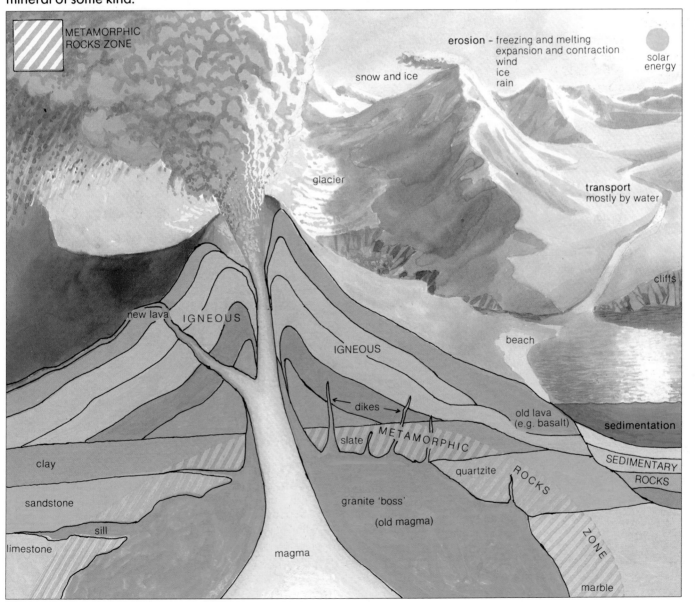

Reference

A simple key for identifying rocks

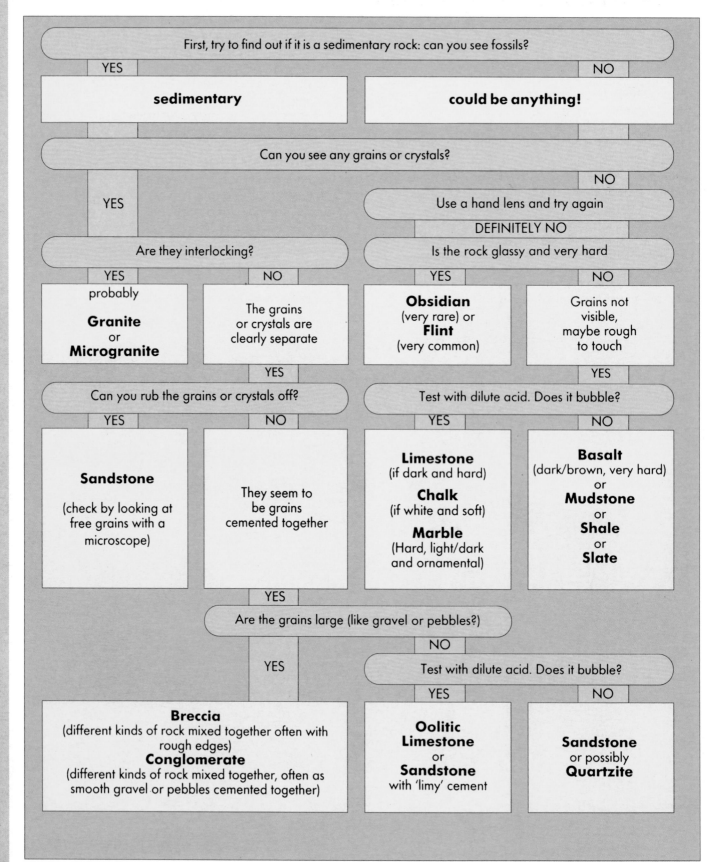

First, try to find out if it is a sedimentary rock: can you see fossils?

YES → **sedimentary**

NO → **could be anything!**

Can you see any grains or crystals?

NO → Use a hand lens and try again
DEFINITELY NO

YES →

Are they interlocking?

Is the rock glassy and very hard

YES → probably **Granite** or **Microgranite**

NO → The grains or crystals are clearly separate

YES → **Obsidian** (very rare) or **Flint** (very common)

NO → Grains not visible, maybe rough to touch

Can you rub the grains or crystals off?

Test with dilute acid. Does it bubble?

YES → **Sandstone** (check by looking at free grains with a microscope)

NO → They seem to be grains cemented together

YES → **Limestone** (if dark and hard) **Chalk** (if white and soft) **Marble** (Hard, light/dark and ornamental)

NO → **Basalt** (dark/brown, very hard) or **Mudstone** or **Shale** or **Slate**

Are the grains large (like gravel or pebbles?)

YES → **Breccia** (different kinds of rock mixed together often with rough edges) **Conglomerate** (different kinds of rock mixed together, often as smooth gravel or pebbles cemented together)

NO → Test with dilute acid. Does it bubble?

YES → **Oolitic Limestone** or **Sandstone** with 'limy' cement

NO → **Sandstone** or possibly **Quartzite**

▽ Faulting, folding and erosion

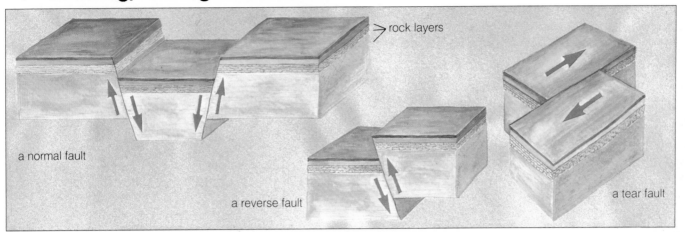

rock layers

a normal fault

a reverse fault

a tear fault

Fault

A geological structure formed when one section of rock moves past another. The fault is the plane along which the rocks slide.

The arrows show how the rock slabs may have moved.

Fold

This describes the effects produced when rocks are squeezed sideways.

The rocks are laid down under the sea in horizontal layers.

Slow, tectonic, Earth movements fold the rocks.

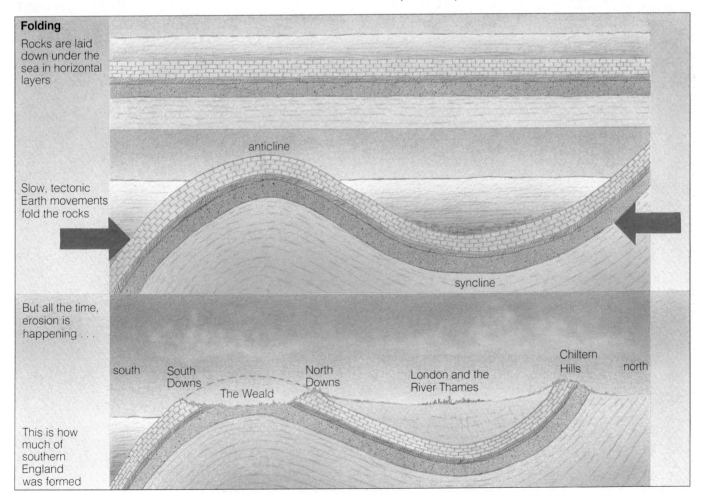

Folding

Rocks are laid down under the sea in horizontal layers

Slow, tectonic Earth movements fold the rocks

anticline

syncline

But all the time, erosion is happening . . .

south   South Downs   North Downs   London and the River Thames   Chiltern Hills   north

The Weald

This is how much of southern England was formed

Erosion

Any process that wears away rocks is called erosion: water, ice, wind, etc. Rain water is slightly acidic because of dissolved carbon dioxide and modern pollutant gases. Some rocks are easily dissolved, e.g. limestone.

 ## Radioactive dating

The radioactivity of rocks decreases with time at a known rate so the ages of rocks and fossils can be found by measuring the radio-activity in them.

 ## The greenhouse gases

Gas	Carbon dioxide (CO$_2$)	Methane (CH$_4$)	Chlorofluoro-carbons (CFC's)	Nitrous oxide (N$_2$O)	Surface ozone (O$_3$), i.e. close to the Earth's surface
Amount it increases each year (% normal)	0.5	1	6		
Time taken to break down (years)	7	10	15000	170	2–3 weeks
How strongly it traps energy, compared with carbon dioxide	1	30-times stronger	10–20000 times stronger	150-times stronger	2000-times stronger
Total contribution to the greenhouse effect (%)	50	18	14	6	10
Source	burning, especially fossil fields	breakdown of organic chemicals by bacteria when there is not enough oxygen, e.g. in rice fields, intestines of cows and sheep; burning coal and wood	made to use as coolants in fridges and air conditioners; used in making foam and aerosol sprays	made by bacteria in the soil and the breakdown of nitrate fertilizers; burning fossil fuels and wood	75% of ozone is made when sunlight affects car exhaust fumes

Changes in the Earth's climate

1. Global temperature: for the past 150-thousand years

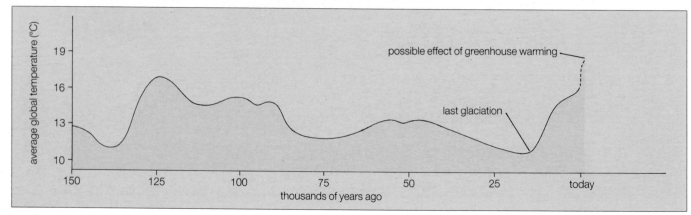

2. European temperature: the past 1000 years

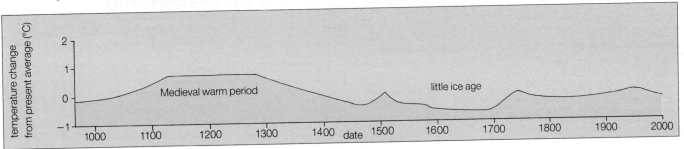

3. Global atmospheric CO₂ increase: the past 200 years

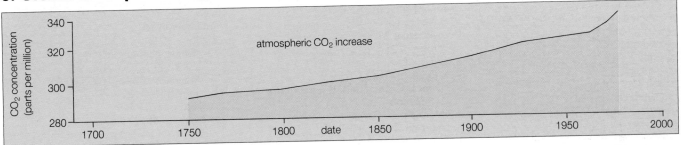

▽ Acid rain

Reference

Reference